THE BEST HUMOR
ANNUAL

THE BEST HUMOR

ANNUAL

Edited by **LOUIS UNTERMEYER**

and **RALPH E. SHIKES**

New York: Henry Holt and Company

FIRST EDITION

Library of Congress Card Catalog Number:

50–10196

Printed in the United States of America

Foreword

Thanks to the encouragement of generous critics and the still more gratifying response of enthusiastic—well, charitable—readers, this is the third of *The Best Humor* series. As in the previous compilations, there is a mingling of famous writers and (as yet) less well-known authors, of professional humorists and practitioners of serious prose whose gravity is relieved with levity. As before, the contributions include fiction pieces from some of the most popular books of the year, articles from periodicals of many different types, and newspaper columns. The period covered is from May, 1951 to May, 1952.

Once again we are indebted to *Collier's* Magazine for providing more selections than any other single source, and we are grateful to *The New Yorker,* our second most fruitful source, for permission to reprint five stories and articles. Among newspapers, the New York *Herald Tribune* most consistently brightens the day for its readers: it can hardly help doing so, with John Crosby and Red Smith contributing regularly to its lively pages.

This collection differs from its predecessors in one important way: it contains fewer short pieces, casuals, and "fillers," and places the emphasis on selections of more considerable size. Thus, although the book has not as many contributors as the first two volumes, it attains (the editors believe) more solid substance and greater readability.

As in previous volumes, here is a wide variety within the broad framework of humor. Here are the outrageous incongruities of S. J. Perelman and the straight-face absurdities of Will Cuppy, the sharp satire of James Reid Parker, the amoral spoofing of Stephen Potter, and the broad burlesque of soap opera by radio comics Bob and Ray. For more extended relaxation, there are several lengthy stories, including Frances Gray Patton's gentle and sensitive portrait of teen-agers, Ludwig Bemelmans' nonchalant portrait of a cosmopolitan freeloader, and Joseph Carroll's wild Irish prose. For briefer moments, the reader will relish pieces by Frank Sullivan, Victoria Lincoln, John Collier, Ralf Kircher, B. M. Atkinson, Jr., and others. If the reader is in a mood for parody, there is Peter DeVries' masterful murder of last year's best-selling novel. If children are your inspiration or your despair, turn to Robert M. Yoder or Parke Cummings for satirical but affectionately recognizable vignettes. If you want to know what's taking place in sports—or taking the place of sports—there is always Red Smith or John Lardner. If you believe women have no sense of humor—or if you believe such a thought subversive and slanderous—turn to Robert T. Allen and James Thurber. If . . . But this is an introduction, not a catalog.

Commenting on what seems to be a dwindling in the number of active humorists in the United States, Frank Sullivan wrote this past year in *The New York Times Book Review*: "The lot of the humorist is more difficult today than it was thirty years ago. . . . His attitude of wary suspicion may stem from a tendency of humorists, especially good ones like Ring Lardner and Mark Twain, to tell the truth, which, though it shall make you free, may also make you uneasy. It is not difficult to understand any reluctance a young writer might feel toward undertaking the writing of carefree humor today. In the Nineteen Twenties the atom was known intimately to only a few scientists. . . . There was plenty wrong with the Nineteen Twenties, but from here they seem halcyon. The climate is not propitious for humor. Nevertheless, if the gods have planted humor in a writer's soul he probably will try to write humor, no matter what Gromyko and McCarthy are up to; either he will do that, or the angry gods may, as punishment, change him into a weeping willow or an NBC vice president."

To which we say "amen." The climate is not propitious for experiments in fun-making, critical or even uncritical wit. But humor is a particularly hardy perennial and will persist in bursting forth as long as men—and women—are not afraid to laugh.

All of which raises the annual query "What is humor?" Our own answers have been accepted with only a few demurrers, but it might be well to state them again. They are a little more inclusive than Webster's definition of humor as "that quality which appeals to the sense of the ludicrous or absurdly incongruous." Humor, we submit, is far more varied than that. The levels of the ludicrous are many; they include (not necessarily here) not only the blandly burlesque physical grotesqueries of Jerry Lewis and Red Skelton, but the verbal nonsense—a chain reaction of logical absurdities—of Groucho Marx. The scope of the incongruous is similarly wide; it ranges from the pratfall to the epigram, from the guffaw to the giggle. But there is also a kind of humor which has little to do with mere fun-making, which lifts the ridiculous to the serene, if not to the sublime. On the physical plane, there is the humor of a Chaplin which, in the midst of rough-and-tumble clowning, surprises us by evoking a sudden sympathy, pity, and even pathos; and there is the humor of such an essayist as E. B. White which, casually teasing, develops into a kindly commentary, a combination of raillery and tenderness, of fooling and philosophy. This is not to imply that the best of humor is necessarily serious; we do not pretend that (according to certain analysts) every flippancy conceals a profundity. But we make a plea for a wider extension of the word, a recognition that, as we originally maintained, "humor is something which leaves you feeling a little lighter in spirit, a little less harassed and a little better equipped to face the difficult problems of the day. . . . In a world of exposed nerve-ends, it can—and does—serve as a necessary relief." Humor is sometimes wildly hilarious and sometimes gently warmhearted, but (to conclude with one last alliteration) humor is basically wholesome and, therefore, healing. At least, this is the sustaining hope of the editors.

LOUIS UNTERMEYER AND RALPH E. SHIKES

Contents

THE BEST HUMOR ANNUAL

Max Shulman

From Minnesota to Manhattan is a grown man's hop, skip, and jump; but Max Shulman took it as a boy in one nonchalant stride. It was his nonchalance as a columnist on *The Minnesota Daily* and his work on the campus humor magazine, *Ski-U-Mah*—which Shulman insists was an Indian word meaning "Close the window, can't you see it's raining?" —which furnished the background for his first book, appropriately entitled *Barefoot Boy with Cheek*. It established Shulman as a campus favorite, was reprinted in an edition which sold more than 200,000 copies, and was made into a musical comedy which played on Broadway for many months. In the period between getting himself out of the classroom and getting his work before the public, Shulman found himself seriously engaged in a war. He wrote a book about it; but his target was not the Army, Navy, or Air Force; he turned a spotlight of satire on the hard-pressed civilians in a book called *The Feather Merchants*. While still in uniform he also wrote another free-swinging farce, *The Zebra Derby*. A logical consequence was the one-volume Shulman collection: *Max Shulman's Large Economy Size*.

The Many Loves of Dobie Gillis is Shulman's latest: eleven stories which use the University of Minnesota, the author's Alma Mater, as the setting for the misadventures—Shulman spells it miss-adventures—of a teen-age Casanova with a crew cut. In his introduction Shulman called attention to the fact that, since his short stories have appeared in magazines of national circulation, they are, therefore, clean, wholesome, and altogether suitable for the parsonage library—and he goes on to announce that substantial discounts will be given to parsonage libraries ordering his book in lots of 40,000 copies or more. Shulman also adds the following cautionary note: "Mean, small, captious, and niggling readers will notice certain discrepancies in the following stories. In some of them, for example, Dobie Gillis is a freshman; in others he is a sophomore. In some he is majoring in law; in others he is majoring in journalism or chemistry or English or mechanical engineering or nothing at all. In some he is shrewd; in others dumb; in some aggressive; in others meek. In some he is seventeen years old; in others eighteen; in others nineteen. These tiny variations will be noticed, as I said, by mean, small, captious, and niggling readers. But to the intelligent, greathearted, truly American reader, they will be matters of no consequence." *The Many Loves of Dobie Gillis* has another claim to distinction: it is the only book of the season—and perhaps the only book of the century—to be dedicated to Ferdinand de Lesseps, "without whom I never could have dug the Suez Canal."

1

It is easy to see why Shulman has become the undergraduate's P. G. Wodehouse, the sorority's S. J. Perelman, and the English major's Marx Brothers all rolled into one.

Love Is a Fallacy*

Cool was I and logical. Keen, calculating, perspicacious, acute, and astute—I was all of these. My brain was as powerful as a dynamo, as precise as a chemist's scales, as penetrating as a scalpel. And —think of it!—I was only eighteen.

It is not often that one so young has such a giant intellect. Take, for example, Petey Bellows, my roommate at the university. Same age, same background, but dumb as an ox. A nice enough fellow, you understand, but nothing upstairs. Emotional type. Unstable. Impressionable. Worst of all, a faddist. Fads, I submit, are the very negation of reason. To be swept up in every new craze that comes along, to surrender yourself to idiocy just because everybody else is doing it—this, to me, is the acme of mindlessness. Not, however, to Petey.

One afternoon I found Petey lying on his bed with an expression of such distress on his face that I immediately diagnosed appendicitis. "Don't move," I said. "Don't take a laxative. I'll get a doctor."

"Raccoon," he mumbled thickly.

"Raccoon?" I said, pausing in my flight.

"I want a raccoon coat," he wailed.

I perceived that his trouble was not physical, but mental. "Why do you want a raccoon coat?"

"I should have known it," he cried, pounding his temples. "I should have known they'd come back when the Charleston came back. Like a fool I spent all my money for textbooks, and now I can't get a raccoon coat."

"Can you mean," I said incredulously, "that people are actually wearing raccoon coats again?"

* From *The Many Loves of Dobie Gillis* by Max Shulman, copyright, 1951, by Max Shulman.

"All the Big Men on Campus are wearing them. Where've you been?"

"In the library," I said, naming a place not frequented by Big Men on Campus.

He leaped from the bed and paced the room. "I've got to have a raccoon coat," he said passionately. "I've got to!"

"Petey, why? Look at it rationally. Raccoon coats are unsanitary. They shed. They smell bad. They weigh too much. They're unsightly. They——"

"You don't understand," he interrupted impatiently. "It's the thing to do. Don't you want to be in the swim?"

"No," I said truthfully.

"Well, I do," he declared. "I'd give anything for a raccoon coat. Anything!"

My brain, that precision instrument, slipped into high gear. "Anything?" I asked, looking at him narrowly.

"Anything," he affirmed in ringing tones.

I stroked my chin thoughtfully. It so happened that I knew where to get my hands on a raccoon coat. My father had had one in his undergraduate days; it lay now in a trunk in the attic back home. It also happened that Petey had something I wanted. He didn't *have* it exactly, but at least he had first rights on it. I refer to his girl, Polly Espy.

I had long coveted Polly Espy. Let me emphasize that my desire for this young woman was not emotional in nature. She was, to be sure, a girl who excited the emotions, but I was not one to let my heart rule my head. I wanted Polly for a shrewdly calculated, entirely cerebral reason.

I was a freshman in law school. In a few years I would be out in practice. I was well aware of the importance of the right kind of wife in furthering a lawyer's career. The successful lawyers I had observed were, almost without exception, married to beautiful, gracious, intelligent women. With one omission, Polly fitted these specifications perfectly.

Beautiful she was. She was not yet of pin-up proportions, but I felt sure that time would supply the lack. She already had the makings.

Gracious she was. By gracious I mean full of graces. She had

3

an erectness of carriage, an ease of bearing, a poise that clearly indicated the best of breeding. At table her manners were exquisite.
I had seen her at the Kozy Kampus Korner eating the specialty
of the house—a sandwich that contained scraps of pot roast,
gravy, chopped nuts, and a dipper of sauerkraut—without even
getting her fingers moist.

Intelligent she was not. In fact, she veered in the opposite direction. But I believed that under my guidance she would
smarten up. At any rate, it was worth a try. It is, after all, easier
to make a beautiful dumb girl smart than to make an ugly smart
girl beautiful.

"Petey," I said, "are you in love with Polly Espy?"

"I think she's a keen kid," he replied, "but I don't know if
you'd call it love. Why?"

"Do you," I asked, "have any kind of formal arrangement with
her? I mean are you going steady or anything like that?"

"No. We see each other quite a bit, but we both have other
dates. Why?"

"Is there," I asked, "any other man for whom she has a particular fondness?"

"Not that I know of. Why?"

I nodded with satisfaction. "In other words, if you were out of
the picture, the field would be open. Is that right?"

"I guess so. What are you getting at?"

"Nothing, nothing," I said innocently, and took my suitcase out
of the closet.

"Where you going?" asked Petey.

"Home for the week end." I threw a few things into the bag.

"Listen," he said, clutching my arm eagerly, "while you're
home, you couldn't get some money from your old man, could you,
and lend it to me so I can buy a raccoon coat?"

"I may do better than that," I said with a mysterious wink and
closed my bag and left.

"Look," I said to Petey when I got back Monday morning. I
threw open the suitcase and revealed the huge, hairy, gamy object that my father had worn in his Stutz Bearcat in 1925.

"Holy Toledo!" said Petey reverently. He plunged his hands

into the raccoon coat and then his face. "Holy Toledo!" he repeated fifteen or twenty times.

"Would you like it?" I asked.

"Oh yes!" he cried, clutching the greasy pelt to him. Then a canny look came into his eyes. "What do you want for it?"

"Your girl," I said, mincing no words.

"Polly?" he said in a horrified whisper. "You want Polly?"

"That's right."

He flung the coat from him. "Never," he said stoutly.

I shrugged. "Okay. If you don't want to be in the swim, I guess it's your business."

I sat down in a chair and pretended to read a book, but out of the corner of my eye I kept watching Petey. He was a torn man. First he looked at the coat with the expression of a waif at a bakery window. Then he turned away and set his jaw resolutely. Then he looked back at the coat, with even more longing in his face. Then he turned away, but with not so much resolution this time. Back and forth his head swiveled, desire waxing, resolution waning. Finally he didn't turn away at all; he just stood and stared with mad lust at the coat.

"It isn't as though I was in love with Polly," he said thickly. "Or going steady or anything like that."

"That's right," I murmured.

"What's Polly to me, or me to Polly?"

"Not a thing," said I.

"It's just been a casual kick—just a few laughs, that's all."

"Try on the coat," said I.

He complied. The coat bunched high over his ears and dropped all the way down to his shoe tops. He looked like a mound of dead raccoons. "Fits fine," he said happily.

I rose from my chair. "Is it a deal?" I asked, extending my hand.

He swallowed. "It's a deal," he said and shook my hand.

I had my first date with Polly the following evening. This was in the nature of a survey; I wanted to find out just how much work I had to do to get her mind up to the standard I required. I took her first to dinner. "Gee, that was a delish dinner," she said

5

as we left the restaurant. Then I took her to a movie. "Gee, that was a marvy movie," she said as we left the theater. And then I took her home. "Gee, I had a sensaysh time," she said as she bade me goodnight.

I went back to my room with a heavy heart. I had gravely underestimated the size of my task. This girl's lack of information was terrifying. Nor would it be enough merely to supply her with information. First she had to be taught to *think*. This loomed as a project of no small dimensions, and at first I was tempted to give her back to Petey. But then I got to thinking about her abundant physical charms and about the way she entered a room and the way she handled a knife and fork, and I decided to make an effort.

I went about it, as in all things, systematically. I gave her a course in logic. It happened that I, as a law student, was taking a course in logic myself, so I had all the facts at my fingertips. "Polly," I said to her when I picked her up on our next date, "tonight we are going over to the Knoll and talk."

"Oo, terrif," she replied. One thing I will say for this girl: you would go far to find another so agreeable.

We went to the Knoll, the campus trysting place, and we sat down under an old oak, and she looked at me expectantly. "What are we going to talk about?" she asked.

"Logic."

She thought this over for a minute and decided she liked it. "Magnif," she said.

"Logic," I said, clearing my throat, "is the science of thinking. Before we can think correctly, we must first learn to recognize the common fallacies of logic. These we will take up tonight."

"Wow-dow!" she cried, clapping her hands delightedly.

I winced, but went bravely on. "First let us examine the fallacy called Dicto Simpliciter."

"By all means," she urged, batting her lashes eagerly.

"Dicto Simpliciter means an argument based on an unqualified generalization. For example: Exercise is good. Therefore everybody should exercise."

"I agree," said Polly earnestly. "I mean exercise is wonderful. I mean it builds the body and everything."

"Polly," I said gently, "the argument is a fallacy. *Exercise is*

6

good is an unqualified generalization. For instance, if you have heart disease, exercise is bad, not good. Many people are ordered by their doctors *not* to exercise. You must *qualify* the generalization. You must say exercise is *usually* good, or exercise is good *for most people*. Otherwise you have committed a Dicto Simpliciter. Do you see?"

"No," she confessed. "But this is marvy. Do more! Do more!"

"It will be better if you stop tugging at my sleeve," I told her, and when she desisted, I continued. "Next we take up a fallacy called Hasty Generalization. Listen carefully: You can't speak French. I can't speak French. Petey Bellows can't speak French. I must therefore conclude that nobody at the University of Minnesota can speak French."

"Really?" said Polly, amazed. *"Nobody?"*

I hid my exasperation. "Polly, it's a fallacy. The generalization is reached too hastily. There are too few instances to support such a conclusion."

"Know any more fallacies?" she asked breathlessly. "This is more fun than dancing even."

I fought off a wave of despair. I was getting nowhere with this girl, absolutely nowhere. Still, I am nothing if not persistent. I continued. "Next comes Post Hoc. Listen to this: Let's not take Bill on our picnic. Every time we take him out with us, it rains."

"I know somebody just like that," she exclaimed. "A girl back home—Eula Becker, her name is. It never fails. Every single time we take her on a picnic——"

"Polly," I said sharply, "it's a fallacy. Eula Becker doesn't *cause* the rain. She has no connection with the rain. You are guilty of Post Hoc if you blame Eula Becker."

"I'll never do it again," she promised contritely. "Are you mad at me?"

I sighed. "No, Polly, I'm not mad."

"Then tell me some more fallacies."

"All right. Let's try Contradictory Premises."

"Yes, let's," she chirped, blinking her eyes happily.

I frowned, but plunged ahead. "Here's an example of Contradictory Premises: If God can do anything, can He make a stone so heavy that He won't be able to lift it?"

7

"Of course," she replied promptly.

"But if He can do anything, He can lift the stone," I pointed out.

"Yeah," she said thoughtfully. "Well, then I guess He can't make the stone."

"But He can do anything," I reminded her.

She scratched her pretty, empty head. "I'm all confused," she admitted.

"Of course you are. Because when the premises of an argument contradict each other, there can be no argument. If there is an irresistible force, there can be no immovable object. If there is an immovable object, there can be no irresistible force. Get it?"

"Tell me some more of this keen stuff," she said eagerly.

I consulted my watch. "I think we'd better call it a night. I'll take you home now, and you go over all the things you've learned. We'll have another session tomorrow night."

I deposited her at the girls' dormitory, where she assured me that she had had a perfectly terrif evening, and I went glumly home to my room. Petey lay snoring in his bed, the raccoon coat huddled like a great hairy beast at his feet. For a moment I considered waking him and telling him that he could have his girl back. It seemed clear that my project was doomed to failure. The girl simply had a logic-proof head.

But then I reconsidered. I had wasted one evening; I might as well waste another. Who knew? Maybe somewhere in the extinct crater of her mind a few embers still smoldered. Maybe somehow I could fan them into flame. Admittedly it was not a prospect fraught with hope, but I decided to give it one more try.

Seated under the oak the next evening I said, "Our first fallacy tonight is called Ad Misericordiam."

She quivered with delight.

"Listen closely," I said. "A man applies for a job. When the boss asks him what his qualifications are, he replies that he has a wife and six children at home, the wife is a helpless cripple, the children have nothing to eat, no clothes to wear, no shoes on their feet, there are no beds in the house, no coal in the cellar, and winter is coming."

8

A tear rolled down each of Polly's pink cheeks. "Oh, this is awful, awful," she sobbed.

"Yes, it's awful," I agreed, "but it's no argument. The man never answered the boss's question about his qualifications. Instead he appealed to the boss's sympathy. He committed the fallacy of Ad Misericordiam. Do you understand?"

"Have you got a handkerchief?" she blubbered.

I handed her a handkerchief and tried to keep from screaming while she wiped her eyes. "Next," I said in a carefully controlled tone, "we will discuss False Analogy. Here is an example: Students should be allowed to look at their textbooks during examinations. After all, surgeons have X rays to guide them during an operation, lawyers have briefs to guide them during a trial, carpenters have blueprints to guide them when they are building a house. Why, then, shouldn't students be allowed to look at their textbooks during an examination?"

"There now," she said enthusiastically, "is the most marvy idea I've heard in years."

"Polly," I said testily, "the argument is all wrong. Doctors, lawyers, and carpenters aren't taking a test to see how much they have learned, but students are. The situations are altogether different, and you can't make an analogy between them."

"I still think it's a good idea," said Polly.

"Nuts," I muttered. Doggedly I pressed on. "Next we'll try Hypothesis Contrary to Fact."

"Sounds yummy," was Polly's reaction.

"Listen: If Madame Curie had not happened to leave a photographic plate in a drawer with a chunk of pitchblende, the world today would not know about radium."

"True, true," said Polly, nodding her head. "Did you see the movie? Oh, it just knocked me out. That Walter Pidgeon is so dreamy. I mean he fractures me."

"If you can forget Mr. Pidgeon for a moment," I said coldly, "I would like to point out that the statement is a fallacy. Maybe Madame Curie would have discovered radium at some later date. Maybe somebody else would have discovered it. Maybe any number of things would have happened. You can't start with a hypoth-

9

esis that is not true and then draw any supportable conclusions from it."

"They ought to put Walter Pidgeon in more pictures," said Polly. "I hardly ever see him any more."

One more chance, I decided. But just one more. There is a limit to what flesh and blood can bear. "The next fallacy is called Poisoning the Well."

"How cute!" she gurgled.

"Two men are having a debate. The first one gets up and says, 'My opponent is a notorious liar. You can't believe a word that he is going to say.' . . . Now, Polly, think. Think hard. What's wrong?"

I watched her closely as she knit her creamy brow in concentration. Suddenly a glimmer of intelligence—the first I had seen —came into her eyes. "It's not fair," she said with indignation. "It's not a bit fair. What chance has the second man got if the first man calls him a liar before he even begins talking?"

"Right!" I cried exultantly. "One hundred per cent right. It's not fair. The first man has *poisoned the well* before anybody could drink from it. He has hamstrung his opponent before he could even start. . . . Polly, I'm proud of you."

"Pshaw," she murmured, blushing with pleasure.

"You see, my dear, these things aren't so hard. All you have to do is concentrate. Think—examine—evaluate. Come now, let's review everything we have learned."

"Fire away," she said with an airy wave of her hand.

Heartened by the knowledge that Polly was not altogether a cretin, I began a long, patient review of all I had told her. Over and over and over again I cited instances, pointed out flaws, kept hammering away without letup. It was like digging a tunnel. At first everything was work, sweat, and darkness. I had no idea when I would reach the light, or even *if* I would. But I persisted. I pounded and clawed and scraped, and finally I was rewarded. I saw a chink of light. And then the chink got bigger and the sun came pouring in and all was bright.

Five grueling nights this took, but it was worth it. I had made a logician out of Polly; I had taught her to think. My job was done. She was worthy of me at last. She was a fit wife for me, a proper hostess for my many mansions, a suitable mother for my well-heeled children.

It must not be thought that I was without love for this girl. Quite the contrary. Just as Pygmalion loved the perfect woman he had fashioned, so I loved mine. I decided to acquaint her with my feelings at our very next meeting. The time had come to change our relationship from academic to romantic.

"Polly," I said when next we sat beneath our oak, "tonight we will not discuss fallacies."

"Aw, gee," she said, disappointed.

"My dear," I said, favoring her with a smile, "we have now spent five evenings together. We have gotten along splendidly. It is clear that we are well matched."

"Hasty Generalization," said Polly brightly.

"I beg your pardon," said I.

"Hasty Generalization," she repeated. "How can you say that we are well matched on the basis of only five dates?"

I chuckled with amusement. The dear child had learned her lessons well. "My dear," I said, patting her hand in a tolerant manner, "five dates is plenty. After all, you don't have to eat a whole cake to know that it's good."

"False Analogy," said Polly promptly. "I'm not a cake. I'm a girl."

I chuckled with somewhat less amusement. The dear child had learned her lessons perhaps too well. I decided to change tactics. Obviously the best approach was a simple, strong, direct declaration of love. I paused for a moment while my massive brain chose the proper words. Then I began:

"Polly, I love you. You are the whole world to me, and the moon and the stars and the constellations of outer space. Please, my darling, say that you will go steady with me, for if you will not, life will be meaningless. I will languish. I will refuse my meals. I will wander the face of the earth, a shambling, hollow-eyed hulk."

There, I thought, folding my arms, that ought to do it.

"Ad Misericordiam," said Polly.

I ground my teeth. I was not Pygmalion; I was Frankenstein, and my monster had me by the throat. Frantically I fought back

11

the tide of panic surging through me. At all costs I had to keep cool.

"Well, Polly," I said, forcing a smile, "you certainly have learned your fallacies."

"You're darn right," she said with a vigorous nod.

"And who taught them to you, Polly?"

"You did."

"That's right. So you do owe me something, don't you, my dear? If I hadn't come along you never would have learned about fallacies."

"Hypothesis Contrary to Fact," she said instantly.

I dashed perspiration from my brow. "Polly," I croaked, "you mustn't take all these things so literally. I mean this is just classroom stuff. You know that the things you learn in school don't have anything to do with life."

"Dicto Simpliciter," she said, wagging her finger at me playfully.

That did it. I leaped to my feet, bellowing like a bull. "Will you or will you not go steady with me?"

"I will not," she replied.

"Why not?" I demanded.

"Because this afternoon I promised Petey Bellows that I would go steady with him."

I reeled back, overcome with the infamy of it. After he promised, after he made a deal, after he shook my hand! "The rat!" I shrieked, kicking up great chunks of turf. "You can't go with him, Polly. He's a liar. He's a cheat. He's a rat."

"Poisoning the Well," said Polly, "and stop shouting. I think shouting must be a fallacy too."

With an immense effort of will, I modulated my voice. "All right," I said. "You're a logician. Let's look at this thing logically. How could you choose Petey Bellows over me? Look at me—a brilliant student, a tremendous intellectual, a man with an assured future. Look at Petey—a knothead, a jitterbug, a guy who'll never know where his next meal is coming from. Can you give me one logical reason why you should go steady with Petey Bellows?"

"I certainly can," declared Polly. "He's got a raccoon coat."

Ludwig Bemelmans

Equipped with a thinking-machine's accurate memory and an oversize imp's oversize imagination, Ludwig Bemelmans tells tales which are a fine combination of the casually plausible and the completely incredible. Cosmopolitan in taste and idiom, Bemelmans is the perfect man-about-literature. He was born in the Austrian Tyrol; his father was a Belgian painter, his mother was the daughter of a Bavarian brewer. He himself was educated in a German lyceum and in a series of Alpine hotels owned by an uncle. "I was born in a hotel and I spent the first years of my life in a beer garden," he wrote. "My nurse was a maître d'hôtel, and the chef himself made up my formula. . . . I think I remember that my diapers were cut-up tablecloths. Instead of a teething ring, a bottle opener hung around my little neck." This background enabled Bemelmans to become the innkeeper's laureate. His experiences in various caravansaries—he once even ran his own restaurant—found their way into the playful, wicked, and wonderful chapters of *Hotel Splendide* and *Hotel Bemelmans*.

But the best of Bemelmans goes far beyond his slightly disguised autobiographies. *My War with the United States* may be a factual record of Bemelmans' naturalization as an American citizen and his service with the U. S. Army, but it is distinguished by the brilliance of a born writer of fiction. *Now I Lay Me Down to Sleep, Small Beer,* and *I Love You, I Love You, I Love You* are some of the volumes which reveal the bland commentator who is also the inspired storyteller. Bemelmans' charm consists of a half-gentle, half-sardonic whimsicality which usually develops into a collection of vignettes of odd people and places. He is not so much the dispenser of the broadly humorous—although he is a master of the comic situation—as the purveyor of good humor. His *How to Travel Incognito* is leisurely reminiscent, sly, sympathetic, foolish, sometimes frightening, and always faintly philosophical.

In a First-class Compartment*

In the first-class compartment of the train from Blois to Paris, sitting next to the window and facing the direction in which it was

*From *How to Travel Incognito* by Ludwig Bemelmans, by permission of Little, Brown & Co. Originally appeared in part in *Holiday,* copyright, 1951, by The Curtis Publishing Company; 1952, by Ludwig Bemelmans.

going, was an American woman, a tourist, a refugee from a conducted tour of the Châteaux de la Loire. She dismissed the historic safari with the words: "Nothing but thick walls and running comment." Opposite her and pressed into the corner sat a man in deep sleep. He had pulled the curtain forward and the air was whipping it back and forth. He was tall, and had immense hands which were folded in his lap over the top of a cane. The conductor entered our compartment and punched my ticket and that of the lady tourist; he carefully did not disturb the sleeping passenger and when he left he very quietly closed the door. The man reminded me of a marsh bird such as I had seen in Flanders, for even in his sleep he seemed conscious of the length of his legs, and had stretched one diagonally into the corner, the other was thrown over it and relaxed. He wore elegant and polished boots, but appeared to have no socks on his feet. His suit was the color of a marsh bird's egg, a dark green speckle on an earth-brown ground, with black lines woven irregularly into the material.

In a land of individuals, he stood out even in his sleep. He was apparently without luggage.

The train was several kilometers out of Blois, when the dining-room steward entered and whispered that he had places left if anyone wished to go to the second sitting. The man in the corner continued peacefully sleeping, the American woman shook her head and suddenly, to my astonishment, burst into tears. She was a nice-looking woman of about forty, as could be seen by the reflection of her face in the window. When I asked her if there was anything I could do, she said, "No, thank you." A moment later, staring at the landscape, she said apologetically: "That always sets me back, the mere mention of food. That's why I finally left him, all on account of a steak. It just seems that he can't be happy unless he is making somebody else unhappy. We went to this château and that château; he always wants to do everything in a systematic way like his stamp collection—he cared more for that stamp collection of his than he even did for me. I tell you, if he knew there was a two-cent stamp lying in Central Park somewhere, he'd grab his hat and run out for it.

"Well, anyway, we stayed overnight in this hotel that was a château. Nothing was the way he liked it, and that poor manager

14

—he's going to have the manager fired—he always writes letters
to the management and tries to have everybody fired. Well, I looked
in the mirror yesterday morning and I took the hairpins out of my
mouth and I said to myself: 'I've had enough.' I just packed up and
left, and you know, last night I had the first good night's sleep
since I married him. And I bought myself a hat, this hat, the first
hat that I bought for myself in fourteen years. I bought it in Blois.
And it started to rain, and a man, the nicest man, offered me
his umbrella. He spoke English with a cleft palate and compli-
mented me on the new hat. I could hardly understand him but it
made me feel real good." I looked at the telegraph poles slanting
past. "I should have known better," she said. "The day before
we got married, he says to me: 'I like Schrafft's.'

"So there we are in Schrafft's and he orders a steak and he
tells the lady captain just exactly how he wants it done. I order
the chef's salad. When the steak comes, he looks at it; he sniffs at
it like a dog and then he snaps his fingers at the lady captain.

" 'I want to see the manager,' he says, 'immediately.'

" 'Yes, sir.'

"She goes and gets a man. 'Ready for the complaint,' he says.

" 'Are you the manager here?' he says.

" 'No, I'm the assistant manager.'

" 'Then go away and get me the manager of this place.'

" 'I'm very sorry, sir, but the manager has just stepped out. Is
there something I can do for you?'

" 'Stepped out at the peak of business?'

" 'Well, to tell you the truth, sir, he has been absent for some
time; he is indisposed, sir; he is at home in bed. Is there anything
I can do, sir?'

" 'Well, yes. You can get me one of those small boxes that you
people put your cupcakes into.'

" 'Yes, sir.'

" 'And then you can bring me some wax paper.'

" 'Yes, sir—anything else, sir?'

" 'No, that's all.'

"Well, when the assistant manager brings the stuff to the table,
my husband wraps up the steak in the wax paper—and mind you
there wasn't a thing wrong with it—and he says to the poor man:

15

" 'You know what I am going to do now? I'm going to the Hotel Pierre, to the thirty-second floor, where the owner of this restaurant lives'—he always seems to know things like that—'and I'm going to walk right in and show him this and ask him to explain to me how it is possible that an inedible piece of meat like this is put in front of a customer at Schrafft's.'

"So the poor man starts to beg:

" 'Oh, please sir, don't do that. Please excuse us, sir. Please let us get you another steak.'

"Well, I couldn't stand it any longer and I took the box and I told him what I thought of him. He got another steak and ate it, and I moved to another table so that people wouldn't think I was with him. Well, something just like that happened day before yesterday in Blois, when we went to visit the castle. Thank God, I'll never have to look at another castle in my life; that's another thing that makes me feel just dandy.

"You take a castle like Blois, with all those empty rooms you have to walk through. So because he speaks French, we have a French guide who speaks so fast that I only get a word now and then like Renaissance—and 'Glorious pages of our history,' which he said every few rooms. Well, we had a longer tour than anybody. Phil—that's my husband—kept asking a lot of questions. This happened with every door, picture, chimney, and tapestry. So when we're finally through the castle, the guide says that by the grace of God none of the churches in Blois were destroyed, so we have to visit them. And then, the guide says that religious architecture, interesting as it is, cannot rival the civilian edifices of Blois, and so we have to visit the house Pierre du Blois, and the Hôtel Sardini. I thought we might get something to eat at the Hôtel Sardini, but I found out that '*Hôtel*' can mean a private house in France as well as a regular hotel, and from there we go to the house of Robert the Magnificent. As we come out of the last house he says, 'We have just time to visit the museum'—so we go to the museum and by that time I am dead on my feet and hungry. The guide knows a good restaurant, he says, and next to this was the place. There were a lot of tourists and a waiter came with a menu, on it is a picture of Brillat-Sarvarin the Great Gourmet." She laughed bitterly at this point of her story,

1 6

and explained, "Phil taught me to appreciate life. The waiter recommended all the specialties of the house: a hot goose-liver paste with raisins, and then a pork sausage cooked in carrot soup. Phil made a face at the goose-liver and the pork sausage, and when the next dish came he got real mad, and called the waiter, and barked at him. But these Frenchmen are not like the people at Schrafft's. Phil asked for the proprietor. So the chef comes out of the kitchen and makes a terrible row. So Phil says he doesn't want to talk to the cook, he wants the proprietor, so the chef tells him that he is the proprietor. He called Phil a lot of names, and then ordered him out of the restaurant. He even followed us halfway up the street with quite a crowd following. Phil was stunned; he wouldn't go to another place, so we just quietly walked home and we had some tea at the hotel. After a while he began to complain. I guess he thought he could take it out on me. Well, I had heard the last complaint I was going to listen to, and for once I yelled right back at him, just like the chef. You should have seen the surprise on his face, when the worm finally turned."

All during this recital, the man opposite had slept peacefully without changing position. When the train stopped, however, he came to life with great suddenness. I had an old umbrella which got in his way and he stepped on it, breaking the ferrule. He seemed not to have noticed it and was out of the car in a great hurry, running with long, springy steps until he disappeared in the crowd of people heading for the exit.

The lady liberated from the château country and Phil said, "You know where I'm going now? I'm going to the American Express Company—he always hated it—he said it was only for tourists. Well, that's where I am going. I'll let them get me a room, and the next ship home, an American ship, I don't care if I have to travel steerage."

In many ways Paris is a large village. A week later, I saw her again in the Place de la Concorde. She still wore her liberty hat, but I was introduced to Phil who, it seems, had traced her through the American Express Company. They were on their way to the Louvre.

I have said that Paris is a village. I encountered the man who had sat opposite me on the train at a cocktail party at the Hôtel Georges V given by a steamship company to inaugurate a new service and to encourage tourist traffic in general. He stood at the end of a long buffet, which was piled high with food, munching quietly and sipping from a glass of champagne. He was attired in a blue suit and a pair of tan and white shoes. I noticed that his shoestrings were untied. His stomach sagged and his shoulders were pushed forward, he turned his head, and suddenly smiled and waved with a sandwich in my direction. Since he had been asleep during the voyage from Blois to Paris, I was astounded that he should appear to recognize me and greet me as though we were old acquaintances.

He put down his glass and came over to me and again I was struck by his resemblance to an agitated bird. He was no longer stooped, and his walk was a series of birdlike hopping movements and sudden stops. The skin of his face was a transparent green, and there was a constellation of black moles on his left cheek. He commented on the rigors of inspecting châteaux and on the woman who had shared our compartment. "You know, I had a sleepless night on her account," he said. "I kept thinking about her story. I felt so sorry for that assistant manager in the American restaurant. One always thinks of Americans as Millionaires, Gangsters, Cowboys, or Detectives—men of action—at any rate not as poor wretches like the assistant manager in Schrafft's."

"But I thought you were asleep," I said.

He offered me a cigarette from a large ivory case with a crown on its cover.

"There is a way of traveling cheaply in France," he said. "One simply gets on a train, sits down in a first-class compartment, and falls asleep. There is a law in France that no first-class passenger asleep may be awakened by a conductor. They may awaken you in second or third class, but never in first. Considering that we are a republic we have more regard for privilege than any other nation on earth." He took a glass dish from the buffet and offered me crackers with *pâté de foie gras*. He ate four of them very rapidly and held out his glass to be replenished by the waiter. He drank thirstily and continued: "There are other ways, but they are more difficult. For example, it is possible for two to travel on only one ticket. In this case, you simply wait for the approach of the conductor, and then you disappear with your friend into the washroom. As the conductor knocks, you open the door a little and hand him the one ticket to punch."

He introduced himself as the Count of St. Cucuface.

"This salad," he said, pointing at a bowl, "is what?"

"Chicken salad, Monsieur le Comte," said the butler. Cucuface took a silver spatula and put some on a plate and turned to eat it. He disposed of it with astonishing speed.

"There's St. Cucuface," said a man nearby to a woman in black velvet with a sparkle of diamonds at her ears, throat, wrists, and shoes. "He's one of the authentic antiques of France. Poor chap, he is now reduced to living off cocktail parties. He's the legs of the buffet; without him the table would fall down at that end. He's the first to come and the last to go."

Pushing people out of his way, advancing like a snow plow through the white summer dresses of the pretty young girls, a heavy man, jovial and self-assured in the company of his equals, bowing, and occasionally lifting a pudgy hand in greeting, moved toward the buffet, and, lifting the covers of the various chafing dishes, announced sadly that he was on a diet. He wandered toward the spot where St. Cucuface was inspecting a good-sized roast turkey. The bird was held by the fangs of a silver rack, and had been sliced into slabs, convenient to pick up and eat. The fat man took three slices of turkey and rolled them up. The turkey roll disappeared in one swallow, and immediately he started on another. St. Cucuface observed him with interest and proceeded to imitate him.

It was the time of plenty again. *Vogue* photographed fashion in Paris. *Life* photographed life in Cannes. The beautiful people were back in Paris, but some of them were still dissatisfied. The fat man munched steadily and then said to the woman in black velvet and diamonds:

"I'm going to open a hotel in Paris. A real hotel. The first thing I'm going to do is get some Canadian telephone operators, bilingual, you know, and trained to talk to you like human beings; not like these yapping old biddies you have to listen to now. Maybe you haven't done much telephoning, but over here the op-

19

erators do the talking and you do the listening. Yes sir, we'll have good telephone service, and you'll also be able to get real shoeshines. I'll get some Italians for that. Look at my shoes—" He held out a foot. "You know, it's impossible to get a decent shoeshine in France. And we won't have any of this lousy French cooking—I want some good American coffee, and dishes like you'd order at home: real toast, ham, and eggs. Do you know that in this whole damn country, from the Atlantic to the Mediterranean, you can't get a decent plate of ham and eggs? In fact, there is a conspiracy against breakfast. The other day I went into a place in Nice and asked for a half grapefruit for breakfast. Well, would you believe it, they served it to me, for breakfast, with liquor on it—they had doused it with Kirsch. Now, in our hotel you'll get a good American breakfast. And no tourists. You'll meet the right people. We'll have to be careful; it's for the rich of course—and by rich I mean rich. In July and August we might have to let the bars down and let in some bums; but for the rest of the time, it'll be just us."

"We're dining at eight at the Princess Stucci's. Come on, dear," said a voice. The fat man turned his back on St. Cucuface and moved away from the turkey of which now only the carcass was left.

St. Cucuface came to me and pulling out his cigarette case, said: "You will give me three thousand francs for this, no?" The franc had been stabilized. Three thousand francs was about ten dollars and I gave him the money. He expressed a wish to see me again and asked for my address.

"You are very fortunate," said a thin Austrian baron. "That is a sign that he likes you and has confidence in you. Cucu doesn't sell his cigarette case to just anybody."

I went home. At that time I lived in an old hotel in a most romantic setting and difficult of approach: the Hôtel St. Julien le Pauvre, on the Left Bank near the church of that same name. It was another authentic antique of France. The ancient silk of the curtains tore when one touched them, chairs occasionally collapsed as one sat down, the mattresses seemed to be stuffed with cabbages and the circular stairs sagged so badly that one could overcome the pull of gravity only by leaning at an angle to them

20

in the fashion of the motorcycle daredevils who negotiate perpendicular walls at county fairs. This hotel *de grand confort* had been my home for years before the war. There is nothing in the whole of America to compare with it; the only such place of old-world charm and discomfort that I have known was the old Bartholdy Inn, an actors' hangout near Times Square which burned down around 1920. The prices of the St. Julien le Pauvre, however, are absolutely first class.

A week after the cocktail party, St. Cucuface called on me. A little self-consciously, he announced that he had received an offer of fifteen thousand francs for the cigarette case he had sold me for three thousand, and he was sure, he said, that I would be happy to return it to him. "We will arrange the details later," he said, putting the cigarette case back in his coat pocket. From the courtyard of the hotel came the sound of dishes and the smell of cooking. Apparently there was no cocktail party that day, and St. Cucuface looked hungry; I asked him to dine with me: he accepted at once, saying, "I hope I can be of use to you."

ABOUT SERVANTS, AND HOW TO DINE
CHEAPLY IN FRANCE

The agility of the French mind in conjuring up appetizing names for eating places is remarkable. There is the Agile Rabbit, the Chope Danton, the Mediterranée, the Porquerolle, the Crémaillère, the Auberge du Fruit Défendu, the Coq Hardi. There are ten thousand restaurants of various categories in Paris serving every sort of appetite, nationality, and pocketbook. Restaurants for diabetics alone number more than a hundred and one of them is even named "Insulin." Besides that, every week someone discovers a new place, better than all the others. I had in one of my pockets a slip of paper with the address of the latest discovery and after I had found it, I wanted to call and reserve a table. Like all things in France, my telephone was an instrument of great personality. One could never bunch conversations; there had always to be pauses. St. Cucuface had just hung up after making a call, and therefore I had to wait for several minutes.

There was always a humming noise when you took off the receiver, the sound of a mosquito hovering near your ear, clear and insistent as on hot summer nights. This was followed by a barrage of rapid noises, rather like the assault of a flotilla of outboard motorboats racing, after which would come a click and then the voices of either of two operators. These ladies I could have drawn both in profile and in full face, simply from hearing their voices. One, a telephone functionary old in service, absolute and obstreperous and with all melody gone from her voice, with a bun of black hair on the back of her head; the other also a veteran of similar format and age, but giving off a few, faint vibrations. In her, the woman was not altogether dead, it flickered only briefly, like the last reflected sunlight in one of the many windows of a large factory: a flash of light and then only the dead dusty panes again. It was the second one, the occasionally illuminated operator, who answered as I took the phone off its hook.

I gave the number of the restaurant and after a while I got it. I said I wanted to reserve a table.

"For whom?"

"For Monsieur Bemelmans—"

"Will you spell it please?"

In France, B is *boe*, e is *oe*—

"*Boe—oe, em, oe*—No no no—*Boe*—as in *boeuf*—"

The telephone girl at the restaurant was apparently also temperamental, for she said, "Never mind, Monsieur, don't disturb yourself, we haven't any tables left," and hung up.

Since in most French restaurants, of this type, the telephone girl and coatroom woman are one and the same and usually either the wife, relative, or a former mistress of the proprietor, there is little use in asking for the owner. Over the hum of the phone, I could hear the voices of the place and then the sound of the outboard motors and the hum of the mosquito. I hung up and as we were debating where to go, the phone rang, and the unexpected, that always happens in France, happened. It was my operator number two, who said she had called the restaurant back and spelled my name for them and had also delivered herself of a few opinions on the treatment of tourists in Paris and that the table was now properly engaged and awaiting us.

The elaborate pleasantries which are necessary to properly express gratitude for such service above and beyond the call of duty are endless. The lamplighter had done the entire square in front of St. Julien le Pauvre when at last all the various compliments and expressions of gratitude were exhausted.

"Now where is this wonderful place?" asked St. Cucuface. I gave him the slip of paper but on it was only the telephone number. I had forgotten the name of the place. So there was the problem of making another call. Since we had just finished a lengthy conversation over the telephone it required a rest, and after a second cooling-off period the address of the new restaurant was finally obtained.

As we walked down the circular stairway, St. Cucuface said: "You know, you have all the attributes of the perfect tourist: patience, meekness, persistence, endurance, and most important of all, perpetual curiosity. I can almost guarantee that from the way this has begun that we are going to spend an uncomfortable evening."

Few things are more difficult to bear than the responsibility for another's well being. We sat silently in the cab, and Cucuface referred again to the matter of the assistant manager at Schrafft's in New York:

"I had no idea that anything like that existed in America. At least I never came across it when I was there. In fact, I found quite the opposite: the cowboy, the gangster spirit. I was at the time very fond of a lady who had invited me to her place on Long Island. She had a butler. In America I suffer your difficulties with my name—here in France St. Cucuface is not unusual. It is an old and distinguished name; there are hundreds of us: dukes, princes, marquises, and counts. In America the name Cucuface makes people laugh. The hostess naturally called me Cucu and so did everybody who came to the house. The only person who had some regard for me was that butler.

" 'Count,' he said to me, 'you don't know what a pleasure it is to serve you. I am so sick of these bastards.' He supervised my

23

valet, who was also very friendly, as he unpacked my bags. I had a bungalow with a pantry with an icebox and in the icebox there was always a ham, a roast chicken, caviar, champagne, beer, milk, soda, and potato salad. In the living room was a bar stocked with whisky and gin so that I could entertain. The formal dinner was of course served at the big house. The butler complained a great deal. He spent more time in my bungalow than at the house and once I said to him, 'You don't have to answer me—but what do you get paid?' 'Oh,' he said, 'not really enough for all the trouble I have. She pays me two hundred and fifty dollars a month and a few extras.' 'What do you mean by extras?' 'Oh, I have a house, and she sends my children to school, and here and there something like a station wagon or some other gift, and she always remembers the wife's and the kids' birthdays.'

"Just before I left, he came again. 'Count, may I take all this junk?' He meant the ham, the chicken that was always there, the champagne and caviar and the liquor. 'Certainly you may,' I told him. He put it all into a hamper and went off with it in the direction of his house.

"He must have stolen thousands of dollars' worth of things a year. The hostess had no conception of the value of things. There was a robbery in her house while I was there, but she never reported it. Her husband had a horror of reporters and of publicity. Anyone could have taken anything at that house. But to go back to servants—

"A few months later in New York I had another bad experience. A friend invited me to dinner at his house. He had told me only the week before what a magnificent cook he had. At the last minute he called and said that instead of dining at his house, we would go to a restaurant in New York called the Pavillion. When I met him there his wife said, 'Forgive us, but our servants decided to leave. We had invited two other people we wanted you to meet, and we had forgotten to tell the cook in time; that is, we told her at five. So she and the butler, the kitchenmaid, and the valet all left.' Just then our waiter came to the table jingling some car keys. He gave them to my friend saying, 'Your chauffeur sent these. He has left the car outside.' He had resigned also.

24

"So we ate a very good dinner and I thought of my good Salvatore, my Italian servant, to whom I have sometimes given my socks at midnight to wash for the next day, saying: 'Here, wash them and darn them so I can put them on tomorrow.' And he will smile and say, 'Certainly, quickly.' He refers to *our* house, *our* garden, and to my three shirts as 'our laundry.' In the country I pay him three dollars a month and when I don't have the three dollars he will not ask for them until he knows I can spare them. I am like his father. My God, that butler in Long Island, he lived more like a prince than I ever did."

With the aid of a policeman and a little boy who ran beside the cab, we finally arrived at the restaurant. The place was crowded and the headwaiter had a list of reservations. He tilted his head and I went into the spelling game again. His pencil moved up and down the row of names written on the back of a menu and he shook his head. We suffered the stares of several attendants and of the coatroom girl. I finally asked for the proprietor and told him that I was a great friend of so-an-so and of others and that the place had been recommended to me by a famous gourmet. He listened with some sympathy and surveyed the room, and then he motioned us to the lobby. We sat down near the swinging door that led out into a dirty corridor and after about half an hour we followed a bill of fare held aloft by the headwaiter and were shown to a table far in the back and so small that as we sat down our knees bumped together.

"Do you mind?" said Cucuface, as he arose. "My poor friend, you must never allow them to do that to you again. Let's get out of here." We got up; Cucuface stopped in the foyer and offered me a cigarette from the beautiful ivory case. "Do you always live like this?" he asked in a tone of compassion, putting an immense hand on my shoulder.

The proprietor, suffering from an automatic reflex, had pulled a match from a box and lighted my cigarette.

"I never eat anywhere where I am not properly received," said Cucuface, taking a light himself.

"Is there anything wrong, Messieurs?" asked the proprietor anxiously.

"Where is the telephone?" asked Cucuface ominously. The telephone was a few feet away attached to a gilded column. St. Cucuface snapped his fingers for the page who attended to the opening and closing of the inner door of the establishment.

"*Chasseur*," he said to him or rather to a spot several feet above the proprietor's head, "get me Maxim's." He made it sound as though he had said, "Get me the police."

When the famous restaurant answered, he said in a voice loud enough for the proprietor to hear: "Albert, a table for two for the Prince de Bavière."

The proprietor laid a trembling hand on the arm of Cucuface and summoned the headwaiter. "You head of veal," he shouted, and turning to Cucuface he began to implore him: "Monsieur le Prince, one moment please." Cucuface said, pointing to me, "That is the Prince, I am merely the Marquis de St. Cucuface." He demanded his hat, cane, and gloves, the coatroom girl stood with a deck of stubs in her hand and looked helplessly at the proprietor; the page boy barred the door. "Come, my dear friend," said Cucuface to me.

"*Mon Prince,* Monsieur le Marquis," pleaded the proprietor, holding both hands up before St. Cucuface's chest, and then bowing, "do not, I beg you, make me suffer for the stupidity of my employees—allow me—"

The coatroom girl had mirrored the various emotions of the owner of the place.

Finally Cucuface allowed himself to be persuaded. The proprietor guided us to a freshly laid table in the best possible position. He begged to be allowed to order the dinner. "Certainly," said Cucuface graciously. "All but the wine." He proceeded to examine the wine card carefully, and the wine waiter and the chastened maître d'hôtel exchanged glances of approval at the selection the Marquis was pleased to make. The menu was superb, the wine was all the name and the year promised and the oldest brandy was served in thin, large, warmed inhalers. It was all exactly as it was supposed to be and so seldom is.

"Allow me," said St. Cucuface as he asked for the bill. The proprietor came running again. He begged, "Monsieur le Prince, Monsieur le Marquis, I beg you, do not make me suffer further. It is all my pleasure. There is no bill."

In a First-class Compartment

Cucuface now reached for his wallet, an extremely thin, worn, and empty-looking envelope of black leather also decorated with a crown. Again the proprietor protested, "Please, it is all taken care of. I hope you have enjoyed your dinner. Is there anything else you desire?"

"Yes," said St. Cucuface. "I have a dog, and I wonder if I might have a small bone for him?"

"Ah, but certainly," said the proprietor. He ran out into the kitchen and came back with a plate of roast beef bones and some meat, which he wrapped in a menu and tied with a string.

We departed through an aisle of bowing waiters.

"I hope I have been of some use to you," said St. Cucuface to me. "I felt I owed you a dinner."

A. K. Lewis

The youngest contributor to this collection, Andy Lewis was born in 1926. True to the best New England tradition, he went to Exeter and Harvard—and in between spent three years in the infantry. After Harvard he got married, and then turned around and worked for the university for two years. The next move took him a little farther, although not too far from Cambridge. With his wife, Sally, and his small son, Danny, he moved to a development in Concord, Massachusetts, where he is learning to become a milkman. Lewis' morning chores should pay for most of the groceries and still leave him the afternoons and evenings free. Since he has a refreshing heartiness—like a brisker and somewhat tougher Max Shulman—it is hoped that his yield, both as milkman and writer, will be amply rewarding.

The Lady or the Sergeant*

"The hand salute," the sergeant said to them, "wich is accompliced in the following manner. Standing at the position of attention, the arm is brought up so as the upper arm—wich is the part between your elbas and your shoulders—is par'lel with the ground. The forearm—wich is the part from the elbas out to the end—is resting just above the eyebra, fingers extendit and joined. You got me?"

"His mother wouldn't let him in the house," said Spirito to Hearn. "So's he come back to the Army."

"And this is your right arm I'm talking about," said the sergeant. "Don't forget that. And I don't want to see none of youse doing these fancy salutes like you was catching flies and throwing them at the officas. Officas attrack enough flies without you throw any more at them. . . . You, soldier."

"Me?" said Spirito.

"That's right," said the sergeant. "You think this is pretty funny. Now you show us the hand salute, and hold it. . . . Thank you; that's very pretty. Now the rest of youse look at here. The right hand is fine. The left hand—wich is supposed to be at

28

the position of attention, down along the trousas—is scratching.
. . . Soldier," he asked Spirito, "why is the left hand scratching?"

"The left leg itches," said Spirito.

"Very funny," said the sergeant. "A real humorous, ain't he?
. . . Soldier, what was you before?"

"A tap dancer," said Spirito. "I worked around the garage
some, but mostly I was a tap dancer."

"A dancer," said the sergeant admiringly. "A entertaina. No
wonda you are so funny. Would you like to show me a step or
two?"

"Ah, now, sarge," said Spirito.

"No, you show me," said the sergeant. . . . "Thank you;
that's very nice. Do another one. My goodness! . . . Ain't that
nice, boys?" They all nodded.

"Now," said the sergeant, "I have another step for you. It's
called the duck-walk, wich is in the position of squatting down,
only you walk. And I would like for you to duck-walk down to
that tree and back."

"Tree?" asked Spirito, peering across the drill field.

"Ther's a tree down there someweres," said the sergeant. "Take
off."

Spirito duck-walked for a long way, past the other basic-
training platoons, until he found a tree. He thought of straighten-
ing up, but every time he looked back in the distance, the sergeant seemed to be watching him. When he returned, his breath
was hot and there was a tear in his eyes.

"My goodness," said the sergeant. "That was the wrong tree.
You go back down to the other tree. And quack this time."

"Wak," said Spirito, starting off.

"Louder," said the sergeant. "You're a big duck."

"Wak," said Spirito.

"That's some better," said the sergeant.

"He is a mean guy," said Hearn to Spirito that evening in barracks. "He don't like for you to clap off to him. You better keep
your clapper shut."

"I bear him no ill will," said Spirito. "I'm going to the Service
Club and dancet."

"Who is going to dance with a basic private like you?" asked Hearn.

"There's two ways," said Spirito. "Either the Army gets you down or you get the Army down. Watch oncet." Out of his foot locker he got the white web belt and the black tie and the dark tan buckle-over shoes. He put them on.

"It ain't regulation," said Hearn doubtfully.

"It's close enough," said Spirito. On his head he put the garrison hat with the crushed edges, and across his chest he hung a ladder of sharpshooter medals and a silver whistle. "See what I mean?"

"I don't know," said Hearn. "Partly you look like an MP, and partly like a birdman." But he was impressed, and Spirito hurried out of the company area with a light heart.

The Service Club was the scene of great violence. The soldiers stood in a ring, three deep, around the dance floor. Inside the ring, the couples threshed about, spun, kicked, threw each other away, dodged, and came hurtling back together again. One after another, the hardy souls on the outside inserted themselves between the flying bodies, seized the women of their choice, and wrestled them loose from their opponents. Spirito moved lightly about the outskirts for a time, watching.

Deep in the interior he saw a young woman in khaki, with fair skin, cherry-red lips, and dark, curly hair that hung down far lower than it should have.

"A lady soldier," said Spirito to himself. "A Wac. On the post —on the very post itself." He flung himself toward her, evaded two elbows, a pillar and a loose blonde, and cut in.

"May I have this dancet?" he asked.

"I——" she said. And someone else cut in on Spirito.

He went back to the edge, dismayed, then turned and fought his way back to her.

"You talk my language," said Spirito with his lips close to her ear. "Leave me buy you a drink."

"O.K.," she said, and slipped her small hand into his. "What do you callit, this fella asked me, when you got a ingrown toenail on your thumb. Curious, ain't it?"

They went over to the soft-drink machine.

"You're gorgeous," said Spirito, standing close to her. "Even in uniform you're gorgeous. Supple, you know what I mean?"

"Thanks," she said. "I wonder if there's any trout in the Wehatchee River. Gee, my old man used to take me fishing all the time."

"They say a beautiful woman shouldn't be clever," said Spirito. "But you're both—beautiful and clever." He opened the bottle for her.

"I seen the man loading one of these up once," she said. "You'd never guess how many bottles they get inside. . . . Lookit; Sun Down, Sun Up is at Theater Number Seven. That's with Essex Flint and Marlene Mako. I really go for that biscuit."

"He sings better than he dances," said Spirito, trying to keep up. "I heard you humming back there. I bet you have a marvelous set of pipes."

"He's the Cazenovia type," said the girl. "They're going back to that now. What do you know about dancetin'?"

"I only do it for a living," said Spirito widely. "Look." He showed her the same steps he had shown the sergeant. "Of course, I work around the garage some too."

"No kidding," she said, interested. "A dancer. I was going to be the green fairy once, but I got the measles. A real dancer. How come they drafted you? My brother was, but he's loose now."

"A dancer?"

"No, drafted."

"Let's get outside," said Spirito. "Away from all this."

"Might as well," she said. "He's kind of a jerk."

"Your brother?"

"No, my boy friend."

They went out of the Service Club and around to the side, into the weed thickets where the water pipes went down into the ground.

"The stars," said Spirito. "I'd like to pick them out of the sky and make a necklace for you."

"I knew a streetcar conductor once," she said, "that had six toes on his foot."

31

The noise from inside the building was subdued. The girl breathed deeply and tucked in her shirt. She was a splendid sight, leaning against the cement blocks, and Spirito's heart leaped to his throat.

"A night like this," he said desperately, "a man will be a man, and a woman will be a woman, if you get me."

"A what?"

"A woman."

"I sure am gonna see that picture at Theater Number Seven," she said. . . . "Oh, is that what you want?" She offered her dark full lips to Spirito.

He was using them vigorously when a vague, familiar shape loomed around the corner.

"Louise," said the sergeant huskily, "I been looking all over. What are you doing here?"

"Neckin'," she said directly.

"Who is this guy?" asked the sergeant. . . . "Do I know you, pal?"

"It's been truly memorable, Louise," said Spirito hastily. "If you'll excuse me, I will see how they are getting on with that phone call to my aunt."

"Are you making a phone call?" she asked. "Stick around; don't let Tiger worry you."

"It's a long-distance call," he said. "To Missoula, Montana. I got to be going."

"Stick around," she said. "We didn't hardly get started. . . . Ain't he cute, Tiger? He's a dancer."

"Louise," said the sergeant humbly, "you can't do this to me."

"My aunt makes blueberry pies," she said. "I sure wish I had some blueberry pie. . . . Run away, Tiger, and bite someone."

Spirito explained the whole thing to Hearn next morning after breakfast. "She says she's in love with me. I'm in love with her too. If it was on the outside, I'd get married or something. . . . What are you looking at?"

"I'm looking at the holes in your head," said Hearn. "The sarge will kill you."

"How corny can he get? Besides, I got a plan."

"You better have a plan," said Hearn. "You better plan to poison yourself."

"If you're a perfect soldier," said Spirito, "what can they do to you? Look again." He showed Hearn all the manuals in the locker. "I hooked them from the day room. Basic Field Manual, Rifle, Machine Gun, Close Combat, Camouflage, Etiquette. Give me a week, I'll know more than the sarge. He can't touch me. What do you think?"

"I think this woman better be a dish," said Hearn. "That's what I think."

"The position of inspection arms," the sergeant said to them, "wich is accomplied in the following manner. Standing at the position of attention, the piece is brought up to port arms. Open the receiver with the ball of your left thumb, looking down as you do so, so as to see there ain't anything inside, returning to a position of port arms, with your eyes looking straight ahead. This is your left thumb I'm talking about. Any questions?"

No one asked any questions.

"Wen you see the inspecting offica drop his left shoulder," said the sergeant, "it means he is reaching for the piece. Cut your hands away, so as when he grabs it, it is standing in the middle of the air. If an offica don't catch it, he is supposed to clean it for you. I will now move down the line, inspecting."

When he came to Spirito, Spirito executed the maneuver with great precision. The sergeant dropped his shoulder. Spirito dropped the rifle. It thudded softly into the thick dust.

"Clean it," said the sergeant, "and bring it to me at nine o'clock tonight."

"How come?" asked Spirito. "You said if an officer missed it, he had to clean it himself."

"Quite right," said the sergeant. "I ain't an offica. Now duck-walk. Anything else?"

"Wak," said Spirito. "Wak-wak."

"You are doing so much duck-walking," said Hearn, "that feathers are growing on your neck."

Spirito gave him a short answer.

"One thing," said Hearn. "With all this special individual exercise you're getting, you should ought to turn into a real specimen."

"It's no good for my legs," said Spirito. "A dancer has got to stay limber, see?"

"You had better give that broad back to him," said Hearn.

"She's my revenge," said Spirito. "Besides, we're in love. Nothing is stronger than love."

"K.P. is stronger than love," said Hearn.

Spirito spent as much time with Louise as he could. She wasn't hard to entertain.

"I told that sergeant to go hide," she said. "I like you better. I like a man that talks while he's lovin'. That Tiger, that bum."

Something like caution came to Spirito. "Maybe you shouldn't be so rough on him. He's not a bad fella; kid him along a little."

"Him?" said Louise with scorn. "He reminds me of my cousin that busted the man with a ax. You know, that's where most of the burlap comes from—prison, I mean."

"I would like to take you away from all this, in a convertible," said Spirito. "You're lovely."

"Well, you don't have to just talk," she said.

When he was not with Louise, Spirito spent most of his time studying the manuals. Over the period of the next few weeks he learned the names of all the parts of the machine gun, how to fold the flag, which side of a general to walk on, the general orders for guard duty, and the names of four different kinds of latrine. His cot was neat and his uniforms hung in order.

"You," said the sergeant. "What is the weight of the rifle?"

Spirito told him.

"How long is it?"

Spirito told him.

"What's its muzzle velocity?"

Spirito told him.

"How far is it to the tree down there?"

"About a hundred and seventy yards," said Spirito. "Give or take ten."

"You're wrong," said the sergeant. "It's a hundred and twenty-five. Duck-walk to it."

"Wak," said Spirito. "Wak-wak."

"There's no use your studying up," said Hearn. "What good is it you know how all the different gases're supposed to smell like? You better give that woman back and forget it."

"I'm learning," said Spirito stubbornly.

"You're learning how to clean the grease trap," said Hearn. "How many times you been on K.P.?"

"I tried to tell her gradual," said Spirito, "but she don't pay any attention. He keeps coming around. You should hear the things she says to him."

"You better cut her loose."

"Not all at once," said Spirito. "Basic don't last forever. Besides, you got to be a gentleman."

Spirito tried to disentangle himself gently from the beautiful Louise—not in order to lose her completely, but in hopes of making room for the sergeant.

It was no use. She waited for him in the Service Club and the PX, and sometimes, when she didn't find him there, over at the company area itself. She sent him notes, and on his birthday, in time for inspection, a pair of red knitted bedroom slippers. "I figure I am nuts about you," she said. "There's a new Essex Flint picture coming to Theater Number Seven."

"Louise," said Spirito, "I don't know how long we can go on this way."

"Why not?" she said. "It used to make me dizzy, but I like it now. Don't you feel good?"

"I don't want to make you cruel to others," said Spirito. "Love is no good if it makes you cruel to others."

"You talking about that Tiger again?" she asked. "Let's us go to see Essex Flint tonight. You know, there was a girl in our county that came in fifth in a bathing-suit contest. Only she married a fight promoter over to Bergen."

35

They went to the theater and saw Essex Flint.

"What's that step he's doing now?" asked Louise.

"It's a three-quarters nelson," said Spirito gloomily. . . . "Louise, we got to think about this thing."

"Do you know what the three biggest lumber-producing states are?" asked Louise. "I was reading it today. . . . What's that step now?"

"A cross body scissors and a wristlock," said Spirito. . . . "You should spend some of your time with somebody else. Get me out of your system, know what I mean?"

"Tiger said once he figured he could kill you in about fourteen weeks," said Louise absently. "How come it would take fourteen weeks to kill anyone?" She chewed gum and thought, while he slid down in the seat. "You know what; I had a Teddy bear once, only the leg came off and we had to send it all the way to Chicago to get it fixed."

"The vertical butt stroke," said the sergeant, "wich is accompliced by bringing the end of your rifle up under his chin full strent' of your shoulder and arm. Keep your elba underneath the swing, and most likely his head will come off. . . . Soldier!"

"Me?" asked Spirito.

"Stand ova there," said the sergeant.

"You got it wrong," said Spirito, backing away. "It was just to make you jealous."

"Stan' still," said the sergeant. "The last time I done this, the fella moved and I killed him. . . . Now then, youse others. Watch this."

"I figured your number was up," said Hearn, later on. "You should 'a' seen the look in that man's eye."

"It was right in front of me," said Spirito. "How many more times we got bayonet this week?"

"Three times," said Hearn. "You had better write your family—and send them manuals along too."

"I got to give that girl up," said Spirito.

"Now you make sense," said Hearn.

"Maybe I could make friends with him," said Spirito.

"Sure," said Hearn. "Like patting a circular saw."

"I got to give her up," said Spirito, "but she don't give easy. I try boffing her around oncet in a whiles. 'I like that,' she says. 'Mean stuff. Valentino stuff.' Once I phoned her up to meet me outside of camp, and I didn't go. She didn't mind; she went to a church fair and they had a community sing. 'I figure you got held up,' she says. 'I sure do like that row, row, row your boat over and over again.' What can I do I ain't already tried?"

"Write her a letter."

"I did," said Spirito. " 'I can't go on living a lie,' I said. 'Our love is dead. Go to one who needs you more.' "

"That's plain enough," said Hearn.

" 'Your letters are crazy,' she says to me. 'I sure do get a laugh out of a crazy letter. I had a sister used to write to the president of the bank. Like to drove him out of his mind.' "

"I don't know," said Hearn. "I don't know what you're going to do."

"Once I seen him walking along," said Spirito. "I sent her out to meet him. 'He wants one last word with you,' I said. 'He's suffering.' So she goes out there. 'Go fry an egg,' is all she said to him. 'Go fry an egg.' "

"Basic don't last forever."

"Neither do I," said Spirito.

The weeks went on. They went out on the range and came back. They went on bivouac and came back. Spirito became almost used to pulling all the details. Whenever he finished, Louise was there, and he became used to that too—as if he had stepped into a bucket of cement.

As the end of basic training approached, he stopped trying to shake her loose. Love had purified him, and he weighed eighteen pounds more than he had ever weighed in his life before.

The sergeant took them all out to the obstacle course—pits, fences, pipes, and hurdles that stretched away farther than the eye could see. "I figure you all ought to do pretty good on this here. I'll be waiting for you at the end. . . . You, soldier."

"Me?" asked Spirito.

"Come here," said the sergeant, and led him away. "I figure your legs been getting a lot of exercise."

Spirito, craftily, said nothing.

"The record on this course is eight minutes, fifteen seconds," said the sergeant. "I figure you are a pretty fast boy, a big, sharp soldier, an' a couple of other things I could think of."

"Well——" said Spirito. There was no hate left in him.

"So, I'll tell you," said the sergeant. "I'll give you just eight minutes, even, to run it—this here obstacle course. And if you don't make it in that time, I am going to have you duck-walk it back. It'll be the longest duck walk in your whole life, and I am going to follow along behind and see you do it."

"Sarge," said Spirito, "I forgive you. You are love's puppet."

"You ain't so bad yourself," said the sergeant. "Eight minutes, even."

Spirito went back to the others. "Hearn," he said, "tell them I was a good guy."

"What'd he say to you?" asked Hearn.

"Go," said the sergeant.

Spirito ran like the wind, jumped over the pits, over the fences, crawled through the pipes, fell down, picked himself up, and ran on. The others fell behind. After a while he stopped feeling bad and listened to the sounds his breath made slithering in and out of his lungs. The image of Louise hung before him for a while, and then went about its own business. He swung across the river on a rope. The sounds of his breathing grew louder and threatened to drown out the thoughts he was thinking about why he was running at all. The picture of the obstacle course began to get black and furry at the edges, and the blackness crept in on him until there was only a pinhole left for him to look through. He climbed over another fence, and there were the sergeant and the colonel, and he crossed the finish line and rolled over on his back.

When he came to, the sergeant was rubbing his stomach. Spirito was still groggy. He rolled over, squatted down, put his hands on his hips, and started back. "Wak-wak."

"You done it in eight minutes, five seconds," said the sergeant.

"I figured," said Spirito. "Wak-wak."

"Come over here, soldier," said the colonel, and Spirito duck-walked back to him.

"Stand up," said the sergeant, and Spirito stood up.

"What is the name of the big spring in the machine gun?" asked the colonel.

Spirito told him.

"What is the fifth general order for guard?" asked the colonel, and Spirito told him.

"Name three different gases and tell me what they smell like," said the colonel.

Spirito did so.

The colonel turned away. "Sergeant," he asked the sergeant, "did you teach this man all these things?"

"He made me learn them," said Spirito, "sir."

"Sergeant," said the colonel, "I am going to make you a staff sergeant and this man here a corporal, and keep him here to train other men."

"Yes, sir," said Spirito and the sergeant.

"I figure this was my day," said Spirito to Hearn that evening. "I figure this was really my day."

"You done all right," said Hearn. "Whereabouts you going?"

"Down to the Service Club," said Spirito. He put on a plain brown web belt, his combat boots, and an overseas cap. He threw the black necktie in the corner with the sharpshooter badges and the tin whistle.

The sergeant came in. "I figure I been pretty rough," he said to Spirito, "but I made a soldier out of you." He sat on the edge of the cot.

"It's O.K., sarge," said Spirito generously. "We all make mistakes."

"You run that obstacle course pretty good," said the sergeant. "You done pretty good."

"Thank you, sarge," said Spirito.

"You know what a soldier should know," said the sergeant. "I figure I been too hard on you. I shouldn't let my sentences interfere with my duty like I did."

"Leave us forget it all," said Spirito. He extended his hand. "Shake."

The sergeant shook his hand. "One last thing," he said. "I put you on K.P. tomorrow, on account of you didn't run it in eight minutes flat." He went away.

Most of the way to the Service Club, Spirito was hating the sergeant worse than anyone he'd ever known in his life. When he got closer to the club and heard the music, he began to feel better. Basic training was going to be over in a week, and he and the sergeant were going to part.

"Louise," he said, half aloud, "this is the beginning of a new life."

As before, the club was the scene of violence. Spirito looked at the dancers calmly, squared his shoulders, and walked around the floor. After he had gone around three times, admiring his reflection in the glass, he went outside to look for her. Instinct led him around the side of the building to the weed patch. There were other couples there.

" 'Scuse me," said Spirito, stumbling over them. There was darkness at the end of the building where the water pipes ran down. "Louise," he said, "is that you there? Who is this joker?"

"A fella," said Louise graciously.

"What're you doing?" Spirito demanded.

"Neckin'," said Louise. "Go fry an egg."

40

Jack Finney

Born in Milwaukee, Wisconsin, married to a beautiful if occasionally belligerent (in a nice way) wife, Jack Finney has been suspected of exploiting his domestic background in many of his short stories. At any rate, Finney's growing saga about Timberlake and Eve Ryan is a round-by-round, story-by-story case history of as charming a couple of loving antagonists as the reader would care to encounter. In "Quit Zoomin' Those Hands Through the Air" Finney temporarily deserts somewhat dramatized autobiography for dramatic science fiction, a form in which he is also expert.

Complying with the editors' request for recent data, Finney replied: "In 1950 I told you, quite accurately, that I had a beautiful Canadian as wife, critic, and collaborator, and that I was 38 years old. But late that year, my wife, although she felt fine, went to the hospital, and returned, pounds lighter, carrying a baldheaded noisemaker. We have been busy ever since, and I am now 63. The noisemaker has become heavier, taller, and louder, and some of the noises are now dimly recognizable as words. Since this has happened, a debate has begun between my wife and me. She insists that the child, while admittedly half American, is also half Canadian, is insultingly specific about which half is which, and has begun educating the upper half in Canadian mythology (the lower half is still completely uneducated). She assures this innocent child, for example, that Canada defeated the Yankees (that's us) in an important Revolutionary battle. This is absurd, of course, but since I got nowhere arguing it, I fell back on American law which claims the entire girl as citizen. This has done no good either, and I suspect that while I am at work writing funny stories (I know for a fact that they're funny because several critics have said, "Finney's attempts at writing are laughable") our daughter is being educated to revere Queen Elizabeth. I am counterattacking with a follow-up on my Civil War story; a tale of the Revolution proving that Benedict Arnold was a Toronto spy.

"Now for some cute sayings by Marguerite, Jr. One night, just before bedtime, she looked up at us with the cutest expression, and . . ." (Because of the publisher's insistence on including other material in this volume, the rest of Finney's material has been omitted.)

Quit Zoomin' Those Hands Through the Air*

Hey, quit zoomin' your *hands* through the air, boy—I know you was a flier! You flew *good* in the war, course you did; I'd expect that from a grandson of mine. But don't get to thinking you know all about war, son, or flying machines either. The war we finished in '65 is still the toughest we've fought, and don't you forget it. It was a big war fought by big men, and your Pattons and Arnolds and Stilwells—they were *good,* boy, no denying it—but Grant, there was a general. Never told you about this before, because I was swore to secrecy by the General himself, but I think it's all right, now; I think the oath has expired. Now, *quiet,* boy! Put those hands in your pockets and listen!

Now, the night I'm talking about, the night I met the General, I didn't know we'd see him at all. Didn't know anything except we were riding along Pennsylvania Avenue, me and the Major, him not saying where we were going or why, just jogging along, one hand on the reins, a big black box strapped to the Major's saddle in front, and that little pointy beard of his stabbing up and down with every step.

It was late, after ten, and everyone was asleep. But the moon was up, bright and full through the trees, and it was nice—the horses' shadows gliding along sharp and clear beside us, and not a sound in the street but their hoofs, hollow on the packed dirt. We'd been riding two days, I'd been nipping some liberated applejack—only we didn't say liberated then; we called it foraging—and I was asleep in the saddle, my trumpet jiggling in the small of my back. Then the Major nudged me, and I woke up and saw the White House ahead. "Yessir," I said.

He looked at me, the moon shining yellow on his epaulets, and said, real quiet, "Tonight, boy, we may win the war. You and I." He smiled, mysterious, and patted the black box. "You know who I am, boy?"

"Yessir."

"No, you don't. I'm a professor. Up at Harvard College. Or

* Reprinted from *Collier's* Magazine.

was, anyway. Glad to be in the Army now, though. Pack of fools up there, most of them; can't see past the ends of their noses. Well, tonight, boy, we may win the war."

"Yessir," I said. Most officers higher than captain were a little queer in the head, I'd noticed, majors especially. That's how it was then, anyway, and I don't reckon it's changed any, even in the Air Force.

We stopped near the White House at the edge of the lawn and sat looking at it—a great big old house, silvery white in the moonlight, the light over the front door shining out through the porch columns onto the driveway. There was a light in an east window on the ground floor, and I kept hoping I'd see the President, but I didn't. The Major opened his box. "Know what this is, boy?"

"Nosir."

"It's my own invention based on my own theories, nobody else's. They think I'm a crackpot up at the School, but I think it'll work. Win the war, boy." He moved a little lever inside the box. "Don't want to send us too far ahead, son, or technical progress will be beyond us. Say, eighty-five years from now, approximately; think that ought to be about right?"

"Yessir."

"All right." The Major jammed his thumb down on a little button in the box; it made a humming sound that kept rising higher and higher till my ears began to hurt; then he lifted his hand. "Well," he said, smiling and nodding, the little pointy beard going up and down, "it is now some eighty-odd years later." He nodded at the White House. "Glad to see it's still standing."

I looked up at the White House again. It was just about the same, the light still shining out between the big white columns, but I didn't say anything.

The Major twitched his reins and turned. "Well, boy, we've got work ahead; come on." And he set off at a trot along Pennsylvania Avenue with me beside him.

Pretty soon we turned south, and the Major twisted around in his saddle and said, "Now, the question is, what do they have in the future?" He held up his finger like a teacher in school, and I believed the part about him being a professor. "We don't know," the Major went on, "but we know where to find it. In a museum. We're going to the Smithsonian Institution, if it's still standing. For us it should be a veritable storehouse of the future."

It had been standing last week, I knew, and after a while, off across the grass to the east, there it was, a stone building with towers like a castle, looking just the same as always, the windows now blank and white in the moonlight. "Still standing, sir," I said.

"Good," said the Major. "Reconnaissance approach, now," and we went on to a cross street and turned into it. Up ahead were several buildings I'd never noticed before, and we went up to them and swung down off our horses. "Walk between these buildings," the Major said, leading his horse. "Quiet, now; we're reconnoitering."

We crept on, quiet as could be, in the shadows between the two buildings. The one to the right looked just like the Smithsonian to me, and I knew it must be a part of it; another building I'd never seen before. The Major was all excited now, and kept whispering. "Some new kind of weapon that will destroy the whole Rebel Army is what we're looking for. Let me know if you see any such thing, boy."

"Yessir," I said, and I almost bumped into something sitting out there in the open in front of the building at the left. It was big and made entirely out of heavy metal, and instead of wheels it rested on two movable belts made of metal; big flat plates linked together.

"Looks like a tank," said the Major, "though I don't know what they keep in it. Keep moving, boy; this thing is obviously no use on a battlefield."

We walked on just a step, and there on the pavement in front of us was a tremendous cannon, three times bigger than any I'd ever seen before in my life. It had an immense long barrel, wheels high as my chest, and it was painted kind of funny, in wavy stripes and splotches, so that you could hardly see it at first in the moonlight that got down between the buildings. "Look at that thing!" the Major said softly. "It would pulverize Lee in an hour, but I don't know how we'd carry it. No," he said, shaking his head, "this isn't it. I wonder what they've got inside, though." He stepped up to the doors and peered in through the glass, shading his eyes with his hand. Then he gasped and turned to me.

I went up beside him and looked through the glass. It was a long, big building, the moonlight slanting in through the windows all along one side; and all over the floor, and even hanging from the ceiling, were the weirdest-looking things I ever saw. They were each big as a wagon, some bigger, and they had wheels, but only two wheels, near the front; and I was trying to figure that out when the Major got his voice back.

"Aircraft, by God!" he said. "They've got aircraft! Win the war!"

"Air what, sir?"

"*Aircraft.* Flying machines. They fly through the air. Don't you see the wings, boy?"

Each of the machines I could see inside had two things sticking out at each side like oversize ironing boards, but they looked stiff to me, and I didn't see how they could flap like wings. I didn't know what else the Major could be talking about, though. "Yessir," I said.

But the Major was shaking his head again. "Much too advanced," he said. "We could never master them. What we need is an earlier type, and I don't see any in here. Come on, boy; don't straggle."

We walked on, leading the horses, toward the front of the other building. At the doors we peeked in, and there on the floor, with tools and empty crates lying around as though they'd just unpacked it, was another of the things, a flying machine. Only this was far smaller, and was nothing but a framework of wood like a big box kite, with little canvas wings, as the Major called them. It didn't have wheels, either, just a couple of runners like a sled. Lying propped against a wall, as though they just were ready to put it up, was a sign. The moonlight didn't quite reach it, and I couldn't read all the words, but I could make out a few. *World's first,* it said in one place, and farther down it said, *Kitty Hawk.*

The Major just stood there for maybe a minute, staring like a man in a trance. Then he murmured to himself, "Very like

45

sketches of Da Vinci's model; only apparently this one worked."
He grinned suddenly, all excited. "This is it, boy," he said. "This
is why we came."

I knew what he had in mind, and I didn't like it. "You'll never
break in there, sir," I said. "Those doors look mighty solid, and
I'll bet this place is guarded like the mint."

The Major just smiled, mysterious again. "Of course it is, son;
it's the treasure house of a nation. No one could possibly get in
with any hope of removing anything, let alone this aircraft—under ordinary circumstances. But don't worry about that, boy; just
leave it to me. Right now we need fuel." Turning on his heel, he
walked back to his horse, took the reins, and led him off; and I
followed with mine.

Off some distance, under some trees, near a big open space like
a park, the Major set the lever inside his black box, and pressed
the button. "Back in 1864, now," he said then, and sniffed. "Air
smells fresher. Now, I want you to take your horse, go to garrison
headquarters, and bring back all the petrol you can carry. They've
got some for cleaning uniforms. Tell them I'll take full responsibility. Understand?"

"Yessir."

"Then off with you. When you come back, this is where I want
you to meet me." The Major turned and began walking away with
his horse.

At headquarters the guard woke a private, who woke a corporal, who woke a sergeant, who woke a lieutenant, who woke a
captain, who swore a little and then woke up the private again
and told him to give me what I wanted. The private went away,
murmuring softly to himself, and came back pretty soon with six
five-gallon jugs; and I tied them to my saddle, signed six sets of
receipts in triplicate, and led my horse back through the moonlit
streets of Washington, taking a nip of applejack now and then.

I went by the White House again, on purpose; and this time
someone was standing silhouetted against the lighted east window
—a big man, tall and thin, his shoulders bowed, his head down on
his chest—and I couldn't help but get the impression of a weary
strength and purpose and a tremendous dignity. I felt sure it was
him, but I can't rightly claim I saw the President, because I've al-

46

ways been one to stick to the facts and never stretch the truth even a little bit.

The Major was waiting under the trees, and my jaw nearly dropped off, because the flying machine was sitting beside him. "Sir," I said, "how did you—"

The Major interrupted, smiling and stroking his little beard: "Very simple. I merely stood at the front door"—he patted the black box at the saddle near his shoulder—"and moved back in time to a moment when even the Smithsonian didn't exist. Then I stepped a few paces ahead with the box under my arm, adjusted the lever again, moved forward to the proper moment, and there I was, standing beside the flying machine. I took myself and the machine out by the same method, and my mount pulled it here on its skids."

"Yessir," I said. I figured I could keep up this foolishness as long as he could, though I did wonder how he had got the flying machine out.

The Major pointed ahead: "I've been exploring the ground, and it's pretty rocky and rough." He turned to the black box, adjusted the dial, and pressed the button. "Now, it's a park," he said, "sometime in the nineteen forties."

"Yessir," I said.

The Major nodded at a little spout in the flying machine. "Fill her up," he said, and I untied one of the jugs, uncorked it, and began to pour. The tank sounded dry when the petrol hit it, and a cloud of dust puffed up from the spout. It didn't hold very much, only a few quarts, and the Major began untying the other jugs. "Lash these down in the machine," he said, and while I was doing that, the Major began pacing up and down, muttering to himself. "To start the engine, I should imagine you simply turn the propellers. But the machine will need help in getting into the air." He kept walking up and down, pulling his beard; then he nodded his head. "Yes," he said, "that should do it, I think." He stopped and looked at me. "Nerves in good shape, boy? Hands steady and reliable?"

"Yessir."

"All right, son, this thing should be easy to fly—mostly a matter of balance, I imagine." He pointed to a sort of saddle at the front of the machine. "I believe you simply lie on your stomach with your hips in this saddle; it connects with the rudder and wings by cables. By merely moving from side to side, you control the machine's balance and direction." The Major pointed to a lever. "Work this with your hand," he said, "to go up or down. That's all there is to it, so far as I can see, and if I'm wrong in any details, you can correct them in the air with a little experimenting. Think you can fly it, boy?"

"Yessir."

"Good," he said, and grabbed one of the propellers at the back and began turning it. I worked on the other propeller, but nothing happened; they just creaked, stiff and rusty-like. But we kept turning, yanking harder and harder, and pretty soon the little engine coughed.

"Now, *heave,* boy!" the Major said, and we laid into it hard, and every time, now, the engine would cough a little. Finally, we yanked so hard, both together, our feet nearly came off the ground, and the motor coughed and kept on coughing and like to choked to death. Then it sort of cleared its throat and started to stutter but didn't stop, and then it was running smooth, the propellers just whirling, flashing and shining in the moonlight till you could hardly see them, and the flying machine shaking like a wet dog, with little clouds of dust pouring up out of every part of it.

"Excellent," said the Major, and he sneezed from the dust. Then he began unfastening the horses' bridles, strapping them together again to make a single long rein. He posted the horses in front of the machine and said, "Get in, boy. We've got a busy night ahead." I lay down in the saddle, and he climbed up on the top wing and lay down on his stomach. "You take the lever, and I'll take the rein. Ready, boy?"

"Yessir."

"Gee up!" said the Major, snapping the rein hard, and the horses started off, heads down, hoofs digging in.

The flying machine sort of bumped along over the grass on its skids, but it soon smoothed out and began sliding along, level as a sled on packed snow, and the horses' heads came up and they began to trot, the motor just chugging away.

"Sound *forward!*" said the Major, and I unslung my trumpet and blew forward; the horses buckled into it, and we were skimming along, must have been fifteen, maybe twenty miles an hour or even faster.

"Now, *charge!*" yelled the Major, and I blew charge, and the hoofs began drumming the turf, the horses whinnying and snorting, the engine chugging faster and faster, the propellers whining in back of us, and all of a sudden the grass was a good five feet below, and the reins were hanging straight down. Then—for a second it scared me—we were passing the horses. We were right over their backs; then they began slipping away under the machine, and the Major dropped the reins and yelled, "Pull back the lever!" I yanked back hard, and we shot up into the air like a rocket.

I remembered what the Major had said about experimenting and tried easing back on the lever, and the flying machine sort of leveled out, and there we were, chugging along faster than I'd ever gone in my life. It was wonderful fun, and I glanced down and there was Washington spread out below, a lot bigger than I'd thought it was and with more lights than I'd known there were in the world. They were *bright*, too; didn't look like candles and kerosene lamps at all. Way off, toward the center of town, some of the lights were red and green, and so bright they lighted up the sky.

"Watch out!" yelled the Major, and just ahead, rushing straight at us, was a tremendous monument or something, a tall big stone needle.

I don't know why, but I twisted hard to the left in the little saddle and yanked back on the lever, and a wing heaved up and the flying machine shot off to one side, the wing tip nearly grazing the monument. Then I lay straight again, holding the lever steady. The machine leveled off, and it was like the first time I drove a team. I could feel in my bones that I was a natural-born flying-machine driver.

"Back to headquarters," said the Major. "Can you find the way?"

"Yessir," I said, and headed south.

The Major fiddled with the dial in his black box and pressed

49

the button, and down below now, in the moonlight, I could see
the dirt road leading out of Washington back to headquarters. I
turned for a last look at the city, but there were only a few lights
now, not looking nearly as bright as before; the red and green
lights were gone.

But the road was bright in the moonlight, and we tore along
over it when it went straight, cut across bends when it curved,
flying it must have been close to forty miles an hour. The wind
streamed back cold, and I pulled out the white knit muffler my
grandma gave me and looped it around my throat. One end
streamed back, flapping and waving in the wind. I thought my forage cap might blow off, so I reversed it on my head, the peak at
the back, and I felt that now I looked the way a flying-machine
driver ought to, and wished the girls back home could have seen
me.

For a while I practiced with the lever and hip saddle, soaring
up till the engine started coughing, and turning and dipping down,
seeing how close I could shave the road. But finally the Major
yelled and made me quit. Every now and then we'd see a light
flare up in a farmhouse, and when we'd look back we'd see the
light wobbling across the yard and know some farmer was out
there with his lamp, staring up at the noise in the sky.

Several times, on the way, we had to fill the tank again, and
pretty soon, maybe less than two hours, campfires began sliding
under our wings, and the Major was leaning from side to side, looking down at the ground. Then he pointed ahead. "That field
down there, boy; can you land this thing with the engine off?"

"Yessir," I said, and I stopped the engine, and the machine began sliding down like a toboggan, and I kept easing the lever
back and forth, watching the field come up to meet us, growing
bigger and bigger every second. We didn't make a sound now, except for the wind sighing through the wires, and we came in like
a ghost, the moonlight white on our wings. Our downward path
and the edge of the field met exactly, and the instant before we
hit, my arm eased the lever back, and the skids touched the grass
like a whisper. Then we bumped a little, stopped, and sat there a
moment not saying a word. Off in the weeds the crickets began
chirping again.

50

The Major said there was a cliff at the side of the field and we found it, and slid the machine over to the edge of it and then we started walking around the field, in opposite directions looking for a path or sentry. I found the sentry right away, guarding the path lying down with his eyes closed. My applejack was gone, so I shook him awake and explained my problem.

"How much you got?" he said; I told him a dollar, and he went off into the woods and came back with a jug. "Good whisky," he said, "the best. And exactly a dollar's worth; the jug's nearly full." So I tasted the whisky—it *was* good—paid him, took the jug back and tied it down in the machine. Then I went back to the path and called the Major, and he came over, cutting across the field. Then the sentry led us down the path toward the General's tent.

It was a square tent with a gabled roof, a lantern burning inside, and the front flap open. The sentry saluted. "Major of Cavalry here, sir"—he pronounced the word like an ignorant infantryman. "Says it's secret and urgent."

"Send the *calvary* in," said a voice, pronouncing it just that way, and I knew the General was a horse soldier at heart.

We stepped forward, saluting. The General was sitting on a kitchen chair, his feet, in old Army shoes with the laces untied, propped on a big wooden keg with a spigot. He wore a black slouch hat, his vest and uniform blouse were unbuttoned, and I saw three silver stars embroidered on a shoulder strap. The General's eyes were blue, hard and tough, and he wore a full beard. "At ease," he said. "Well?"

"Sir," said the Major, "we have a flying machine and propose, with your permission, to use it against the rebs."

"Well," said the General, leaning back on the hind legs of his chair, "you've come in the nick of time. Lee's men are massed at Cold Harbor, and I've been sitting here all night dri— thinking. They've got to be crushed before— A *flying* machine, did you say?"

"Yessir," said the Major.

"H'mm," said the General. "Where'd you get it?"

"Well, sir, that's a long story."

"I'll bet it is," said the General. He picked up a stub of cigar

51

from the table beside him and chewed it thoughtfully. "If I hadn't been thinking hard and steadily all night, I wouldn't believe a word of this. What do you propose to do with your flying machine?"

"Load it with grenades!" The Major's eyes began to sparkle. "Drop them spang on rebel headquarters! Force immediate surrend—"

The General shook his head. "No," he said, "I don't think so. Air power isn't enough, son, and will never replace the foot soldier, mark my words. Has its place, though, and you've done good work." He glanced at me. "You the driver, son?"

"Yessir."

He turned to the Major again. "I want you to go up with a map. Locate Lee's positions. Mark them on the map and return. Do that, Major, and tomorrow, June 3, after the Battle of Cold Harbor, I'll personally pin silver leaves on your straps. Because I'm going to take Richmond like—well, I don't know what. As for you, son"—he glanced at my stripe—"you'll make corporal. Might even design new badges for you; pair of wings on the chest or something like that."

"Yessir," I said.

"Where's the machine?" said the General. "Believe I'll walk down and look at it. Lead the way." The Major and me saluted, turned and walked out, and the General said, "Go ahead; I'll catch up."

At the field the General caught up, shoving something into his hip pocket—a handkerchief, maybe. "Here's your map," he said, and he handed a folded paper to the Major.

The Major took it, saluted and said, "For the Union, sir! For the cause of—"

"Save the speeches," said the General, "till you're running for office."

"Yessir," said the Major, and he turned to me. "Fill her up!"

I filled the tank, we spun the propellers, and this time the engine started right up. We climbed in, and I reversed my forage cap and tied on my scarf.

"Good," said the General approvingly. "Style; real calvary style."

We shoved off and dropped over the cliff like a dead weight, the ground rushing up fast. Then the wings bit into the air, I pulled back my lever, and we shot up, the engine snorting, fighting for altitude, and I swung out wide and circled the field, once at fifty feet, then at a hundred. The first time, the General just stood there, head back, mouth open, staring up at us, and I could see his brass buttons gleam in the moonlight. The second time around he still had his head back, but I don't think he was looking at us. He had a hand to his mouth, and he was drinking a glass of water —I could tell because just as we straightened and headed south, he threw it off into the bushes hard as he could, and I could see the glass flash in the moonlight. Then he started back to headquarters at a dead run, in a hurry, I guess, to get back to his thinking.

The machine was snorting at the front end, kicking up at the hindquarters, high-spirited, and I had all I could do to keep her from shying, and I wished she'd had reins. Down below, cold and sparkly in the moonlight, I could see the James River, stretching east and west, and the lights of Richmond, but it was no time for sightseeing. The machine was frisky, trembling in the flanks, and before I knew it she took the bit in her mouth and headed straight down, the wind screaming through her wires, the ripples on the water rushing up at us.

But I'd handled runaways before, and I heaved back on the lever, forcing her head up, and she curved back into the air fast as a calvary mount at a barrier. But this time she didn't cough at the top of the curve. She snorted through her nostrils, wild with power, and I barely had time to yell, "Hang on!" to the Major before she went clear over on her back and shot down toward the river again. The Major yelled, but the applejack was bubbling inside me and I'd never had such a thrill, and I yelled, too, laughing and screaming. Then I pulled back hard, yelling, "Whoa!" but up and over we went again, the wings creaking like saddle leather on a galloping horse. At the top of the climb, I leaned hard to the left, and we shot off in a wide, beautiful curve, and I never had such fun in my life.

Then she quieted down a little. She wasn't broken, I knew, but she could feel a real rider in the saddle, so she waited, figuring out what to try next. The Major got his breath and used it for cursing. He didn't call me anything I'd ever heard before, and I'd been in the calvary since I joined the Army. It was a beautiful job and I admired it. "Yessir," I said when his breath ran out again.

He still had plenty to say, I think, but campfires were sliding under our wings, and he had to get out his map and go to work. We flew back and forth, parallel with the river, the Major busy with his pencil and map. It was dull and monotonous for both me and the machine, and I kept wondering if the rebs could see or hear us. So I kept sneaking closer and closer to the ground, and pretty soon, directly ahead in a clearing, I saw a campfire with men around it. I don't rightly know if it was me or the machine had the idea, but I barely touched the lever and she dipped her nose and shot right down, aiming smack at the fire.

They saw us then, all right, and heard us, too. They scattered, yelling and cursing, with me leaning over screaming at them and laughing like mad. I hauled back on the lever maybe five feet from the ground, and the fire singed our tail as we curved back up. But this time, at the top of the climb, the engine got the hiccups, and I had to turn and come down in a slow glide to ease the strain off the engine till she got her breath, and now the men below had muskets out, and they were mad. They fired kneeling, following up with their sights the way you lead ducks, the musket balls whistling past us.

"Come on!" I yelled. I slapped the flying machine on her side, unslung my trumpet, and blew charge. Down we went, the engine neighing and whinnying like crazy, and the men tossed their muskets aside and dived in all directions, and we fanned the flames with our wings and went up like a bullet, the engine screaming in triumph. At the top of the curve I turned, and we shot off over the treetops, the wing tip pointing straight at the moon. "Sorry, sir," I said, before the Major could get his breath. "She's wild— feeling her oats. But I think I've got her under control."

"Then get back to headquarters before you kill us," he said coldly. "We'll discuss this later."

"Yessir," I said. I spotted the river off to one side and flew over it, and when the Major got us oriented he navigated us back to the field.

"Wait here," he said when we landed, and he trotted down the path toward the General's tent. I was just as glad; I felt like a drink, and besides I loved that machine now and wanted to take care of her. I wiped her down with my muffler, and wished I could feed her something.

Then I felt around inside the machine, and then I was cussing that sentry, beating the Major's record, I think, because my whisky was gone, and I knew what that sentry had done: sneaked back to my machine and got it soon as he had me and the Major in the General's tent, and now he was back at the guardhouse, probably, lapping it up and laughing at me.

The Major came down the path fast. "Back to Washington, and hurry," he said. "Got to get this where it belongs before daylight or the space-time continuum will be broken and no telling what might happen then."

So we filled the tank and flew on back to Washington. I was tired and so was the flying machine, I guess, because now she just chugged along, heading for home and the stable.

We landed near the trees again, and climbed out, stiff and tired. And after creaking and sighing a little, the flying machine just sat there on the ground, dead tired, too. There were a couple of musket ball holes in her wings and some soot on her tail, but otherwise she looked just the same.

"Look alive, boy!" the Major said. "You go hunt for the horses, and I'll get the machine back," and he got behind the flying machine and began pushing it along over the grass.

I found the horses grazing not far off, brought them back, and tethered them to the trees. When the Major returned we started back, just as dawn was breaking.

Well, I never did get my promotion. Or my wings either. It got hot, and pretty soon I fell asleep.

After a while I heard the Major call, "Boy! Boy!" and I woke up saying, "Yessir!" but he didn't mean me. A paper boy was running over with a newspaper, and when the Major paid for it, I drew alongside and we both looked at it, sitting there in our saddles near the outskirts of Washington. *BATTLE AT COLD HARBOR*, it said, and underneath were a lot of smaller headlines one after the other. *Disaster for Union Forces! Surprise At-*

tack at Daybreak Fails! Repulsed in Eight Minutes! Knowledge of Rebel Positions Faulty! Confederate Losses Small, Ours Large! Grant Offers No Explanation; Inquiry Urged! There was a news story, too, but we didn't read it. The Major flung the paper to the gutter and touched his spurs to his horse, and I followed.

By noon the next day we were back in our lines, but we didn't look for the General. We didn't feel any need to, because we felt sure he was looking for us. He never found us, though; possibly because I grew a beard, and the Major shaved his off. And we never had told him our names.

Well, Grant finally took Richmond—he was a great general—but he had to take it by siege.

I only saw him one more time, and that was years later when he wasn't a general any more. It was a New Year's Day, and I was in Washington and saw a long line of people waiting to get into the White House, and knew it must be the public reception the Presidents used to hold every New Year's. So I stood in line, and an hour later I reached the President. "Remember me, General?" I said.

He stared at me, narrowing his eyes; then his face got red and his eyes flashed. But he took a deep breath, remembering I was a voter, forced a smile, and nodded at a door behind him. "Wait in there," he said.

Soon afterward the reception ended, and the General sat facing me, behind his big desk, biting the end off a short cigar. "Well," he said, without any preliminaries, "what went wrong?"

So I told him; I'd figured it out long since, of course. I told him how the flying machine went crazy, looping till we could hardly see straight, so that we flew north again and mapped our own lines.

"I found that out," said the General, "immediately after ordering the attack."

Then I told him about the sentry who'd sold the whisky, and how I thought he'd stolen it back again, when he hadn't.

The General nodded. "Poured that whisky into the machine, didn't you? Mistook it for a jug of gasoline."

"Yessir," I said.

He nodded again. "Naturally the flying machine went crazy. That was my own private brand of whisky, the same whisky Lincoln spoke of so highly. That damned sentry of mine was stealing it all through the war." He leaned back in his chair, puffing his cigar. "Well," he said, "I guess it's just as well you didn't succeed; Lee thought so, too. We discussed it at Appomattox before the formal surrender, just the two of us chatting in the farmhouse. Never have told anyone what we talked about there, and everybody's been wondering and guessing ever since. Well, we talked about air power, son, and Lee was opposed to it, and so was I. Wars are meant for the ground, boy, and if they ever take to the air they'll start dropping bombshells, mark my words, and if they ever do that, there'll be hell to pay. So Lee and I decided to keep our mouths shut about air power, and we have—you won't find a word about it in my memoirs or his. Anyway, son, as Billy Sherman said, war is hell, and there's no sense starting people thinking up ways to make it worse. So I want you to keep quiet about Cold Harbor. Don't say a word if you live to be a hundred."

"Yessir," I said, and I never have. But I'm past a hundred now, son, and if the General wanted me to keep quiet after that he'd have said so. Now, take those hands out of the air, boy! Wait'll the world's *first* pilot gets through talking!

John Crosby

John Crosby's radio and television column is one of the most sagacious as well as one of the most scintillating features of the New York *Herald Tribune*. His audiences, of which the editors of this volume are an enthusiastic part, confidently believe that Crosby will someday leave his restricted field for the larger arena of general living, politics, sports, science, arts and letters, and (possibly) World Affairs. Meanwhile they are happy within the confines of Crosby's self-imposed limitations and look forward to his dissections of the absurdities that go on over the air waves.

Crosby was born May 18, 1912, in Milwaukee, Wisconsin. Graduated from Phillips Exeter Academy, he attended Yale University for two years and returned to Wisconsin to become a hometown journalist. Back East after a few years, he was sent out on multiple assignments by the *Herald Tribune,* and just as he learned the routine of police stations and court trials—and also a few Broadway routines—was snatched by the U. S. Army. In 1946, after a five-year hitch in uniform, Crosby found himself back on the *Herald Tribune* in charge of a radio column. Undeterred by the prospect of listening to—and, worse, writing about —the daily horror of rapidly accumulating soap operas, singing commercials, punch-drunk comedians, exhumed operettas, hourly murders, violent give-away jackpots, and phony problem dramas, Crosby set to work. The rest, in a manner of speaking, is history.

Chestnuts Are in Bloom Again *

I've been working on my war film which should be ready for television release some time next year. But I know you people can't wait that long so I'm going to give you a preview right now. This scenario, I ought to explain, was undertaken only after an exhaustive study of the other war films that have belted around the TV circuit all summer; it contains only the ripest old chestnuts that money can buy; it doesn't break any new ground but it makes excellent use of the old soil.

There is what I consider a wonderful scene near the end of this film. Battersby, bearded and haggard, is in the prisoner-of-

* Copyright, 1951, New York *Herald Tribune,* Inc.

war enclosure, staring out at the bleak parade ground, the barbed wire, the stark barracks. And he says, as you rather suspect that he will: "I was just thinking that now the heather will be in bloom in Devon."

Earlier in the film, Battersby, accompanied by young Grimsby, enters the shell-riddled, apparently abandoned village. "Quiet around here," says young Grimsby. Battersby, the more experienced officer, glances around, chewing his underlip. "Yes—too quiet." He glances up the empty street and somehow he can't prevent himself from adding: "I don't like it . . . I don't like it at all."

The action switches from the battlefield back to the laboratory. Naturally, I'm not going to neglect the nuclear physicist, most brilliant scientist in the free world, and the only man capable of holding all the secrets of the super-atomic ray gun in his head. They're in the laboratory—Murchison from G-2, Dr. Wellsbach, the scientist—examining the ray gun. "Devilish machine," says Murchison, awed. Then after a moment of reflection. "But—can you imagine what would happen if it fell into the wrong hands." (Next reel: It falls into the wrong hands. So does Wellsbach. Pandemonium at GHQ. Chaos at Scotland Yard. Only the Prime Minister maintains a semblance of calm. "You did all you could, Murchison. All any one could.")

Well, naturally we have to get back the devilish machine and also, if it's not too late, Wellsbach. Comes the secret, highly dangerous mission. Murchison and Battersby flying at 35,000 feet through a hail of flack, their parachutes at the ready, the intercom chattering away.

"Two ack emma—one minute more, old boy."

"Thickish out there, what?"

"Steady the plips. Fast with the ploffs. Roger and over."

"I say, old boy . . ."

"Righto?"

"If anything happens . . ."

"Stout fella."

"Say pip-pip to Dee for me, will you, like a good lad?"

"Righto."

"Well—cheerio."

"Cheerio."

Bang! That's the end of Murchison.

Battersby gets through into the enemy country. Instantly falls in love with a girl who belongs to the other side. "We've fought this thing. My God, how we've fought it!" Great scene when Battersby, who should be skipping back to his own territory, returns to the enemy girl's farmhouse.

"Why did you come?"

"I had to."

"Don't say anything—just let me look at you."

"Tonight, at least, is ours."

Oh, I forgot to tell you the beginning of this film. Murchison, in civvies, and his wife at their little cottage in Surrey, having breakfast.

"Anything in the paper, dear?"

"Nothing. Some archduke's been murdered."

"This Is Madness! Sheer Madness!" *

My wife and I are as derivative as lizards, changing the color of our thoughts and our speech habits according to our environment. Since we have been exposed to television, it has left a deep mark on our conversation. It was just the other night, speeding the departing guests, that I found myself exclaiming:

"Good-by for now. You've been a perfectly *wonderful* audience."

The guests, a non-TV crowd turned a little pale, I thought. Uneducated people.

My wife, who knows her lines as well as Wendy or Faye or any of the girls, threw in that classic, almost unavoidable line: "You must come back again—real soon."

The guests fled. Haven't seen them since. It's just possible they

* Copyright, 1951, New York *Herald Tribune,* Inc.

60

didn't have a good time. My wife and I were discussing it just the other day, employing only the very best clichés.

"John, you don't think . . ."

"I don't know *what* to think."

If you follow the well-established precedents laid down by television's emcees and quizmasters, "the wonderful audience" and "come back again real soon" are the only respectable formulas for getting the guests out of the house. Getting them *into* the house is another matter. Our favorite, a line that must be declaimed with the utmost joviality, is:

"Almost anything can happen in this house—and it usually does."

I think this is a perfectly wonderful opening gambit but it does seem to unsettle the guests. Not nearly so much, though, as our new form of introduction, something we also picked up from TV: "I want you to meet the most wonderful girl in the world AND HERE SHE IS—MARY CROSBY!" The cheers and wolf whistles and tumultuous applause are provided by my small son, another devotee of television, who can imitate an audience of five hundred persons with the utmost ease.

My wife's opening line here is: "We have some perfectly marvelous drinks coming up. But first, a word about something that I'm sure will be of interest to *every one.*"

She has another line, this one for use when we are doing the visiting in other people's houses. She says brightly: "I feel as though I'm sitting right in your living room." The last time she used it, the host snapped back: "You *are* sitting right in my living room." I ought to explain that he is a nontelevision churl, a man unacquainted with the ordinary civilities of life, especially televised life.

It was a stiffish and, in the end, disastrous visit we had that night, though we tried everything to put them at their ease. "Here we are again, folks," I exclaimed, "with a half hour of fun and frolic all for *you.*" They didn't seem to think it was all for them and they didn't take very kindly to the fun and frolic, even the custard-pie throwing which has always been a surefire bit in our repertoire.

In fact; it was just about then that we got thrown out of the house. My wife got in a good line, though, just before she was tossed out: "This is madness! Sheer madness! I should never have come."

I got in an even better one. Just as I hurtled out the front door, I fixed my host with a steely glance—difficult thing to do in mid-air—and declared, ringingly: "I'm seeing you now—for the first time—as you really are!"

We don't see them any more either. As a matter of fact, we don't seem to *have* any friends any more.

Wanna Buy a Drunken Duck?*

Afternoon television, whatever else you can say about it, has an air of wonderfully engaging innocence about it. You get the idea they're making it all up as they go along, and consequently you can't blame the children if they stumble over the words from time to time, if the thoughts get a little misty and unreal.

Just the other day, I tuned in on Ed and Pegeen Fitzgerald, the philosophers of the breakfast table, in time to hear him explain earnestly to a rather bewildered guest: "You know the island we live on is completely surrounded by water." The guest chewed on this intelligence a moment and then plunged into a discussion of fire prevention in the home. On the same program Mrs. Fitzgerald asked her husband if he thought Navy marriages were happier than Army marriages because sailors spent so much time at sea. No, said Ed thoughtfully, he didn't think absence made the heart grow fonder.

That's the way it goes on afternoon TV. One minute you hear about an island completely surrounded by water, the next minute you're up to your hips in profound reflections on the effect of prolonged absence on matrimony. You never know what's coming next. It may not be show business; it doesn't even resemble con-

* Copyright, 1951, New York *Herald Tribune,* Inc.

versation exactly; but it has a sort of dreamlike charm—these giblets of wisdom and information. After partaking of the Fitzgeralds, who are generally credited with the invention of the multiple-sponsored marriage, I spent a profitable half hour with another TV couple, Woody and Virginia Klose, who are on the same station (WJZ-TV in New York). They were discussing drunken ducks. "I don't think I've ever seen a drunken duck and I don't think I want to," said Mr. Klose to Mrs. Klose, closing the topic of drunken ducks, conceivably for all time.

But not the subject of drunkenness. Pretty soon, the Kloses welcomed their guest of the day, Isabel Leighton, who plunged right back into insobriety. "Very, very happy people don't get thoroughly plastered all the time," declared Miss Leighton, among other things. These remarks are admittedly torn from their contexts, which is unfair. But then it's hard to keep your attention from wandering during afternoon TV fare; you lose the thread and pretty soon you wake up and somebody's discussing drunken ducks.

In our house we use the TV set like a hearth, a place to keep warm on cold fall afternoons. Well, I was dozing in front of this contemporary fireplace, warming my feet on Kate Smith one afternoon, when I woke up to find myself in the middle of a fashion show. A bunch of models in beachwear parading back and forth. Miss Smith's guest, a fashion expert, was saying: "In the privacy of your own pool or patio the outer garment may be removed."

I fell right back asleep again and dreamed about Miss Kate's millions of devoted women listeners all over the country divesting themselves of their outer garments in the privacy of their own pools or patios. There must be two or three babes around who don't own a pool or even a patio and they're stuck with the outer garment till the right millionaire comes along. After all, television is for the masses, not for the unprivileged few who haven't got patios.

Why, it was just the other day that Carmel Myers, the silent film star who now has her own TV show, was telling one of her guests about what fun they had on the set in the old days, which is to say, back when they kept the money. It was a nice little anecdote. A director had driven her to a restaurant in his Cadillac. When the doorman asked him what to do with the car, the director said "Keep it." No one ever saw the car again. Or the doorman either.

Sing a Song of Ballantine's*

The other day on television, a lovely young woman was discovered writing a love letter—no, not to Cary Grant, junior—to her refrigerator. Men, I'm fully aware, are being eliminated in every other line of work, but in this one I thought we'd hang on a few more years. But no. This lady's heart had been won by the stainless, sixty-cubic-inch, lifetime-guaranteed contrivance with the extra-large freezing compartment. Next year, I expect, the refrigerator people will add a new wrinkle—a letter-writing gadget so that the darned thing can answer its mail.

It's not entirely surprising, either, this amorous feeling toward mechanical objects. Our lust for them is being cultivated on television in some wonderfully ingenious ways. I'm not one of those people, you understand, who gets upset by commercials. In fact, I rather like them. What, I keep asking myself when the pitchman comes on, are they going to do to me now? Just how are they going to frame this appeal to my pocketbook?

Next thing I know, Frankie Laine appears driving a mule train through the wilderness. Presently, he comes on a pair of starving mountaineers, whips back the canvas of his wagon, and what do you think? It's stuffed with Kellogg's Corn Flakes, whose nutritive qualities he sings about to the tune of the song he's most closely associated with—and if you don't know what that is, you oughtn't to be reading radio columns.

They creep up on you, these modern commercials. No matter who the guy (or girl) is, no matter how he's dressed or what he's doing—sooner or later the package of SPIV, the all-purpose cleanser, is unveiled, usually to the accompaniment of song. Along about Thanksgiving keep a wary eye out for John Alden and Priscilla. They always get a heavy play and they're always selling something. One year, I remember, John and Priscilla were discovered in pleasant dalliance in an all-steel Hotpoint kitchen, which, they decided, exemplified all the virtues the pilgrims came over here to practice. Another year, if my memory isn't playing me tricks, John was out gunning for a turkey, missed the fowl, and was then comforted by Priscilla on Thanksgiving Day with a can of Campbell's soup.

As a matter of fact, most of the history I know has been learned at the knee of my television set. The Ballantine people have been especially helpful.

> "Nero fiddled while Rome burned down,
> "He played sweet music in his velvet gown,
> "He played till flames just filled the sky'n
> "Then he asked for Ballantine."

That last rhyme, incidentally, is high among my all-time favorite bits of poesy. I'm also partial toward another bit of historic verse from the Ballantine collection.

> In a royal barge upon the Nile so green,
> Sat Cleopatra the Egyptian queen,
> Her slaves brought nectar from the vine,
> But she clapped her hands for Ballantine.

Suds in your eye, Cleo. And that brings to mind another unlikely toast. Miss Faye Emerson toasting her trip to Paris on her recent "Wonderful Town" show in, of all things, Pepsi-Cola. There are three people I'd like to get together in a sort of general all-purpose beverage commercial—Cleopatra and her Ballantine, Faye and her Parisian Pepsi-Cola, and Arthur Godfrey lifting a glass of Lipton's while advising us—as he always does around this time of year—to stick to tea and lay off that other stuff.

I'm indebted to Miss Emerson for another of my favorite television commercials. She was dressed as a cowboy and was shooting Pepsi-Cola bottles off a bar, suggesting—as I see it—that if

65

you didn't want to drink the stuff you could always use it for target practice.

Then there's the weather commercial. Whenever a man starts telling you about weather—it's going to be a nice day, it's going to rain, everyone out for a typhoon—watch out. He's got a product up his sleeve. It's sort of a game around our house to figure out what the product is. I remember one weather commercial which showed a toothsome young lady on a street corner, the wind blowing her skirts up to her neck. I thought we were in for a pitch about seamless nylons. But no. A guy drives up in a Chevrolet, doffs his hat and, well, she climbed right in. I went right out and bought a Chevrolet, but the wind hasn't blown very hard in our neighborhood ever since.

Al Capp

When, on November 6, 1950, *Time* elected Al Capp as its cover man, it ran a gaudy, fact-filled, and cartoon-crammed story about him. The twelve packed paragraphs were headed with a punning title, "Die Monstersinger," and they began, "Al Capp, the cartoonist-creator of *L'il Abner,* probably has a sharper eye for slobs, monsters, hags, and fiends than anyone alive. This means that his eye is very sharp indeed, for the modern slob seldom slobbers and in the 20th Century even monsters are apt to use both Vitalis and Zip, grease themselves liberally with Mum or Dew, and consult a dentist twice a year."

If, as *Time* intimated, Capp's world is inhabited by "bloated businessmen, brainless editors, venal politicians," and other knaves and annoyances, Capp delights in his creatures. He loves to expose their frenzies and idiocies in howling caricatures; his savagely portrayed villains are not merely drawn but drawn and quartered. Born Alfred Gerald Caplin, in New Haven, Connecticut, he struggled through a childhood of poverty and a schooling which is graphically reflected in "Memories of Miss Mandelbaum." At nine he had an almost fatal accident. Hitching a ride on a truck, he slipped, fell, and was run over. His left foot had to be amputated, and he had to make his way through adolescence with ever-increasing difficulties. He began to wander, thumbed his way through the South and, at nineteen, settled temporarily in Boston. He had always amused himself—and, as the following excerpt shows, partly supported himself—by making funny pictures. In his twentieth year he made the rounds of the art schools, jumped to New York's Greenwich Village, where he ground out advertising drawings at two dollars each. When the Associated Press paid him $50 a week to draw a stock cartoon, Capp planted his good foot firmly on the first rung of the ladder. His ascent was rapid. By the time he was thirty, his now famous strip, *L'il Abner,* was being syndicated in some 400 newspapers and Capp was receiving some $2000 a week. Eight years later he sued the syndicate for fourteen million dollars to keep control of his creations and, although the suit was settled out of court, Capp was well satisfied.

Although only a few of Capp's admirers realize it, the cartoonist is also a writer. However, unlike his drawings, which are farcically wild, purposely illiterate, and exaggerated to the point of absurdity, Capp's prose is straightforward, unaffected, amusing, touching, and completely convincing. Millions know him as the man who, in a hitherto crude and vulgar medium, produced new elements in humor, "a skirling of irony and satire such as the comic page had never known."

Memories of Miss Mandelbaum*

I

Recently a man from Santa Barbara, California, wrote to a weekly news magazine to complain that I am overpaid for the pictures I draw, in contrast to what other people get for doing something useful. Well, I may be overpaid now, but I wasn't when I started out in the world as a professional artist, which was when I was eleven years old and in the seventh grade of P.S. 62, in Brooklyn. I was paid ten cents a picture then, and risked being clapped into the reformatory every time I drew one. Today, thanks to the willingness of the average American to laugh at a group of characters even more bedeviled than he is (a necessarily fictitious group, of course), my price has risen somewhat and I now risk nothing more than having my income disapproved of by people who live in places I can't afford to live in.

My career as a professional artist started during the year we lived in the teeming hot-pastrami and block-gang-warfare jungle of the Brownsville (or Murder, Inc.) section of Brooklyn. My father had moved us (my mother, my two younger brothers, and sister) there from the serenity of New Haven, Connecticut, because he had just gone bankrupt in a new business.

My father's new businesses never lasted long enough to become old ones. These businesses were based on my father's ever-new ideas (part of which, always, was to move his family to a new community, a new city, a new state even—where we would find a new and glorious life). My father was a gifted artist and a brilliant idea man. He should have used his ideas in a comic strip, like I do, in which he could create a world he could manage, like I can. But there weren't enough comic strips in the early 1900's, and so my father's ideas had to be tried in an inferior, unmanageable real world. These business ideas would have worked out perfectly in a comic strip, for they all had just the right touch of fantasy, but they inevitably ended in disaster in real life. For events in a comic strip can be controlled to follow reason and

6 8

sanity; the characters in one can be made to behave with kindness, humor, and faith. But in uncontrollable reality, unreasonable misfortunes overtook my father's brilliant ideas (nobody bought his stuff) and the characters he dealt with behaved unspeakably (they wanted their money) and so we were constantly moving out of used-up communities and into bright, new El Dorados, and my father was constantly going out of new businesses and into even newer ones, with new ideas, and new, romantic backers.

And so, in 1920, we came to Brooklyn, and I was enrolled at P.S. 62, a huge, barren, penitentiary-like structure, bursting with a brawling horde of children of all races, presided over by a senile, dipsomaniacal political appointee, and staffed by frantic, overworked, and bad-tempered teachers, as unlike the Connecticut type as vodka is from milk.

It was my luck to enter P.S. 62 at the time when Mr. Lawless was organizing his Experimental Class. When I tell you that a few months later the Experimental Class was discontinued because Mr. Lawless himself was hauled off to an insane asylum (where he spent the rest of his days) you may get some idea of the thinking behind the experiment itself, and, indeed, of that of the School Authorities, which permitted this project.

Mr. Lawless' idea was that if you combined twenty of the school's worst boys (subnormals, petty thieves, rapists, and thugs) with twenty of its best boys, association with the good kids would make the bad kids better. What actually happened, of course, was that the good kids were so enchanted with the bad kids that, from the first day on, we tried to be like them, and, in some cases, so spectacularly surpassed them that, in the end, they were hard put to it to be as lousy as we were.

You'll notice that, by using the word "we," I include myself among the good kids. This was never officially established. I just supposed I was, and always have.

II

One fact about me did get established immediately. I was the "best drawrer" in the class. I was always the "best drawrer" in every class (for there is seldom more than one kid who can draw decently at all, in any class). In Connecticut, this had given me about twenty minutes of distinction once a week, for in a school curriculum sanely designed to prepare kids for life, this was all the drawing considered necessary. But in Mr. Lawless' Experimental Class, drawing became increasingly important as the experiment became increasingly disordered. In fact, drawing became a lifesaver. For instance, when Mr. Lawless would announce a quiz, based on reading presumably done at home the night before, the Smart Kids (who had done their reading) would settle back and yawn. They knew that Mr. Lawless wouldn't call on them, because he knew they'd done their homework. (By the way, as this sort of thing went on, the Smart Kids stopped doing any homework. They were smart enough to realize that Mr. Lawless would always believe they had). But the Bad Kids would stiffen up, alert, rebellious, and ready for trouble. They knew they'd get called on, because Mr. Lawless knew they never did their homework the night before, if for no other reason than that they never went home nights.

These quizzes would begin with the clouding of Mr. Lawless' face and the clenching of his teeth. He'd start getting mad at the answers he knew he'd get before he had asked the first question. For the first answer would, inevitably, be a request to repeat the first question. Mr. Lawless' face would then get darker, his jaw muscles would twitch violently, and he would repeat the question. This, in itself, was a victory for Badness over Authority, and the other Bad 'Uns, knowing what was coming, would titter, with a few of the weak-willed Good 'Uns, even, joining in. The question having been repeated (which Mr. Lawless knew very well the Bad 'Un had clearly heard in the first place—and which the Bad 'Un knew Mr. Lawless knew he'd heard), the formula for the destruction of Mr. Lawless' control went relentlessly on.

It was a simple formula. You just answered a question by asking another question, until Mr. Lawless exploded. Like this:—

"Who was the first president of the United States?"

"I didn't getcha, sir. Would you please repeat th' question?"

"Who — was — the — first — president — of — the — United — States?"

"Of the United States?"

"Yes. The United States."

"Oh. I getcha." Then you sat down, with the air of one to whom everything had been made clear, and was now satisfied. This accomplished the first stage of the destruction of Mr. Lawless' control. His jaw muscles would twitch more violently. He would clench and unclench his fists, and he would rise behind his desk.

"GET UP!" His voice would have the hint of a scream in it. "You haven't answered my question!!!"

You arose, and asked, "What question?"

"The question about the first president."

"I toldja. He was the first president of the United States."

"Who was??"—and now Mr. Lawless was screaming. You pretty nearly had him. You just had to keep answering his questions by asking him questions.

The answer to "WHO was?" was, of course, "Who was WHAT?" Any moron in the class knew that, and knew too that, any minute now, Mr. Lawless' control would snap and he'd call you a sonofabitch and you could say, "You got no right to call me no sonofabitch, sir," and the poor dazed man would realize that somehow he'd been maneuvered into being in the wrong, that he was licked again, give the whole thing up, and announce a drawing class. These drawing classes became, as I said, life-savers. The passing out of "drawring paper" and crayons and the borrowing of rulers and erasers gave legality to the jabbering and conviviality that always went on anyhow.

Mr. Lawless pretended to himself that these drawing classes weren't just outs from hopeless situations, but, rather, shrewd psychological probes, by announcing "Themes" for each drawing. Like "What I Would Like to Do Tonight When I Get Out of School." Announcements like these caused a great deal of foul merriment among the subnormal. They were stupid, all right, but not stupid enough to confess what THEY'D like to do that night when they got out of school.

The "What I Would Like to Be When I Am a Man" theme first indicated to the Bad Kids that my drawing, which up to then was merely admired and envied, could be put to some practical use. Most of them wanted to be gunmen, bookies, and thieves when they grew up, but these hopes and dreams they preferred to keep sacred. For Mr. Lawless' eyes, they represented themselves as yearning to become policemen, firemen, and senators. Now policeman, fireman, and senator uniforms are not easy to draw, if you are subnormal, and so they began to drift over to my desk for help with their idiot scratchings.

I extended myself for them. Being slowed up by having lost my left leg at nine, I couldn't win the respect of such heroes as Cowboy Scalenzo, Six-Toe Tanglebaum, or Crooksie Rattigan in the ordinary way—namely, by attacking my classmates from behind, and running off with their possessions before they could scramble up.

III

At first, all I got for my efforts, and all I wanted, was respect. This is how money came into it, and after that, Miss Mandelbaum.

One day Cowboy Scalenzo came into class with a black eye and many purple bruises on his face. He didn't offer to tell us how badly moidered the other two or three guys were and so we knew these were not the scars of victory, but something that the Cowboy preferred not to discuss. The drawing session came early that day when Six-Toe Tanglebaum wittily replied to a statement by Mr. Lawless that if he (Six-Toe) was a little rat then he (Mr. Lawless) must be a big rat. The theme that day was "My Greatest Ambition."

After I had drawn Crooksie Rattigan as a G-Man and Jackson Jackson, a colored boy, being inaugurated President of the United States, Cowboy Scalenzo came over with his usual request—to draw him like a cowboy. As always he would fascinatedly watch me draw his pinched, swarthy little face in a huge Stetson, and then put a kerchief, star-studded Western vest, boots, and spurs on his drawn-much-healthier-than-life body. As always he would offer no suggestions with these technicalities of costume, but just breathe harder as his image became like a cowboy. It was never until I reached the drawing of the gun and holster that the cowboy ever spoke. At that point, he would carefully describe just what kind of gun he was carrying that day, how the gun barrels were shaped, exactly how the handle was curved. He was very particular about these things. You had the feeling that up to that time we were in fantasy and artistic license was tolerated, but when we came to the gun, we had come down to business and that had to be right. On this day, however, the little bruised, bitter face said, "I ain't only holdin' the gun, see—I'm shootin' it."

I drew him shooting it.

The Cowboy looked at the billows of smoke coming from the nozzle with grim satisfaction.

"Got room for anudder guy?" he asked.

There was room.

"I'm shootin' it at my brudder. Drawr the bullet goin' right into him."

"What does your brother look like?" I asked.

"His name is Angelo. He's older than me. He looks lousy."

With this description, it was the work of only a few minutes to draw Angelo accurately, a look of anguish on his face, a bullet going right into him, and his legs kicking wildly in the air.

The Cowboy studied the drawing with pleasure meanwhile tenderly rubbing his blackened eye and bruised jaw.

He didn't turn the drawing in. He continued to study it at his desk the rest of the day, seeming to forget the pain of his injuries in the joy of his revenge on Angelo.

When school was over, he laid two pennies on my desk. "You done good," he said.

And that's how I became a merchant of dreams. For all my little subnormal classmates had their little subnormal dreams which were, generally, of assault and battery on those larger than themselves. At first I was glad to draw their dreamings for free, for their respect. But, then, my commissions became so many and so intricate, and I, with my increasing importance, became such a prima donna, that the shrewder little morons began offering me pennies, then nickels, and finally, a dime apiece to do theirs first.

That dime a drawing cut the number of requests down, but there still came in more than I could comfortably handle, and I was looking around for an assistant. I had read in *The Book of*

Knowledge how Peter Paul Rubens, an artist of another age but with practically the same problem as I, had hired assistants to help him with detail, and I had my eye on a comer in the third grade, when Miss Mandelbaum appeared and all hell broke loose.

Miss Mandelbaum taught drawing, and was the first female teacher (in fact, the first female of any kind) to enter our classroom. Miss Mandelbaum was new and young and no one had told her. She had simply noticed that the quality of drawings coming from Mr. Lawless' class (mostly done by me) was pretty high for a class composed mainly of morons.

It quickly became apparent to Miss Mandelbaum that I was the Talent, and she showed a great interest in my work, coming in every day, bending over my desk to watch me draw, and (nothing is more distracting or destructive to the artist) coaching me as I went along. My classmates showed a great interest in Miss Mandelbaum's coaching, mainly because of what happened to her neckline when she bent over to coach me.

Their respectful crowding around Miss Mandelbaum during her daily visit to my desk, and their silent, rapt attention, delighted Miss Mandelbaum and gave poor Mr. Lawless his first glimmer of hope that the Experiment was stimulating those little subnormal minds. He was right. After Miss Mandelbaum, my commissions changed.

For the first time, Cowboy Scalenzo didn't order a murder. "Drawr me Miss Mandelbaum wit' a one-piece bathin' suit on," he said. In the early 1920's, the one-piece bathing suit was no more than a mad rumor then appearing in the more sensational press. No one had ever actually seen anyone wearing one, and even the most advanced and hopeful among us doubted that anyone ever would. I was a little hazy about the arrangement of a plump lady teacher with a one-piece bathing suit on, but the Cowboy helped me with details. He was visibly pleased by the drawing, gave me a dime, and took it to his desk to study it.

After a while, he came back. I was busy drawing Miss Mandelbaum in a one-piece bathing suit (the idea had caught on) for Six-Toe Tanglebaum, who had canceled his order for a picture of him knifing Cowboy Scalenzo in the back (I played no favorites).

74

"Can that one," proposed Cowboy Scalenzo, "and I'll make it a quarter if ya finish this one." He laid on my desk the original One-Piece Bathing Suit Miss Mandelbaum.

"Finish it?" I asked, perplexed. "Didn't I draw everything you told me was there?"

"Sure you did, Al," said the Cowboy, "but I want you to draw me lookin' at her."

I drew Cowboy Scalenzo, in a cowboy suit, looking at Miss Mandelbaum in a one-piece bathing suit.

This caught on.

I then drew Tanglebaum looking at HIS Miss Mandelbaum.

Before the end of that day I had drawn dozens of Portraits of Young Morons Looking at Miss Mandelbaums. It had been my biggest day, at the new rate of two bits a Portrait, and I was loaded with commissions for the next day. I took some of the more urgent jobs home with me, and felt that I could no longer delay my talk with that comer in the third grade. Rubens was right.

The next day Fourfingers Bastardo came over to my desk.

"You finish that pitcher o' me an' Miss Mandelbaum yet?" he asked.

"Not yet, Fourf, I'm still kinda working it up," I replied in a lying tone that was, in later years, to become familiar to dead-line-worried syndicate editors.

"That means you ain't started on it yet," said Fourfingers, who even as a twelve-year-old subnormal was a better judge of my character than syndicate editors, "an' that's okay, because I don't want you should do it."

"Well, that's okay with me, Fourf," I replied, confident that this wouldn't become a trend. "I've got plenty o' others I can—"

"I don't want you to work on no others," said my patron. "I don't want you should drawr me simply LOOKIN' at Miss Mandelbaum." He bent over and whispered, "I'll give you a extra dime if you drawr Miss Mandelbaum in that one-piece bathin' suit and me in a policeman's uniform, and she's sittin' in my lap."

I followed his instructions, putting everything down very lightly, so that I wouldn't have to erase if I made any mistakes. It was

7 5

all very complicated, and terribly engrossing, and before we realized it, Miss Mandelbaum had slipped into the room and was bending over my desk.

"Doing a wrestling scene, I see," she remarked brightly. "But the penciling is so light, so timid—as if you weren't sure of the anatomical details." She beamed at me, and picked up my pencil. "The only way out—to bring out the real meaning—is to *emphasize* all the main construction lines, with good, *bold* strokes!!"

She proceeded to do this, penciling vigorously over my light lines. Fourfingers' face emerged, and then the positions of both figures. It wasn't until she put in the few good bold strokes that brought out her own lightly, but accurately, sketched-in face that she realized what she was doing. She screamed a terrible scream of anguish and betrayal, dropped the pencil as though it were red-hot, and ran out of the room. She never came back. My father's business failed, we moved to Massachusetts, and my career as a professional artist didn't get going again for ten years.

P. G. Wodehouse

Pelham Grenville Wodehouse is almost as fabulous a character as his own characters who go by the implausible names of Frederick Altamount Cornwallis Twistleton, Barmy Fotheringay-Phipps, Stanley Featherstonehaugh Ukridge, Smallwood Bessemer, the incredible Psmith, and the incomparable Jeeves. Wodehouse was born in England in 1881, and his first book was published as soon as he got out of his teens. Since 1908 he has written an average of a book a year—short stories, novels, lyrics, farces, and books for musical comedy. Opposite the title page of his latest volume, *Nothing Serious,* his present publishers list over forty titles, all of them presumably extant, and all of them occurring in the topsy-turvy country which is Wodehouse's special domain. His is a world which is peopled entirely by eccentrics: brash young idlers willing to give up their liberty for a girl with a million dollars; elderly uncles, whose stuffed shirts conceal a heart that is eager for one more madcap leap; prim philistines who turn into grimly passionate golfers—in short a set of queer characters who are happy being caricatures. The late Sinclair Lewis paid Wodehouse his finest compliment when he declared that he was "the master of the touchingly inane, of the ultimate and lordly deadpan." No writer of our day has provoked so many gasps of incredulity—and so many gargantuan and grateful laughs.

Excelsior *

Alfred Jukes and Wilberforce Bream had just holed out at the end of their match for the club championship, the latter sinking a long putt to win, and the young man sitting with the Oldest Member on the terrace overlooking the eighteenth green said that though this meant a loss to his privy purse of ten dollars, his confidence in Jukes remained unimpaired. He still considered him a better golfer than Bream.

The Sage nodded without much enthusiasm.

"You may be right," he agreed. "But I would not call either of them a good golfer."

"They're both scratch."

"True. But it is not mere technical skill that makes a man a good golfer, it is the golfing soul. These two have not the proper attitude of seriousness toward the game. Jukes once returned to the clubhouse in the middle of a round because there was a thunderstorm and his caddie got struck by lightning, and I have known Bream to concede a hole for the almost frivolous reason that he had sliced his ball into a hornet's nest and was reluctant to play it where it lay. This was not the Bewstridge spirit."

"The what spirit?"

"The spirit that animated Horace Bewstridge, the finest golfer I have ever known."

"Was he scratch?"

"Far from it. His handicap was twenty-four. But though his ball was seldom in the right place, his heart was. When I think what Horace Bewstridge went through that day he battled for the President's Cup, I am reminded of the poem, Excelsior, by the late Henry Wadsworth Longfellow, with which you are doubtless familiar."

"I used to recite it as a child."

"I am sorry I missed the treat," said the Oldest Member courteously. "Then you will recall how its hero, in his struggle to reach the heights, was laid stymie after stymie, and how in order to achieve his aim, he had to give up all idea of resting his head upon the maiden's breast, though cordially invited to do so. A tear, if you remember, stood in his bright blue eye, but with a brief 'Excelsior!' he intimated that no business could result. Virtually the same thing that happened to Horace Bewstridge."

"You know," said the young man, "I've always thought that Excelsior bird a bit of a fathead. I mean to say, what was there in it for him? As far I can make out, just the walk."

"Suppose he had been trying to win his first cup?"

"I don't recollect anything being said about any cup. Do they give cups for climbing mountains 'mid snow and ice?"

"We are getting a little muddled," said the Oldest Member. "You appear to be discussing the youth with the banner and the clarion voice, while I am talking about Horace Bewstridge. It may serve to clear the air and disperse the fog of misunderstanding if I tell you the latter's story. And in order that you shall miss none of the finer shades, I must begin by dwelling upon his great love for Vera Witherby."

It was only after the thing had been going on for some time (said the Oldest Member) that I learned of this secret romance in Horace's life. As a rule, the Romeos who live about here are not backward in confiding in me when they fall in love. Indeed, I sometimes feel that I shall have to begin keeping them off with a stick. But Bewstridge was reticent. It was purely by chance that I became aware of his passion.

One rather breezy morning, I was sitting almost exactly where we are sitting now, thinking of this and that, when I observed fluttering toward me across the terrace a sheet of paper. It stopped against my foot, and I picked it up and read its contents. They ran as follows:—

MEM

OLD B. *Ribs. But watch eyes.*
MA B. *Bone up on pixies. Flowers. Insects.*
I. *Symp. breeziness.*
A. *Concil. If poss. p., but w.o. for s.d.a.*

That was all, and I studied it with close attention and, I must confess, a certain amount of alarm. There had been a number of atom-bomb spy scares in the papers recently, and it occurred to me that this might be a secret code, possibly containing information about some local atoms.

It was then that I saw Horace Bewstridge hurrying towards me. He appeared agitated.

"Have you seen a piece of paper?" he asked.

"Would this be it?"

He took it, and seemed to hesitate for a moment.

"I suppose you're wondering what it's all about?"

I admitted to a certain curiosity, and he hesitated again. Then there crept into his eyes the look which I have seen so often in the eyes of young men. I saw that he was about to confide in me.

And presently out it all came, like beer from a bottle. He was in love with Vera Witherby, the niece of one Ponsford Botts, a resident in the neighbourhood.

In putting it like that, I am giving you the thing in condensed form, confining myself to the gist. Horace Bewstridge was a little long-winded about it all, going rather deeply into his emotions and speaking at some length about her eyes, which he compared to twin stars. It was several minutes before I was able to enquire how he was making out.

"Have you told your love?" I asked.

"Not yet," said Horace Bewstridge. "I goggle a good deal, but for the present am content to leave it at that. You see, I'm working this thing on a system. All the nibs will tell you that everything is done by propaganda nowadays, and that your first move, if you want to get anywhere, must be to rope in a *bloc* of friendly neutrals. I start, accordingly, by making myself solid with the family. I give them the old salve, get them rooting for me, and thus insure an impressive build-up. Only then do I take direct action and edge into what you might call the *blitzkrieg*. This paper contains notes for my guidance."

"With reference to administering the salve?"

"Exactly."

I took the document from him, and glanced at it again.

"What," I asked, "does 'Old B. Ribs. But watch eyes' signify?"

"Quite simple. Old Botts tells dialect stories about Irishmen named Pat and Mike, and you laugh when he prods you in the ribs. But sometimes he doesn't prod you in the ribs, merely stands there looking pop-eyed. One has to be careful about that."

"Under the heading 'Ma B.,' I see you say: 'Bone up on pixies.' You add the words 'flowers' and 'insects.' "

"Yes. All that is vitally important. Mrs. Botts, I am sorry to say, is a trifle on the whimsy side. Perhaps you have read her books? They are three in number—*My Chums the Pixies, How to Talk to the Flowers,* and *Many of My Best Friends Are Mosquitoes.* The programme calls for a good working knowledge of them all."

"Who is 'I,' against whose name you have written the phrase: 'Symp. breeziness'?"

"That is little Irwin Botts, the son of the house. He is in love with Dorothy Lamour, and not making much of a go of it. He talks to me about her, and I endeavour to be breezily sympathetic."

"And 'A'?"

"Their poodle, Alphonse. The note is to remind me to conciliate him. He is a dog of wide influence, and cannot be ignored."

" 'If poss., p., but w.o. for s.d.a.'?"

"If possible, pat, but watch out for sudden dash at ankles. He is extraordinarily quick on his feet."

I handed back the paper.

"Well," I said, "it all seems a little elaborate, and I should have thought better results would have been obtained by having a direct pop at the girl, but I wish you luck."

In the days which followed, I kept a watchful eye on Horace, for his story had interested me strangely. Now and then, I would see him pacing the terrace with Ponsford Botts at his side and catch references to Pat and Mike, together with an occasional "Begorrah," and I noted how ringing was his guffaw as the other suddenly congealed with bulging eyes.

Once, as I strolled along the road, I heard a noise like machine-gun fire and turned the corner to find him slapping little Irwin's shoulder in a breezy, elder-brotherly manner. His pockets were generally bulging with biscuits for Alphonse, and from time to time he would come and tell me how he was getting along with Mrs. Botts' books. These, he confessed, called for all that he had of resolution and fortitude, but he told me that he was slowly mastering their contents and already knew a lot more about pixies than most people.

It would all have been easier, he said, if he had been in a position to be able to concentrate his whole attention upon them. But of course he had his living to earn and could not afford to neglect his office work. He held a subordinate post in the well-known firm of R. P. Crumbles Inc, purveyors of Silver Sardines (The Sardine with a Soul), and R. P. Crumbles was a hard taskmaster. And, in addition to this, he had entered for the annual handicap competition known as the President's Cup.

It was upon this latter topic, as the date of the tourney drew near, that he spoke almost as frequently and eloquently as upon the theme of his love. He had been playing golf, it appeared, for some seven years, and up till now had never come within even measurable distance of winning a trophy. Generally, he said, it was his putting that dished him. But recently, as the result of reading golf books, he had adopted a superscientific system, and was now hoping for the best.

It was a stimulating experience to listen to his fine, frank enthusiasm. He spoke of the President's Cup as some young knight of King Arthur's Round Table might have spoken of the Holy Grail. And it was consequently with peculiar satisfaction that I noted his success in the early rounds. Step by step, he won his way into the semifinals in his bracket, and was enabled to get triumphantly through that critical test owing to the fortunate circumstance of his opponent tripping over a passing cat on the eve of the match and spraining his ankle.

Many members of the club would, of course, have been fully competent to defeat Horace Bewstridge if they had sprained both ankles or even broken both arms, but Mortimer Gooch, his antagonist, was not one of these. He scratched, and Horace walked over into the final.

His chances now, it seemed to me, were extremely good. According to how the semifinal in the other bracket went, he would be playing either Peter Willard, who would be as clay in his hands, or a certain Sir George Copstone, a visiting Englishman whom his employer, R. P. Crumbles, had put up for the club, and who by an odd coincidence was residing as a guest at the house of Ponsford Botts. I had watched this hand across the sea in action, and was convinced that Horace, provided he did not lose his nerve, could trim him nicely.

A meeting on the fifteenth green the afternoon before the match enabled me to convey these views to the young fellow. We were there to watch the finish of the opposition semifinal, and when Sir George Copstone had won this, I linked my arm in Horace's and told him that in my opinion the thing was in the bag.

"If Peter Willard, our most outstanding golfing cripple, can

82

take this man to the fifteenth, your victory should be a certainty."

"Peter was receiving thirty-eight."

"You could give him fifty. What is this Copstone? A twenty-four like yourself, is he not?"

"Yes."

"Then you need feel no anxiety, my boy," I said, for when I give a pep talk I like it to be a pep talk. "If you are not too busy tonight reading about pixies, you might be looking around your living room for a spot to put that cup."

He snorted devoutly, and I think he was about to burst into one of those ecstatic monologues of his, but at this moment we reached the terrace. And, as we did so, a harsh, metallic voice called his name, and I perceived, standing at some little distance, a beetle-browed man of formidable aspect, who looked like a cartoon of Capital in a Labor paper. He was smoking a large cigar, with which he beckoned to Horace Bewstridge imperiously, and Horace, leaving my side, ambled up to him like a spaniel. From the fact that, as he ambled, he was bleating "Oh, good evening, Mr. Crumbles. Yes, Mr. Crumbles. I'm coming, Mr. Crumbles," I deduced that this was the eminent sardine fancier who provided him with his weekly envelope.

Their conversation was not an extended one. R. P. Crumbles spoke rapidly and authoritatively for some moments, emphasizing his remarks with swift, captain-of-industry prods at Horace's breast-bone, and then he turned on his heel and strode off in a strong, economic royalist sort of way, and Horace came back to where I stood.

Now, I had noticed once or twice during the interview that the young fellow had seemed to totter on his axis, and as he drew nearer, his pallid face, with its starting eyes and drooping jaw, told me that all was not well.

"That was my boss," he said, in a low, faint voice.

"So I had guessed. Why did he call the conference?"

Horace Bewstridge beat his breast.

"It's about Sir George Copstone."

"What about him?"

Horace Bewstridge clutched his hair.

"Apparently this Copstone runs a vast system of chain stores

throughout the British Isles, and old Crumbles has been fawning
on him ever since his arrival in the hope of getting him to take
on the Silver Sardine and propagate it over there. He says that
this is a big opportunity for the dear old firm and that it be-
hooves all of us to do our bit and push it along. So——"

"So——?"

Horace Bewstridge rent his pullover.

"So," he whispered hoarsely, "I've got to play Customer's
Golf to-morrow and let the man win that cup."

"Horace!" I cried.

I would have seized his hand and pressed it, but it was not
there. Horace Bewstridge had left me. All that my eye encountered was a swirl of dust and his flying form disappearing in the
direction of the bar. I understood and sympathized. There are
moments in the life of every man when human consolation cannot avail and only two or three quick ones will meet the case.

I did not see him again until we met next afternoon on the
first tee for the start of the final.

You, being a newcomer here (said the Oldest Member) may
possibly have formed an erroneous impression regarding this
President's Cup of which I have been speaking. Its name, I admit, is misleading, suggesting as it does the guerdon of some terrific tourney battled for by the cream of the local golfing talent.
One pictures perspiring scratch men straining every nerve and
history being made by amateur champions.

As a matter of fact, it is open for competition only to those
whose handicap is not lower than twenty-four, and excites little
interest outside the ranks of the submerged tenth who play for it.
As a sporting event on our fixture list, as I often have to explain,
it may be classed somewhere between the Grandmothers' Umbrella and the All Day Sucker competed for by children who
have not passed their seventh year.

The final, accordingly, did not attract a large gate. In fact, I
think I was the only spectator. I was thus enabled to obtain an
excellent view of the contestants and to follow their play to the
best advantage. And, as on the previous occasions when I had
watched him perform, I found myself speculating with no little

84

bewilderment as to how Horace's opponent had got that way.

Sir George Copstone was one of those tall, thin, bony Englishmen who seem to have been left over from the eighteen-sixties. He did not actually wear long sidewhiskers of the type known as Piccadilly Weepers, nor did he really flaunt a fore-and-aft deerstalker cap of the type affected by Sherlock Holmes, but you got the illusion that this was so, and it was partly the unnerving effect of his appearance on his opponents that had facilitated his making his way into the final. But what had been the basic factor in his success was his method of play.

A deliberate man, this Copstone. Before making a shot, he would inspect his enormous bag of clubs and take out one after another, slowly, as if he were playing spillikens. Having at length made his selection, he would stand motionless beside his ball, staring at it for what seemed an eternity. Only after one had begun to give up hope that life would ever again animate the rigid limbs, would he start his stroke. He was affectionately known on our links as The Frozen Horror.

Even in normal circumstances, a sensitive, highly strung young man like Horace Bewstridge might well have found himself hard put to it to cope with such an antagonist. And when you take into consideration the fact that he had received those special instructions from the front office, it is not surprising that he should have failed in the opening stages of the encounter to give of his best. The fourth hole found him four down, and one had the feeling that he was lucky not to be five.

At this point, however, there occurred one of those remarkable changes of fortune which are so common in golf and which make it the undisputed king of games. Teeing up at the fifty, Sir George Copstone appeared suddenly to have become afflicted with some form of shaking palsy. Where before he had stood addressing his ball like Lot's wife just after she had been turned into a pillar of salt, he now wriggled like an Ouled Nail dancer in the throes of colic. Nor did his condition improve as the match progressed. His movements took on an even freer abandon. To cut a long story short, which I am told is a thing I seldom do, he lost four holes in a row, and they came to the ninth all square.

And it was here that I observed an almost equally surprising change in the demeanour of Horace Bewstridge.

Until this moment, Horace had been going through the motions with something of the weary moodiness of a Volga boatman, his face drawn, his manner listless. But now he had become a different man. As he advanced to the ninth tee, his eyes gleamed, his ears wiggled, and his lips were set. He looked like a Volga boatman who has just learned that Stalin has purged his employer.

I could see what had happened. Intoxicated with this unexpected success, he was beginning to rebel against those instructions from up top. The almost religious fervour which comes upon a twenty-four handicap man when he sees a chance of winning his first cup had him in its grip. Who, he was asking himself, was R. P. Crumbles? The man who paid him his salary and could fire him out on his ear, yes, but was money everything? Suppose he won this cup and starved in the gutter, I could almost hear him murmuring, would not that be better than losing the cup and getting his three square a day?

And when on the ninth green, by pure accident, he sank a thirty-foot putt, I saw his lips move and I knew what he was saying to himself. It was the word "Excelsior."

It was as he stood gaping at the hole into which his ball had disappeared that Sir George Copstone spoke for the first time.

"Jolly good shot, what?" said Sir George, a gallant sportsman. "Right in the old crevasse, what, what? I say, look here," he went on, jerking his shoulders in a convulsive gesture, "do you mind if I go and shake out the underlinen? Got a beetle or something down my back."

"Certainly," said Horace.

"Won't keep you long. I'll just strip off the next-the-skins and spring upon it unawares."

He performed another complicated writhing movement, and was about to leave us, when along came R. P. Crumbles.

"How's it going?" asked R. P. Crumbles.

"Eh? What? Going? Oh, one down at the turn."

"He is?"

"No, I am," said Sir George. "He, in sharp contradistinction, is one up. Sank a dashed fine putt on this green. Thirty feet, if an inch. Well, excuse me, I'll just buzz off and bash this beetle."

He hastened away, twitching in every limb, and R. P. Crumbles turned to Horace. His face was suffused.

"Do I get no cooperation, Bewstridge?" he demanded. "What the devil do you mean by being one up? And what's all this nonsense about thirty-foot putts? How dare you sink thirty-foot putts?"

I could have told him that Horace was in no way responsible for what had occurred and that the thing must be looked on as an Act of God, but I hesitated to wound the young man's feelings, and R. P. Crumbles continued.

"Thirty-foot putts, indeed! Have you forgotten what I told you?"

Horace Bewstridge met his accusing glare without a tremor. His face was like granite. His eyes shone with a strange light.

"I have not forgotten the interoffice memo. to which you refer," he said, in a firm, quiet voice. "But I am ignoring it. I intend to trim the pants off this stranger in our midst."

"You do, and see what happens."

"I don't care what happens."

"Bewstridge," said R. P. Crumbles, "nine more holes remain to be played. During these nine holes, think well. I shall be waiting on the eighteenth to see the finish. I shall hope to find," he added significantly, "that the match has ended before then."

He walked away, and I think I have never seen the back of any head look more sinister. Horace, however, merely waved his putter defiantly, as if it had been a banner with a strange device and the other an old man recommending him not to try a pass.

"Nuts to you, R. P. Crumbles!" he cried, with a strange dignity. "Fire me, if you will. This is the only chance I shall ever have of winning a cup, and I'm going to do it."

I stood for a moment motionless. This revelation of the nobility of this young man's soul had stunned me. Then I hurried to where he stood, and gripped his hand. I was still shaking it, when an arch contralto voice spoke behind us.

"Good afternoon, Mr. Bewstridge."

Mrs. Botts was in our midst. She was accompanied by her husband, Ponsford, her son Irwin, and her dog, Alphonse.

"How is the match going?" asked Mrs. Botts.

Horace explained the position of affairs.

"We shall all be on the eighteenth green, to see the finish," said Mrs. Botts. "But you really must not beat Sir George. That would be very naughty. Where is Sir George?"

As she spoke, Sir George Copstone appeared, looking quite his old self again.

"Bashed him!" he said. "Whopping big chap. Put up the dickens of a struggle. But I settled him in the end. He'll think twice before he tackles a Sussex Copstone again."

Mrs. Botts uttered a girlish scream.

"Somebody attacked you, Sir George?"

"I should say so. Whacking great brute of a beetle. But I fixed him."

"You killed a beetle?"

"Well, stunned him, at any rate. Technical knockout."

"But, Sir George, don't you remember what Coleridge said —He prayeth best who loveth best all things both great and small?"

"Not beetles?"

"Of course. Some of my closet chums are beetles."

The other seemed amazed.

"This friend of yours, this Coleridge, really says—he positively asserts that we ought to love beetles?"

"Of course."

"Even when they get under the vest and start doing buck and wing dances along the spine?"

"Of course."

"Sounds a bit of a silly ass to me. Not the sort of chap one would care to know. Well, come on, Bewstridge, let's be moving, what? I say," went on Sir George, as they passed out of earshot, "do you know that old geezer? Potty, what? Over in England, we'd have her in a padded cell before she could say 'Pip, pip.' Beetles, egad! Coleridge, forsooth! And do you know what she said to me this morning? Told me to be careful where I stepped on the front lawn, because it was full of pixies. Can't

88

stand that husband of hers, either. Always talking rot about Irishmen. And what price the son and heir? There's a young blister for you. And as for that flea storage depot she calls a dog . . . Well, I'll tell you. If I'd known what I was letting myself in for, staying at her house, I'd have gone to a hotel. Carry on, Bewstridge. It's your honour."

It was perhaps the exhilaration due to hearing these frank criticisms of a quartette whom he had never liked, though he had striven to love them for Vera Witherby's sake, that lent zip to Horace's drive from the tenth tee. Normally, he was a man who alternated between a weak slice and a robust hook, but on this occasion his ball looked neither to right nor left. He pasted it straight down the middle, and with such vehemence that he had no difficulty in winning the hole and putting himself two up.

But now the tide of fortune began to change again. His recent victory over the beetle had put Sir George Copstone right back into the old mid-season form. Once more he had become the formidable Frozen Horror whose deliberate methods of play had caused three stout men to succumb before his onslaught in the preliminary rounds. With infinite caution, like one suspecting a trap of some kind, he selected clubs from his bulging bag; with unremitting concentration he addressed and struck his ball. And for a while there took place as stern a struggle as I have ever witnessed on the links.

But gradually Sir George secured the upper hand. Little by little he recovered the ground he had lost. He kept turning in steady sevens, and came a time when Horace began to take nines. The strain had uncovered his weak spot. His putting touch had left him.

I could see what was wrong, of course. He was being much too scientific. He was remembering the illustrated plates in the golf books and trying to make the club head move from Spot A. through Line B. to ball C. and that is always a fatal thing for a high-handicap man to do. I have talked to a great many of our most successful high-handicap men, and they all assured me that the only way in which it was possible to obtain results was to shut the eyes, breathe a short prayer, and loose off into the unknown.

Still, there it was, and there was nothing that could be done about it. Horace went on studying the line and taking the Bobby Jones stance and all the rest of it, and gradually, as I say, Sir George recovered the ground he had lost. One down on the thirteenth, he squared the match at the fifteenth, and it was only by holing out a fortunate brassie shot to win on the seventeenth that Horace was enabled to avoid defeat by two and one. As it was, they came to the eighteenth on level terms, and everything, therefore, depended on what Fate held in store for them there.

I had a melancholy feeling that the odds were all in favor of the older man. At the time of which I am speaking, the eighteenth was not the long hole which we are looking at as we sit here, but that short, tricky one which is now the ninth—the one where you stand at the foot of the hill and pop the ball up vertically with a mashie, trusting that you will not overdrive and run across the green into the deep chasm on the other side. At such a hole, a cautious, calculating player like Sir George Copstone inevitably has the advantage over a younger and more ardent antagonist, who is apt to put too much beef behind his tee shot.

My fear, however, that Horace would fall into this error was not fulfilled. His ball soared in a perfect arc, and one could see at a glance that it must have dropped very near the pin. Sir George's effort, though sound and scholarly, was not in the same class, and there could be no doubt that on reaching the summit we should find that he was away. And so it proved. The first thing I saw as I arrived, was a group consisting of Ponsford Botts, little Irwin Botts, and the poodle, Alphonse; the second, Horace's ball lying some two feet from the flag; the third, that of his opponent at least six feet beyond it.

Sir George, a fighter to the last, putted to within a few inches of the hole, and I heard Horace draw a deep breath.

"This for it," he said. And, as he spoke, there was a rapid pattering of feet, and what looked like a bundle of black cotton-wool swooped past him, seized the ball in its slavering jaws, and bore it away. At this crucial moment, with Horace Bewstridge's fortunes swaying in the balance, the poodle Alphonse had got the party spirit.

The shocked "Hoy!" that sprang from my lips must have sounded to the animal like the Voice of Conscience, for he started visibly and dropped the ball. I had at least prevented him from going to the last awful extreme of carrying it down into the abyss.

But the spot where he had dropped it, was on the very edge of the green, and Horace Bewstridge stood motionless, with ashen face. Once before, in the course of this match, he had sunk a putt of this length, but he was doubting if that sort of thing happened twice in a lifetime. He would have to concentrate, concentrate. With knitted brow, he knelt down to study the line. And, as he did so, Alphonse began to bark.

Horace rose. Almost as clearly as if he had given them verbal utterance, I could read the thoughts that were passing through his mind.

This dog, he was saying to himself, was the apple of Irwin Botts' eye. It was also the apple of Ponsford Botts' eye. To seek it out and kick it in the slats, therefore, would be to shoot that system of his to pieces beyond repair. Irwin Botts would look at him askance. Ponsford Botts would look at him askance. And if they looked at him askance, Vera Witherby would look at him askance, too, for they were presumably the apples of her eye, just as Alphonse was the apple of theirs.

On the other hand, he could not putt with a noise like that going on.

He made his decision. If he should lose Vera Witherby, it would be most unfortunate, but not so unfortunate as losing the President's Cup. Horace Bewstridge, as I have said, was a golfer.

The next moment, the barking had broken off in a sharp yelp, and Alphonse was descending into the chasm like a falling star. Horace returned to his ball and resumed his study of the line.

The Bottses, Irwin, and Ponsford, had been stunned witnesses of the assault. They now gave tongue simultaneously.

"Hey!" cried Irwin Botts.

"Hi!" cried Ponsford Botts.

Horace frowned meditatively at the hole. Even apart from the length of it, it was a difficult shot. He would have to allow for the undulations of the green. There was a nasty little slope there to the right. That must be taken into consideration. There was

91

also, further on, a nasty little slope to the left. The thing called for profound thought, and for some reason he found himself unable to give his whole mind to the problem.

Then he saw what the trouble was. Irwin Botts was standing beside him, shouting "Hey!" in his left ear, and Ponsford Botts was standing on the other side, shouting "Hi!" in his right ear. It was this that was affecting his concentration.

He gazed at them, momentarily at a loss. How, he asked himself, would Bobby Jones have handled a situation like this? The answer came in a flash. He would have taken Irwin Botts by the scruff of his neck, led him to the brink of the chasm and kicked him into it. He would then have come back for Ponsford Botts.

Horace did this and resumed the scrutiny of the line. And at this moment, accompanied by a pretty, soulful-looking girl in whom I recognized Vera Witherby, R. P. Crumbles came on to the green. As his eye fell on Horace, his face darkened. He asked Sir George Copstone how the match stood.

"I should have thought," he said, chewing his cigar ominously, "that it would have been over long before this. I had supposed that you would have won on about the fifteenth or sixteenth."

"It is a point verging very decidedly on the moot," replied Sir George, "if I'm going to win on the eighteenth. He's got this for it, and I expect him to sink it, now that there's nothing to distract his mind. He was being a bit bothered a moment ago," he explained, "by Botts senior, Botts junior, and the Botts dog. But he has just kicked them all into the chasm, and can now give his whole attention to the game. Capable young feller, that. Just holed out a two hundred yard brassie shot. Judged it to a nicety."

I heard Vera Witherby draw in her breath sharply. R. P. Crumbles, switching his cigar from one side of his mouth to the other, strode across to where Horace was bending over his ball, and spoke rapidly and forcefully.

It was a dangerous thing to do, and one against which his best friends would have advised him. There was no "Yes, Mr. Crumbles," "No, Mr. Crumbles," about Horace Bewstridge now. I saw him straighten him with a testy frown. The next moment, he had attached himself to the scruff of the other's neck and was adding him to the contents of the chasm.

92

This done, he returned, took another look at the hole with his head on one side, and seemed satisfied. He rose, and addressed his ball. He was drawing the club head back, when a sudden scream rent the air. Glancing over his shoulder, exasperated, he saw that their little group had been joined by Mrs. Botts. She was bending over the edge of the chasm, endeavoring to establish communication with its inmates. Muffled voices rose from the depths.

"Ponsford!"

"Wah, wah, wah."

"Mr. Crumbles!"

"Wah, wah, wah."

"Irwin!"

"Wah, wah, wah."

"Alphonse!"

"Woof, woof, woof."

Mrs. Botts bent still further forward, one hand resting on the turf, the other cupped to her ear.

"What? What did you say? I can't hear. What are you doing down there? What? I can't hear. What is Mr. Crumbles doing down there? Why has he got his foot in Irwin's eye? Irwin, take your eye away from Mr. Crumbles' foot immediately. What? I can't hear. Tell whom he is fired, Mr. Crumbles? I can't hear. Why is Alphonse biting Mr. Crumbles in the leg? What? I can't hear. I wish you would speak plainly. Your mouth's full of what? Ham? Oh, sand? Why is your mouth full of sand? Why is Alphonse now biting Irwin? Skin whom, Mr. Crumbles? What? I can't hear. You've swallowed your cigar? Why? What? I can't hear."

It seemed to Horace Bewstridge, that this sort of thing, unless firmly checked at the source, might go on indefinitely. And to attempt to concentrate while it did, was hopeless. Clicking his tongue in annoyance at these incessant interruptions, he stepped across to where Mrs. Botts crouched. There was a sound like a pistol shot. Mrs. Botts joined the others. Horace came back, rubbing his hand, studied the line again and took his stance.

"Mr. Bewstridge!"

The words, spoken in his left ear just as he was shooting,

were little more than a whisper, but they affected Horace as if an ammunition dump had exploded beneath him. Until this moment, he had evidently been unaware of the presence of the girl he loved, and this unexpected announcement of it caused him to putt rather strongly.

His club descended with a convulsive jerk, and the ball, as if feeling that now that all that scientific nonsense was over, it knew where it was, started off for the hole at forty miles an hour in a dead straight line. There were slopes to the right. There were slopes to the left. It ignored them. Sizzling over the turf, it struck the back of the cup, soared into the air like a rocket, came down, soared up again, fell once more, bounced and rebounded and finally, after rattling round and round for perhaps a quarter of a minute, rested safe at journey's end. The struggle for the President's Cup was over.

"Nice work," said Sir George Copstone. "Your match, what?"

Horace was gazing at Vera Witherby.

"You spoke?" he said.

She blushed in pretty confusion.

"It was nothing. I only wanted to thank you."

"Thank me?"

"For what you did to Aunt Lavender."

"Me, too," said Sir George Copstone, who had joined them. "Precisely what the woman needed. Should be a turning point in her life. That'll take her mind off pixies for a bit. *And* beetles."

Horace stared at the girl. He had thought to see her shrink from him in loathing. Instead of which, she was looking at him with something in her eyes which, if he was not very much mistaken, was the lovelight.

"Vera . . . Do you mean . . .?"

Her eyes must have given him his answer, for he sprang forward and clasped her to his bosom, using the interlocking grip. She nestled in his arms.

"I misjudged you, Horace," she whispered. "I thought you were a sap. I mistrusted anyone who could be as fond as you seemed to be of Aunt Lavender, Uncle Ponsford, little Irwin, and Alphonse. And I had always yearned for one of those engagements where my man, like Romeo, would run fearful risks to come near me, and I would have to communicate with him by means of notes in hollow trees."

"Romantic," explained Sir George. "Many girls are."

Into the ecstasy of Horace Bewstridge's mood there crept a chilling thought. He had won her love. He had won the President's Cup. But, unless he had quite misinterpreted the recent exchange of remarks between Mrs. Botts and R. P. Crumbles at the chasm side, he had lost his job and so far from being able to support a wife, would now presumably have to starve in the gutter.

He explained this, and Sir George Copstone pooh-poohed vehemently.

"Starve in the gutter? Never heard such bally rot. What do you want to go starving in gutters for? Join me, what? Come over to England, I mean to say, and accept a prominent position in my chain of dashed stores. Name your own salary, of course."

Horace reeled.

"You don't mean that?"

"Of course I mean it. What do you think I meant? What other possible construction could you have put on my words?"

"But you don't know what I can do."

Sir George stared.

"Not know what you can do? Why, I've seen you in action, dash it. If what you have just done isn't enough to give a discerning man an idea of your capabilities, I'd like to know what is. Ever since I went to stay at that house, I've wanted to find someone capable of kicking that dog, kicking that boy, kicking old Botts and giving Ma Botts a juicy one right on the good old spot. I'm not merely grateful to you, my dear chap, profoundly grateful, I'm overcome with admiration. Enormously impressed, I am. Never saw anything so adroit. What I need in my business is a man who thinks on his feet and does it now. Ginger up some of my branch managers a bit. Of course, you must join me, dear old thing, and don't forget about making the salary big. And now that's settled, how about trickling off to the bar and having a few? Yoicks!"

"Yoicks!" said Horace.

"Yoicks!" said Vera Witherby.

"Tallo-ho!" said Sir George.

"Tallo-ho!" said Horace.

"Tally-ho!" said Vera Witherby.

"Tally-bally-ho!" said Sir George, driving the thing home beyond any possibility of misunderstanding. "Come on, let's go."

Julia Truitt Yenni

Readers of *House for the Sparrow* and *This Is Me, Kathie* will remember the sensitivity of the author's characters as well as the easy grace of her style. Her gifts are emphasized in her most recent novel, *The Spellbound Village*, published in 1951. However, only the most perceptive readers of Miss Yenni's preceding work would look for the broad irony and slashing burlesque of "My Friend Valerie," an unexpectedly dexterous and devastating exposure of feminine affectations.

A native of Birmingham, Alabama, Julia Truitt Yenni (born February 21, 1913) was one of eight talented children. Her grandmother, Julia Truitt Bishop, was well known as a newspaper woman and magazine writer. Leaving the Southland to take care of itself, Miss Yenni came North, made her home in Pennsylvania, and proceeded to ensconce herself there with her husband and two young daughters.

My Friend Valerie*

I am hypnotized by the little paragraphs that appear at the front —or the back—of a magazine and furnish sprightly bits of information about the authors whose work appears on its pages. I know far more about the authors in these little sketches than I do about their works. For, while any isolated paragraph, with its own heading and possibly a blurred snapshot in one corner, acts on me as a flute on a cobra, I become selective and critical once I turn the pages into the body of the magazine.

It was in these paragraphs that I met—and have now known intimately for years—a woman who holds, in my judgment, the title Most Revolting. For my own satisfaction, I have dreamed up a name for her—Valerie Bounce. Mercifully, Valerie and I have never met in person, but I have a perfect and detailed picture of her.

Valerie is tall, not tall enough to be statuesque, just tall enough to be horsy; a bit on the heavy side, but none of it fat, mind you, not on Valerie! Every ounce of it good, solid muscle, which it darned well ought to be, considering the life she leads. Her teeth are large, inclined to be prominent; but if you think this makes Valerie self-conscious, you're crazy. Teeth and all, Val's rich, healthy laughter rings out from early in the morning until far into the night, or what Valerie always refers to as the wee, small hours.

She is addicted to dirndls, which she herself runs up, and for which she dyes the material, too, with beetroot, black walnuts, and old onion skins. When she's in really fine fettle—and Valerie is practically never in any other kind of fettle—she spins and weaves the stuff, too, out of hair she combs out of a couple of Angora cats she's got around the place.

I have a fairly distinct picture of Valerie's husband, though for obvious reasons it is not quite so sharp as the portrait of Valerie herself. He is slight of build, vague of coloring, and smokes a pipe. He attempts a mustache with more courage than vigor, and wears scratchy tweeds that irritate his skin terribly; he can't very well avoid the tweeds, since Valerie weaves them.

Valerie's situation in life varies according to what snapshot she decides to send in that week. Along with that little job in which she's wearing tight dungarees ("Levis, we call them out here," she writes) and sitting on the corral fence with a brace of stallions nuzzling her behind the ears, she sends a delightfully casual account of her life on a two-thousand-acre ranch in Idaho. Here she brands all the cattle, feeds several thousand orphaned lambs out of a bottle, cooks, washes, and plans innumerable gay picnics and parties for her four "bairns" and her "partner," and fills in the rest of the day with breaking in the cow ponies the toughest ranch hands have given up as pure poison.

And you want to know what Val does when the steers are in bed, the last lamb left with its bottle and a Teddy bear beside it? You might think she'd get out of those tight pants, put on a housecoat, and relax. Not Valerie! What she does then is write books and stories. And not just a few, either. Between Robin (the eldest of the "bairns") and Bunny (second eldest), she turned out three novels, a mystery yarn, and "half a dozen short pieces." (Short pieces, indeed! Short pieces of what?) Between Bunny and Christopher, she wrote and illustrated ten children's stories, and between Christopher and Thad—All right, I'm as tired of this as you are.

Do you think we're through with Valerie? Not by a jugful! Next month she's in again. This time she snagged a snapshot out of Cousin Lutie's Cape Cod album, showing a blurred female figure against a definite down East background, and now we leave ranch life behind us.

This is a quite different Valerie—with a feeling for Fine Old Pieces and Fine Old Traditions. She and her husband (squirming uncomfortably in his tweeds) have bought a three-hundred-year-old New England farmhouse, and have been busily and lovingly restoring it to its original glory. Inch by inch (and every inch by hand, of course) they have removed old paint and varnish, sacrilegious gimcrackery. They have whittled out an exact duplicate of the Original Staircase (as I am convinced Valerie is two-thirds beaver, it is my opinion she gnawed it out), and they are now baking bricks in the kitchen oven for an exact duplicate of the original fireplace. Since they are also curing boards, so as to recreate the original floors, and piling up shingles (hand-hewn), to recreate the original side walls, I take a dim view of what they must have bought in the first place. But then, I haven't Valerie's spirit, a fact of which I become more convinced when I reach the last few sentences of the paragraph and once more find out what Valerie is up to come nightfall—when the sandpaper is tucked away, the last board rubbed, the last nail chewed.

What Valerie does *then* is take out a quill pen ("Silly, I know," she writes, "but it seems to have a spirit, a will of its own, which knows more what this rich background should produce than the hand that holds it!"), and without batting her somewhat sparse eyelashes, she pours forth three full-length novels a year, five children's books (her husband drew the pictures for these), and a "dozen or so short pieces."

These are two of Valerie's many aspects. I've spotted her writing from the Maine woods, where, between sugaring-off and lumbering time, she scratches out enough wordage to fill a five-foot shelf. She does all this by cozy, kerosene lamplight, with the four "babes" rolling happily on the floor and her husband quietly pulling at his pipe opposite her. (Valerie never refers to her chil-

99

dren as children. They are always bairns, babes, or Tall Sons.)

Very occasionally she deserts the country and becomes a busy doctor's wife. Then, after doing all her husband's clerical work and pitching in on a few emergency amputations (which I suspect she enjoys), she washes the dishes, does all the ironing and cleaning, and then ("because time hangs heavy on my hands," she exclaims, with delightful simplicity), places her battered old portable on a card table and tosses off a witty book on the trials of a doctor's wife, a serious book of advice for career girls, three mystery stories, a magazine serial, and "half a dozen short pieces."

Mostly, though, Valerie sticks to the country. The furrowed field, the vast horizon, the towering timber—obviously she recognizes her best locale—and farm, fishing shack, and converted barn all have echoed to the clack of her typewriter, the scrape of her pen.

But something about Valerie has begun to puzzle me lately, almost worry me. And that is, don't the editors of the magazines recognize the fact that all these women are, one and all, my friend Valerie?

Or do they innocently suppose the world contains more than one woman who can write, with a straight face (as straight as Valerie can get her face, that is), "And I found that after the fields were plowed, the farm hands fed, and the babes tucked in bed for the night, time hung heavy, and I decided to try my hand at writing"?

Answer me this—has any of them ever *seen* Valerie? No. You'll notice that almost invariably her stuff is shipped from some distant hamlet, with a comment to the effect that she and her husband rarely leave their own little bit of paradise to face the dirt and noise that attend Civilization.

Or could it be—this is the worry that has begun to gnaw at me—that the editors themselves *make up* those little paragraphs? Why is the face in the snapshot always so blurred, the address (if any is given) so far off the beaten track that nobody would be likely to check up on it?

Could it be that they *quite deliberately* face us, at the beginning of their publications, with Valerie the Indomitable—us, poor weak sisters, dead at the end of a day in which we have done nothing but cope with two or three children and a relatively well-equipped house, yet ready for no activity more energetic than a long bath and a look at a magazine? We cower in our chairs and approach the pages of fiction and advertising with a feeling of inferiority so great that the first advertisement, which tells us that if we do not at once get our hands in better shape, our husband will elope with his secretary, finds us cringingly ready to believe the worst— softened for the impression, like a lock of hair prepared to receive the permanent wave.

For months now, off and on, I have been alternately attracted and repelled by this idea. It is tempting, for it would mean the end of Valerie the Revolting. Once more, as I read those small paragraphs, I could hold up my head and face the accounts of Valerie's activities with the calm sneer of disbelief.

But that is the frightening part of it. I find that, even if it means blessèd release, I cannot part with Valerie. There is a quality of mesmerism about her. Valerie Bounce is loathsome, she is revolting—but she belongs to me, she is mine, and I cannot let her go!

Red Smith

A sportswriter who is also a writer's writer, Red Smith has been praised by a host of literary eminents. Such a notable author as Robert E. Sherwood has hailed Smith as the successor of Ring Lardner and Heywood Broun. His pages, wrote Sherwood, "give you a much better idea of what the American people are really thinking and feeling, what they are laughing at or irritated by, than you get from the best-informed Washington correspondents."

He was born in 1905 in Green Bay, Wisconsin, and christened Walter Wellesley Smith. As soon as he got his B. A. degree at Notre Dame he became a newspaperman. Starting as a cub reporter on the Milwaukee *Sentinel*, he wrote his way up through rewrite man on the St. Louis *Star-Times* and sports reporter on the Philadelphia *Record* to his present position, the nationally known columnist of the New York *Herald Tribune*. His "Views of Sports" began appearing in 1945 and the column (a worthy companion to John Crosby's radio and television paragraphs in the same daily) is read as Gospel by sports fans and quoted by teachers as a model of journalism. Smith's volume, *Out of the Red*, justifies not only its punning title but also a reader's (and Longfellow's) conclusion: "The Smith, a mighty man is he."

Social Notes from Hell's Kitchen*

Two exemplary little gentlemen, who wouldn't dream of clutching an antagonist by the eyeballs unless the referee's back was turned, are to entertain the Eighth Avenue eleganti this evening with an exchange of Chesterfieldian courtesy and Old World politesse.

Sandy Gawain Saddler, a verray parfit gentil knight, and Paddy Fauntleroy DeMarco, *le chevalier sans peur et sans reproche*, are to meet in Madison Square Garden for their third passage at arms. Each will be formally attired in silken drawers, Taylor Foul Proof armor, and an air of injured innocence. For the guests, white or black tie is optional.

Sir Sandy is a graduate knight who has studied chivalry at the feet—and thumbs and elbows—of the master, Willie Pep.

* Copyright, 1951, New York *Herald Tribune*, Inc.

102

Last time he and his tutor appeared here, they gave such a rousing exhibition of polished gentility that Mr. Robert Christenberry, New York's arbiter of ring etiquette, chased both of them clear across the state line. Not until now has Saddler been allowed back without a muzzle.

Sir Paddy is an unschooled cavalier who never studied etiquette and makes up his manners out of his own head. That last phrase is used advisedly; the outside of DeMarco's head is practically the first thing his opponents meet socially.

It should not be inferred from the foregoing that either of tonight's entertainers is the rowdy or mischievous type. Each is the soul of punctilio, pacific, gallant, and forgiving. Not for a moment would either man consider gnawing an adversary's ear, unless the other guy started it.

Saddler insists that he never gets rough except in self-defense. A man practically has to pull a knife on him before Sandy will resort to judo; only on the gravest provocation would he smite a fellow creature below the neutral zone. To Sandy, such tactics are almost unspeakably repellent.

DeMarco is just as sternly opposed to raffish behavior in the ring. To be sure, he does bob and duck and jump and jiggle a good deal during working hours. It isn't his fault if some awkward slob gets his bridgework in the way when Paddy puts his head down and bores in.

Saddler, who is given to introspection, once undertook to psychoanalyze himself for the benefit of visitors to his training camp.

"In the ring before a fight," a fellow said, "you look so glum and forlorn a guy would think you'd lost your last friend in the world. Are you unhappy? Do you brood?"

"I dunno," Sir Sandy said, "guess I'm just evil."

Evil or not, he is featherweight champion of the world and a thoroughly competent fist fighter when he elects to box instead of making like the Green Hornet with half-nelsons and Indian deathlocks.

In eight years of professional fighting, he has lost only once when there was something of value at stake. That was in his second fight with Pep, whom he had stiffened in their first engagement for the championship. In their second match he slugged

103

Willie with great severity, digging one large fox hole in Pep's features, but the artful dodger from Hartford outhustled and outmaneuvered him to regain the title on points.

When they met for a third time, Pep came unraveled after seven rounds, and the championship changed hands again. This gave Saddler two legs on the boxing title and retired the trophy as far as the Marquis of Queensberry was concerned. Forsaking the manly art, they presented one more performance, this time under catch-as-catch-can and Greco-Roman rules, and Saddler chased Willie out of the ring at a time when Pep had a clear lead of three hammerlocks, one gouge, and two hook-scissors to one body slam.

Having thus disposed of Pep in all fields of endeavor except thuggee, Saddler has destroyed his own opportunities for gainful employment in the featherweight division. He now plans to challenge for the lightweight championship as soon as he has perfected himself in the step-over toehold and flying mare.

Before he can wangle an introduction to Jimmy Carter, the leader of 135-pound society, Sandy must settle his account with DeMarco, who is ranked fifth in the lightweight class. The only bout Saddler has lost this year was an overweight match with DeMarco, who won on points.

That was their second engagement. In 1949 Saddler opened an incision in Paddy's profile and was credited with a nine-round knockout. Two of the three official score cards gave DeMarco no worse than a draw when the lads were pried apart.

Commissioner Christenberry, who is both a rassling fan and the Emily Post of cauliflower society, will be watching for evidence that these young men have grown in social grace. Both have impeccable backgrounds. DeMarco is a Brooklyn post-deb of the 1945 season. Saddler was born in Boston, barely a knuckleduster's throw from Beacon Hill.

James Thurber

James Thurber's boyhood was, he says in a modest third-person esti-
mate, "pretty well devoid of significance. He fell down a great deal
during this period, and his gold-rimmed glasses forever needed straight-
ening, which gave him an appearance of a person who hears somebody
calling but can't make out where the sound is coming from."

Later he could tell (and did tell) exactly where the sound—and the
fury—came from. He told it well, with a wonderful combination of
humor and realism. Pretending to be bewildered by noise and people,
Thurber unmasked pomposity, lambasted buncombe, and deflated the
pretenses of stuffed shirts of every size. Such books (and such titles) as
*My Life and Hard Times; Men, Women and Dogs; The Seal in the
Bedroom; The Middle-aged Man on the Flying Trapeze; The Thurber
Carnival;* and *The Beast in Me and Other Animals* are typical of his
humor and his startling excursions into the macabre. Thurber has gone
as far in the limbo between daydream and nightmare as it is possible
to go. He can extend a whimsicality into logical lunacy, turn a fairy
tale into a parable, and mix nonsense with satire. He can do all this
naturally because he is something far beyond the traditional laugh-
provoker. Thurber is a humorist who is, first of all, a humanist.

What's So Funny? *

A young lady, Miss E. H., of Oklahoma City, has written me asking if there are any standing rules for writing humor. I am naturally
flattered to have been selected as an official spokesman in this matter, and I hope I will not intone as I go along or become too pon-
tifical, or turn surly.

Perhaps we might begin with a caption for a drawing I have
had around for years: "Where were you last night, Chastity?" I
have never done a drawing to accompany this, or even sketched
out the characters in my mind. I can't even remember now what
I saw in it. In the cold light of my fifties, it appears to me as a
Formula Caption against which a standing rule might well be
drawn. By a Formula Caption I mean one that can be endlessly

* Reprinted by permission from *The Bermudian*.

paraphrased, and usually is. For example: "Quit messing around with that loaded pistol, Prudence," and "For Heaven's sake, Patience, will you please give me a chance to explain?" So much for Formula Captions.

I have established a few standing rules of my own about humor, after receiving dozens of humorous essays and stories from strangers over a period of twenty years. 1). The reader should be able to find out what the story is about. 2). Some inkling of the general idea should be apparent in the first five hundred words. 3). If the writer has decided to change the name of his protagonist from Ketcham to McTavish, Ketcham should not keep bobbing up in the last five pages. A good way to eliminate this confusion is to read the piece over before sending it out, and remove Ketcham completely. He is a nuisance. 4). The word "I'll" should not be divided so that the "I" is on one line and " 'll" on the next. The reader's attention, after the breaking up of "I'll," can never be successfully recaptured. 5). It also never recovers from such names as Ann S. Thetic, Maud Lynn, Sally Forth, Bertha Twins, and the like. 6). Avoid comic stories about plumbers who are mistaken for surgeons, sheriffs who are terrified by gunfire, psychiatrists who are driven crazy by women patients, doctors who faint at the sight of blood, adolescent girls who know more about sex than their fathers do, and midgets who turn out to be the parents of a two-hundred-pound wrestler.

I have a special wariness of people who write opening sentences with nothing in mind, and then try to create a story around them. These sentences, usually easy to detect, go like this: "Mrs. Ponsonby had never put the dog in the oven before," " 'I have a wine tree, if you would care to see it,' said Mr. Dillingworth," and "Jackson decided suddenly, for no reason, really, to buy his wife a tricycle." I have never traced the fortunes of such characters in the stories I receive beyond the opening sentence, but, like you, I have a fair notion of what happens, or doesn't happen, in "The Barking Oven," "The Burgundy Tree," and "A Tricycle for Mama."

An aging author who receives but never has the time or strength to read humorous stories written by women that invariably run to 8500 words, can usually get a pretty good idea of the material

106

from the accompanying letters, many of which contain snapshots of the writer's husband, baby, and beach cottage. These pieces have usually been written in a gay, carefree vacation mood, and it is a sound rule to avoid self-expression at such a time, since it leads to overemphasis, underlining, unnecessary quotation marks, and the odd notion that everything that happens is funny. The American housewife, possibly as the result of what might be called the "Blandings Influence," also seems to believe that amusement is inherent in everything that goes wrong about the house and in everybody that comes in to fix it. My own experience has not been that fortunate. In my view, a carpenter named Twippley is likely to be as dull as a professor named Tweedle, and I think we are safe in setting this up as a standing rule.

Another reliable rule, Miss E. H., is that nocturnal urges to get out of bed and write something humorous should be strongly resisted. The woman who springs up, lights the light, wakes her husband, and starts "writing it out" is not only a nuisance but is almost certainly laboring under the common illusion of the sleepy that the commonplace is remarkable. These night pieces are usually dashed off in less than twenty minutes, and when written by the female, seem to grow out of the conviction that writing late at night lends a special magic to prose, like writing in a rose arbor or on a houseboat. The magic, alas, rarely survives the cynical light of day. Tender is the night, but it has neither literary style nor creative talent, and no more enhances the quality of a lady's output than does the assumption of such cute and booksy *noms de plume* as Suzanna Prynne or Priscilla Winkle.

Since I was twelve, I have had an antipathy to ladies or gentlemen who write comic stories in baby talk, Deep Southern dialect, or other exasperating lingos, or whose characters lisp or stammer or talk like Red Skelton. I am also distinctly cool to writers who try to interest me in tribal dialect, African, Mayan, or American Indian. My worst personal experience in that field was when I read, or tried to read, a manuscript dealing with the confused whimsies of the Shoshone Indians. Its author sent a letter with it that began: "I have lived among the Shoshones for twenty years, and have thought for some time that their humor, which consists mainly of heavy banter, would be a valuable con-

107

tribution to American folklore. In some instances, as in the case of OGLA WAHGU, which is not easily rendered into English, I have made no attempt at translation. OGLA WAHGU means, variously, 'not for me,' and 'I am going,' and, more rarely, 'strook him.' " My secretary returned the manuscript with a polite letter saying that I had died.

There ought to be a law, Miss E. H., and not merely a rule, against the sort of thing that emerges when an authoress—she is usually either very young or in her treacherous fifties—"invents" what she calls a new kind of humor. This stuff, out of "Tender Buttons" by "Jabberwocky," is even less clear than the kidding around of the Shoshones. One example began: "He was in bad, but she knew he was not a sloop." Another exhibit, as hard to believe as it was tedious to decipher, started off like this: " 'Where have you asked?' Sylvia been. 'No answer in particular,' Roger whered." It is possible that a new and valid kind of humor may be invented some day, but I hope the inventor will send it to someone else, not me.

My final standing rule, Miss E. H., is that the young wife and mother should sedulously avoid the cowsie-wowsie type of humor. This genus invariably begins something like this: "Now that she had become a humming bird she wondered what George had become and *where* he was! Then she *knew!* Of course, how silly of her! George would be a flower with a bell much too deep for her to reach into. Wasn't that *just* like spiteful, inconsiderate George! She hoped suddenly that he would be eaten by a cow. It would serve him. . . ." I do not know what in the name of God causes this, but there is a lot of it, and most of it is sent to me. From the snapshots the authoresses enclose of themselves, their husbands, and their babies, I gather that they are healthy, reasonably sane, well-mated, and happy. I hate to think that humor is not compatible with a successful marriage, but what else am I to think?

We now come to the perennial parody of Noel Coward of which the ladies are so fond, and there is, in my house, a standing rule about that, too. And, if, after your marriage, you ever send me a burlesque of "Private Lives," Miss E. H., signed with the name "Knowall Coward," I will burn the snapshot of you and your husband and the beach cottage. As for your poor baby—but

108

I am getting surly now and will close, with best wishes, love and kisses, and a friendly warning that humor can be a headache, dear Miss E. H. Why don't you become a bacteriologist, or a Red Cross nurse, or a Wave, like all the other girls?

Hazel Heckman

Hazel Price (now Heckman), daughter of an English father and a Pennsylvania Dutch mother, was born on a farm near Liberty, Kansas, population 361. She attended the rural school and the Liberty grade school through the tenth grade, becoming the valedictorian of her class. There were five other pupils. After graduating from the Independence (Kansas) high school, she attended Kansas University and worked her way through by reading for a blind law student, washing dishes at the faculty club, and working at the institution's news bureau. For a while she taught in rural schools in Montgomery County, then she married and moved to an oil boomtown. There (Blackwell, Oklahoma) she read proof and wrote features for the local paper.

In 1946 Hazel Heckman moved West again, this time to Tacoma, Washington, and began experimenting in practically every form of writing. She wrote poetry—which was published—radio plays which were produced, and short articles on subjects ranging from stars to starlings. Her first fiction story won a two hundred dollar prize in a *Country Home* contest. After that she sold her fiction to the solidest as well as the slickest journals. She divides her time between Tacoma and Anderson Island in lower Puget Sound, but she says, "my first love is and always will be the oak-and persimmon-covered hills and the sycamore-lined streams of Southeast Kansas."

*The Quarter-pound Loss**

The feud between Nate Alden and Della Summers, if indeed such an amiable prolongation of cold warfare could be called a feud, began the day Della, a big raw-boned woman with a no-account husband and a brown wart on her nose, first walked into Nate's native-stone store in Picket Rock, Kansas, with a basket of eggs she had taken from underneath a broody hen. It ended the day Nate paced solemnly down the aisle of the little Picket Rock M. E. church, some thirty years later, wearing a pair of white cotton gloves on his big chapped hands, and took his place beside the gray plush casket that contained Della's mortal remains. Nate's

* Reprinted from *Collier's* Magazine.
110

name had led the list of pallbearers they found on the night table beside Della's bed. If this was a final gesture on Della's part to get the best of Nate, you might say Della had won the last round. She was no featherweight.

"There's a woman who'll bear watching," Nate advised his new clerk, Syd Benton, when Syd started working steady in Nate's store. "I've known Della Summers, girl and woman, for as long as I can remember; and she's as full of tricks as a hound dog is of fleas." He laughed silently, his big belly and his loose jowls shaking. "It's not that she's dishonest exactly. Della just lives by a different code than most folks."

He let the sugar dribble from the scoop into the sack he was filling and peered through his scratched lenses at the worn figures on the counter scale. Nate always used a balance scale and he always weighed on the down-balance, giving his customer the advantage. "Take the time she made her Thousand Star quilt," he went on. "I got in a lot of new piece goods that spring and she took a sample off every bolt. Maybe more than one, I never kept track. She kept saying she was trying to decide on a new dress pattern and couldn't make up her mind. 'Don't be so parsimonious, Alden,' she'd say when I got my scissors down and laid the bolt on the counter. 'I want something big enough Tom can see the print.' As though Tom Summers would have noticed what she had on if she'd worn a gunny sack."

He slid the filled sack along the counter and took up an empty. "Well, she just kept on taking swatches. And later that fall when she had the Ladies' Aid in to quilt her new Thousand Star, she bragged that it hadn't cost her a cent and that it was all new stuff. Made out of sample snips from Nate Alden's store. . . . Furthermore," he added with a kind of pride, "she took a blue ribbon on the quilt at the county fair."

Della Summers always reminded Syd of a battleship under forced draught. "Where's Alden?" she would demand, barging into the store and slamming the door behind her. "Why ain't he here tending to his knitting?" Her sharp eyes would search the piece-goods shelves and her gold bridgework gleam in a sociable smile. "I see he's got in a new shipment of domestic. But if it's got no more body than the last he can just keep it."

111

"He's gone to the bank," Syd said. "He told me to tell you if you came in that he's got the dried apples you've been asking for to make your *schnitz un knepp.*"

Della helped herself to a handful of apples from the box. "More likely stopped into Hamblett's for a swig of red-eye," she said. "That's not a furniture store. It's a den of iniquity. You can smell it clear out into the street."

When Della's broad back was turned, Syd pulled the apples out of convenient reach. The last time she had come in there had been fresh grapes and Della had eaten at least a pound. She had left the seeds and skins in the cat's dish. "Sure she makes out a free lunch once a week," Nate said mildly when Syd complained. "But she's a good steady customer. There are some things you just have to abide."

Della took up a muslin remnant and rubbed it between the heels of her hands. "This stuff's full of sizing, too," she told Syd. "I don't know where Alden gets it. Once it's been through the wash the only thing it's fit for is dish mops." Having thoroughly stirred the remnant table, she went in search of further forage.

"There's a case of eggs in the buggy," she said, bearing down on the prune box. "And an empty demijohn for vinegar."

When Syd returned, laden, Nate had come in through the side door and was scooping pea beans from the drawer underneath the counter into the scale pan. Della, the store cat in her capacious lap, sat on a heap of stock salt blocks eating a fig newton.

"I don't see how your conscience allows you to sleep of nights, Alden," she said. "Fifteen cents for eggs. I feed the hens and you pocket the profits."

"Well, I sell them out for sixteen," Nate said. "That gives me a penny for handling and makes me a profiteer." He reached for an end of twine and wrapped it twice around the bean sack.

"I think I'll put out my own shingle," she said, helping herself to another newton. "Why should folks pay you sixteen when they can get them from me for fifteen?"

"Go ahead," Nate said. "Save me a lot of trouble. Bring up an empty egg case for Mrs. Summers," he told Syd. "And fill her vinegar jug."

"And I don't want any of Alden's cistern water with mother in

112

it," Della said. "The last he sold me didn't smell strong enough to attract a sour-gnat."

Nate weighed out a pound of Four-X coffee beans and set the grinder for "fine," the way Della liked her coffee. "Never mind the water this time," he told Syd. "Give her the pure stuff. If any mother slips out, drop it into the rain barrel. We'll use it to start a new batch."

Actually, Nate was a "crank" about vinegar. There were storekeepers, he knew, who poured a gallon of water into the barrel whenever they drew a gallon of vinegar out, trusting to the accumulation of mother and the occasional addition of a few apple peelings to maintain a pale strength. But Nate bought pure cider vinegar and only handled the best.

In the back room Syd set the egg case on the table and pried the lid open. Once a week Nate shipped the filled cases, without opening them, to the wholesale house in Meade, ten miles away, exchanging an empty case, with cardboard fillers, to his customer. But once during molting season, puzzled by the fact that one end of Della's case was lighter than the other, Syd had looked inside and had found an entire empty filler. Nate had fussed and fumed when Syd told him.

"I ought to have guessed she'd be up to something," he said. "She never figured on us knowing where the loss came. We'll check *her* case from now."

"Aren't you going to tell her we found it?" Syd asked.

"Why, no," Nate said. "Of course not. You can't insult a good customer by calling her a thief."

Nate's forbearance concerning Della was a thing Syd never quite understood. Nate himself was almost painfully honest; and, ordinarily, he had no use for a man or woman who was not. Too, he prided himself on his ability to judge character. "Let me study a man's face for half a minute," he told Syd, "and I can tell you whether or not he's to be trusted." He carried many farmers on his books from harvest to harvest, taking his money once a year, at threshing time. If a crop failed, as Kansas crops frequently did, he accepted a note from the farmer in lieu of payment; and then stuffed the note into his safe and forgot about it until another harvest time rolled around. Sometimes there were two crop failures in succession, but Nate never complained. His tastes were simple, and a decent living was all he asked.

Actually he did very well. Occasionally a competitor opened a rival store; but none of them stayed in business long. People preferred to trade with Nate. And Picket Rock drew on a large trading area. The nearest town, Meade, was ten miles away, a considerable distance with a horse and buggy. It was true that a few automobiles were beginning to appear on the roads, snorting and popping and scaring the horses half out of their wits; but a strip of bottom land lay between Picket Rock and Meade, the roads an unnegotiable quagmire in wet weather.

It sometimes seemed to Syd that Nate's confidence in Della, in spite of his warning to Syd, approached a kind of gullibility. "I can't think for the life of me why I don't turn the box *out* while she's here," he would complain sheepishly to Syd, setting out the top layer of a box of sweet potatoes or a crate of strawberries he had bought from Della and finding an inferior product underneath. But he never did.

Sometimes, too, it seemed to Syd that Della's trickery amounted to sheer meanness, and sometimes he couldn't determine whether it was deliberate or not. There was, for example, the time she brought in the black Langshan rooster and traded him to Nate "on account." The Langshan was a shabby bird. His comb was black and frozen and one eye was missing. On his scaly legs he boasted a pair of evil-looking spurs. He regarded Nate out of his one remaining yellow eye and crowed loudly.

"He's got pretty long spurs for a youngster," Nate said.

"I didn't say I wouldn't take old cock's price."

"You don't usually cull until spring," Nate said. "Something wrong with him?"

"He's got a green feather in his tail," Della admitted. "But that's not going to taste in the soup."

"Put him into the pen with the others," Nate told Syd. He handed a peppermint stick to Della's grandson Lacey, a cotton-haired boy with pink eyebrows, who stood with his palms and his nose pressed flat against the glass candy case. "I'll ship him to Meade if he don't die of old age before Saturday."

On the following morning, when Nate stepped outside the back

114

door of the store, he was greeted by a scene of carnage. The air was filled with floating feathers and feathers of all colors lay about the chicken pen and decorated the hollyhocks and clung to the meshes of the enclosure. On the floor of the pen a battered Plymouth Rock rooster lay dead; and several other cocks, in various stages of indisposition, cowered in a corner. The Langshan, his spurs bloody, and surrounded by an admiring circle of chittering hens, scratched triumphantly among the litter.

Nate wrung the Langshan's neck. "I ought to have known," he told Syd bitterly. "He was wrecking her own pens. Someday I'm going to lose my temper and tell Della where to take her custom."

But he never did. Only twice during all of Syd's time at the store did he actually see Della get her comeuppance; and both times Nate expressed a certain compunction. Both occasions had to do with butter.

Della made good butter. She churned frequently, while the cream was still fresh, and she worked and washed her butter well and kept it cool in the springhouse. Occasionally Nate took home a pound of Della's butter for his own use; his wife would have no one else's. But, like most of the citizens of Picket Rock, Nate kept a cow in the town herd, and Mrs. Alden churned her own butter.

The butter Nate bought from customers he shipped to the creamery at Meade, and he took no profit. He handled the butter purely as a favor to his customers, who expected list price. Indeed, on the bad butter, and there was a good deal of it, he took a considerable loss. He kept a jar in the coolest part of the store cellar, and into this, as soon as he had bought it, he dumped the butter which he considered unfit for consumption. When the jar was full he sold the butter for five cents a pound to the creamery in Meade, where it was "reprocessed." Nate himself would not touch a pound of creamery butter. Nor would he eat butter in a restaurant. He fancied that it was all "reprocessed." And he referred to it and to his own jar as "boot grease." Sometimes he grumbled to Syd, especially in hot weather. But he went right on taking the butter, the way he carried ice and stood the meltage, and the way he kept the store open at all hours and on Sunday mornings, for the benefit of his customers.

115

That summer two things happened in regard to butter. Drought set in early, so that the cows fell off and butter kept a good price. And along about June a traveling drummer came into Nate's with a supply of rectangular wooden butter molds and an accompanying supply of tablets of waxed paper of a proper size for wrapping.

Nate was skeptical about the molds. "With the old round prints," he told the drummer, "I can tell one customer's butter from another. They each use a different pretty on top. Mrs. Reese has got a bunch of grapes and Mrs. Hamblett has got a butterfly. Mrs. Summers, who makes the best butter, has got an oak leaf with an attached acorn. I'd miss that."

"I'm not asking you to *buy* any," the drummer said. "Just let me leave one on your counter. Let the ladies be the judge."

The molds sold like flypaper in July.

"Smartest buy I've seen you make in a long time, Alden," Della said. "It will make a real professional-looking pound, that will look like store-bought butter on the table."

The day Della brought the short basket of butter into town, she was wedged solidly behind the wheel of a spanking new Ford car and accompanied by her grandson Lacey. Hearing a series of violent explosions, Syd and Nate ran to the door in time to see the Ford come to an abrupt stop, its front wheels on the sidewalk a few feet short of Nate's wooden Indian.

Della climbed out and straightened her skirt. "It didn't stop when I said 'whoa,'" she told Nate jocularly. "What do you think of it, Alden?"

"Tony!" Nate said.

Lacey emerged, pale and shaken, from the back seat. "I'm thirsty," he announced in a small voice. "I want a drink of *cold* ice water."

"Grandma told you she'd get you here safe," Della told him. "And she did, didn't she?"

"I want a drink," Lacey said.

Della handed a basket of butter to Nate and led the way to the cooler, where a tin cup hung suspended from a twine string. She pressed the spigot and filled the cup and gave it to Lacey.

116

"Little short this week," Nate said, lifting the cover from the butter basket.

"It's the drought," Della said. She helped herself to a sweet cracker. "Cows are off some."

Lacey's eyes met Syd's, mischievously, over the brim of the cup. "Rat got in the jar," he announced, moving a little away from Della. "Splashed out half the cream before Grandma could catch him and give him to the cat!"

Della, her face flaming, picked at a bit of silk on the remnant counter.

Emboldened by the counter between him and Della, and aware of an electrified audience, Lacey relived the excitement of the chase. "He *jumped* out," he said. "But he was too bogged down with cream to run. When Grandma stepped on him he went squi-ish. And then he weren't nothing hardly but a big spot of grease."

Nate, his face grim, set the full basket on the counter.

"It was a *live* rat," Della flared. "After some of the butter Alden takes in, people needn't gag at a *live* rat. . . . But if he wants to be persnickity . . ." She took up the butter basket, and Nate let her go.

Lacey exploded into laughter again, but kept a wary eye on Della. "Rat butter!" he chortled. "Grandma was the *only* one would eat it."

As soon as Della had gone, Nate sat down, abruptly, on a herring keg. Anger left him and he shook with silent laughter. Tears coursed down his cheeks and he wiped them away with the hem of his apron.

"Did you ever see anything like it?" he asked Syd. "She looked like she'd been hit in the face with a kettle of hot mush."

And then he stopped laughing.

"I felt a little sorry for her," he said. "I almost wish I'd took it." Syd said, "I wouldn't want to be in Lacey's shoes."

Nate took the feather duster from the counter and ran it thoughtfully across the faces of the kraut cans. "I almost wish I'd took it," he repeated. "And dumped it into the chicken trough."

When Syd brought Nate the news that Della's husband, Tom, had filed for township trustee of Picket Rock township against

Zack Kaufmann, the incumbent, Nate was incredulous but unperturbed.

"Why Tom Summers is too shiftless and no-account to tie his own shoes," he said. "He'd starve to death if it wasn't for Della. Everybody knows that. Why, township trustee's a *responsible* job. He's got all the road building to see to. Tom Summers! Rat catcher would be more like it. If anybody voted for that bumbailey for township trustee, he'd need his head examined."

"Mrs. Summers is working tooth and nail," Syd said. "She's out every day in her Ford. She's got signs tacked on telegraph poles as far as Meade township. I was squirrel hunting down to Fallon's grove yesterday, and she's even got them nailed on the trees."

"For the squirrels and skunks no doubt," Nate chuckled. "They'll likely come out heavy for Tom. He's just their stripe."

The first time Della came into the store after Tom's filing, she announced blandly, "Well, I reckon you've heard the news, Alden. I guess we can count on your support."

"Well," Nate said. "I can't very well take sides in a political scrap you know." She knew very well he wouldn't vote for Tom, even if Tom were capable, which he was not. There wasn't a more upright and conscientious man in Picket Rock township than Zack Kaufmann, the incumbent. In ten years in office Zack had built all-weather roads through every farming community in the township, and all of them leading into Picket Rock.

Della took up a loaf of bread and squeezed it in order to test its freshness, and then put it back and selected another for her basket. "That's too bad," she said. "I'd planned to ask if I could nail a placard on your hitching rack. I've been a customer for a good long time you know."

"And I hope you'll keep on being," Nate said. He laid a slab of bacon on the block and honed his broad-bladed knife. "Thick or thin?" he asked, feeling mean.

"Middling," Della said cautiously. She had asked for her bacon "thick," once, moving Nate's knife testily along the slab. When six slices had come to a pound, she had hit the rooftree. "We were out to Round Mound last night," she said, taking a handful of seedless raisins and going to look out through the window.

118

"That so?" Nate asked politely.

"The Mounders are all lined up for Tom," Della said. "They know a good thing when they see one."

"Pound of Four X?" Nate asked. He felt a little sorry for Della. It must be humiliating sometimes to be married to a man like Tom.

He carried Della's groceries to the car and stood for a moment with his foot on the step. "Looks like we're in for a spell of weather," he said, slapping at a fly on his ankle.

"Yes," she said. "Dogpecker gnats are bad, too. Well, much obliged for your support, Alden." The gears clashed and she departed in a spurt of gravel.

"Now what did she mean by thanking me for my support?" Nate asked Syd. "I just the same as told her I wasn't going to vote for Tom."

"Maybe she meant the sign," Syd said. "She set it in the window while you were slicing the bacon."

Pressed against the glass, a gaudy red and yellow placard advised passers-by flamboyantly: WE VOTE FOR TOM SUMMERS AND RIDE ON ALL-WEATHER ROADS. Nate plucked it from the window with distaste. "Put this in the bottom of the cat's box," he told Syd. "She ought to sleep good on it." He rescued a fly that was struggling in his poison saucer. "All-weather roads," he said. "Picket Rock township's already got the finest all-weather roads in the county."

The weather turned muggy and the flies hung in clouds on the outside of the screen door and buzzed disconsolately in Nate's netting trap. Farmers, busy with the year's harvest, came and went with a harried air, and little was heard about the approaching runoff. One thing was certain. Whoever won the Republican nomination, Zack or Tom, was sure to be elected, even if a Democrat filed, which was not likely. Picket Rock had always been a dyed-in-the-grain Republican township.

"Looks like you've got quite a campaign here," a traveling drummer remarked to Nate. "There are signs on every second telegraph pole in the township. Two to one for Tom Summers. Who is this Summers anyway?"

"Nobody," Nate said. Della was carrying things a little too far.

119

When hot weather came and Nate brought the egg candler up from the cellar, Della regarded it, as always, with pretended dudgeon. "I've got a good mind to take my custom to Meade," she said, "now I've got the Ford." She helped herself to a banana from the stalk.

"Why don't you?" Nate asked good-naturedly. "You'll find they're candling, too, though. It's the law now."

"Bother the law," Della said. "I don't have time to sit around while you look through every egg to see whether the hen's had truck with a rooster."

Nate lighted the lamp and dropped the match into the coal scuttle and eased his weight onto the herring keg in front of the candler. "I pen *my* cockerels away," he said, "when breeding season's done."

"There's a *man* for you," Della told Syd. "No wonder his hens look roupy . . . Give me a taste of that cheese with blood in it, will you, Syd?"

She took the sliver of pimiento cheese off the broad blade of Syd's knife, and moved around the corner to the cracker barrel. "A piece of pickle would go good," she said, "if Alden wasn't so stingy."

"Give her a pickle," Nate told Syd. "One of those kosher dills." He held an egg to his ear and shook it gently. "That one ought to have hatched," he said. "You didn't leave it under the hen long enough."

Della brushed the crumbs from her generous bosom and picked at the remnants. "When you get through," she said, "I'll go home and make a cake from them you've candled out."

"Well, just don't bring me any of it," Nate said. "That's all I ask." He had marked a reject once and had found it back in Della's case when she came in the next week.

The bell on the front screen jangled and Charlie Hamblett came in, not quite steady on his feet. "Howdy, Mrs. Summers," he said, bowing elaborately. "How's Tom's campaign coming?"

Della favored him with a chilly smile. "Mr. Hamblett," she said. "We've got Round Mound and Hardpan in the bag. It looks like the whole west half of the township is solid for Summers, since we've promised them the graveled road."

Nate's ears lifted. "What's this about a road?" he asked. "I thought the township had plenty of graveled roads."

"Why, an all-weather road across that quagmire into Meade," Della said. "Now that folks are getting automobiles, they'll be wanting to get into Meade to the picture shows in bad weather as well as good. It's what we're campaigning on. Roads all through that quagmire!"

"Of all the gnat-brained, impractical notions I've ever heard," Nate told Syd, "that takes the loving cup! Nobody lives in that bottom. It's flood land. Building roads across it high enough to travel on would break the township. And all the Picket Rock trade on that side would go into Meade, and ruin Picket Rock. It's that new Ford. It's turned Della's head light."

He folded and refolded the disheveled remnants. "Turning road funds over to a man like Tom Summers, who's never had one nickel to jangle against another, would be like turning the Dalton boys loose in the U. S. mint."

"Do you think he has a chance?"

"I don't know," Nate said. "I just don't know. With last summer's good wheat crop, automobiles are getting as thick as flies in a honey pot." He went to the meat box and took out a small crock of milk and poured it, cream and all, into a saucer for Big Red, the store cat. "Picket Rock would be a ghost town," he said. "There's no rhyme nor reason to it. If a road had been needed across that bottom, if it had been practical, Zack would have built it long ago. Putting road funds into the hands of a man like Tom Summers would be like dropping a dead cat into a flock of vultures. They'd have its bones picked before you could say the Ten Commandments!"

He stewed about it all week. As he sorted the potatoes and scraped the meat block and put fresh sawdust on the floor he kept muttering to himself about the road. He only went across to Charlie's once, and then he was back in a few minutes, more disturbed than ever.

"They say she's really got folks eating out of her hand," he told Syd. "The tenant farmers will all vote for Tom. They've got nothing to lose. She never says anything against Zack. There's nothing *to* say. Zack's proved his mettle. She just keeps dangling

121

that graveled road in front of their faces. Even the homestead-
ers. They forget they're the ones who are going to have to pay for
it. It's like Big Red when she goes on the prowl of nights. She
never thinks about having to feed another litter. It's a regular
boondoggle trap, and they're walking into it with their eyes wide
open."

"Why don't you tell Mrs. Summers?" Syd asked. "Why don't
you explain it to her?"

"It wouldn't do any good," Nate said. "She'd think I was just
trying to block Tom to help Zack. When she gets the bit in her
teeth, there's no stopping her."

When Nate put the carefully lettered sign: VOTE FOR ZACK
KAUFMANN AND SAVE YOUR TOWNSHIP in his window, Della pretended not to notice. Nor did she appear to be aware that Nate was
hardly his old cordial self. While he unpacked her produce, she
munched dried apricots from the case and made frequent trips to
the water cooler, keeping up her usual run of chatter.

"Sam Jeter's had his spring bath," she said. "Mrs. Jeter told me
about it herself. She said she'd got so she couldn't stand Sam in the
bed. So she filled the wash tub with hot water one morning and
took a bar of lye and crackling soap and lugged it up the stairs
before Sam was up. Then she locked the stair door and told Sam
he could have his eggs and side meat just as soon as he'd washed
himself."

"And what did Sam say to that?" Nate asked coldly. People
said the only things Sam Jeter knew water was good for was for
drinking or for fishing.

"Mrs. Jeter said he screamed like a stuck hog," Della said.
"He yelled so loud and beat on the stair door so hard that she
went down to the crick to get out of earshot. But he finally washed
himself. She said the water was thick as mush, and she made a fire
of hedge trimmings and burned his overalls."

When, late that afternoon, Nate came across the street from
the bank, he noticed for the first time that the Zack Kaufmann window card had been carefully covered by a square of muslin from
the remnant counter.

122

The Quarter-pound Loss

The affair about the butter looked like pure providence. In the first place Nate almost never sold a pound of butter in Picket Rock. And in the second place, when he had the call from Mrs. Bombach, why should he have selected that particular print of Della's butter? With the new molds, the prints all looked identical, and Della had brought in an even dozen.

"Half a pound will be enough," Mrs. Bombach told Nate. "If you don't mind cutting one. I'm churning in the morning. But I've got company in the house and not a scrap of butter for supper."

"Mrs. Summers' is the freshest in," Nate told her. "And it's always the best." He liked Mrs. Bombach. She minded her own business and she didn't put on airs, the way some of the other doctors' wives had.

"Mrs. Summers' will be fine," she said. "And many thanks."

"Leave the sweeping," Nate told Syd. He set a pound of Della's butter on the block and wiped his knife on his apron. "Take this butter up to Mrs. Bombach's. Take the Maxwell and stop back by the icehouse. We're getting low . . ." He broke off with a murmured ejaculation.

"Look here!" he told Syd. Red spots of color dyed his fat cheeks and his blue eyes sparked with anger. "Of all the conniving shenanigans! She didn't have enough to finish filling the mold, so she dropped in the first thing she laid eyes on."

In the center of the butter print, neatly rolled in butter paper against the rust, was a quarter-pound scale weight.

When, an hour later, Zack Kaufmann came in for his weekly pound of beefsteak, Nate was still sputtering.

"How's the campaign coming?" he asked Zack, fingering the weight in his pocket.

"From what I hear," Zack said, "from the unofficial poll, I might as well withdraw and save face. It's not that I mind so much losing; it's a thankless job. You know that, Nate. But you know as well as I do what that road is going to cost and what it's going to do to Picket Rock."

Nate pulled a length of twine down and wrapped it around his stubby fingers. "Maybe he won't build it," he said hopefully. "He's lazy as a spavined mule."

123

"He'll build it," Zack said. "She'll see he builds it. She's done the promising."

Nate wrapped the twine around the package of steak and snapped it off. "Zack," he said. "Don't give up yet. I've got a little kind of a plan in mind. It might not work. And it will probably lose me a good steady customer . . ."

When Della came into the store, on the following Saturday, she was friendly and beaming, full of sugar. "I'd like to taste the cheese," she told Nate, bearing down on the meat case. "Tom likes it nippy."

"How's Tom's campaign shaping?" Nate asked, getting out the cheese.

"Fine," Della said. "Fine as frog hair. We were over to Gravel Hill last night. They're all lined up. It looks like Kaufmann's left at the post."

Nate wiped the broad-bladed knife on his apron and sank it into the soft cheese. "Tom ever think of withdrawing from the ballot?" he asked casually.

Della looked up in amusement, her hand in the cracker barrel. "Why, no," she said. "Of course not, Alden. Why should he? He's got the whole west side counted, and half the east."

Nate held out the cheese, his knife and his gray eyes steady. "You ever think of asking him to?"

Della came to lean against the meat case, but ignored the offering. "What are you driving at, Alden?"

Nate laid the scale weight on the counter between them. "Suppose," he said conversationally, "I were to put this into my window, with a card telling where I found it?"

Red crept from Della's collar, slowly, across her plump cheeks and into the roots of her sun-faded hair. But her eyes held steady.

"Is that a condition?" she asked quietly.

Nate fondled the weight with his fingers.

"It might be a hard thing to do, Alden," she said. "A month . . . six weeks ago, I could have done it easy. He was sick of the whole thing. He said it would be a lot of hard work, and you know how he hates that, and that I'd talked him into it. But now it's coming close, he's got his head up and tail over the dashboard. All he thinks about is the glory of winning."

124

Nate withdrew the scale. "Please yourself," he said. "I'm not a man to tell what I know. Under *ordinary* circumstances . . . But the day I hear Tom's dropped out of the race, you can have this . . . bauble back. With Syd's and my pledge to silence."

Nate bit thoughtfully into the slice of cheese he had cut for Della and watched her go, shutting the door easy. "You can come in now," he called to Syd, "and finish the onions."

"What did she say?" Syd asked. "How did she look? Do you think she'll do it?"

Nate set the cheese back in the case and untied his apron. "I'm going over to Charlie's," he told Syd, ignoring the questions. "I feel like a ginger beer, to pick me up. Maybe I won't be back for an hour or two."

It was two weeks before Della again entered the store. Thoughtfully, in anticipation of her coming, Nate had withdrawn the VOTE FOR ZACK KAUFMANN placard from the front window. It had served its purpose. Tom Summers had withdrawn from the race and Zack had a clear field.

"If there was another store," Della announced stiffly, "I wouldn't trouble you with my patronage." Her eyes passed without interest over the neatly folded remnants. A glass jar of pink coconut puffs stood invitingly open, but she did not take any. She waited, in stony silence, while Nate candled the eggs.

He set the egg case on the counter and took out his order book. For once he hadn't candled out a single egg. He hadn't had to. They were as clear as crazy water.

Silently Della laid her list on the counter; and as silently Nate set about filling it. Gravely, he rechecked, added a bundle of licorice sticks, gratis, for her grandson Lacey. That was everything but the coffee.

He ground it fine, the way Della liked it. He poured it, fresh and aromatic, into the sack, and set the sack on the scale. It weighed, as he had estimated, exactly three-fourths pound, on the down balance. He glanced up.

Della, her head held high, was gazing haughtily down her nose at the meat block. Nate opened the coffee sack and dropped in the quarter-pound scale weight.

Russell Lynes

A native of the Berkshires, Russell Lynes was born in Great Barrington, Massachusetts, in 1910 and, after various peregrinations, settled down in New York and (as frequently as he can manage) in North Egremont, a few miles from his birthplace. Lynes learned the vicissitudes of hospitality in rectories in New Jersey, and suffered the joys and trials of hosthood and guesthood at Vassar, as Director of Publicity; at Bryn Mawr, where he and his wife were coprincipals of the Shipley School; in Washington, where he was with the War Department as training specialist; and even in New York, where he is an editor of *Harper's* Magazine.

When Lynes' *Snobs* appeared about a year ago, first as an article and, later, as a book, it was evident that its mocking but penetrating analysis would provoke controversy. It also provoked a successor: *Guests, or How to Survive Hospitality*. The new volume consists of four slightly catastrophic chapters, of which "Weekend Guests" is the funniest if not the most critical. "This book," said Groucho Marx, "should do for manners what Kinsey did for sex." And Lynes added, "Any resemblance that the reader may find between the characters of this book and any actual persons, living or dead, should be a lesson to him about the company he keeps."

Weekend Guests *

If you have a house on an upland meadow, or a cottage by the sea, or a cabin in the woods, you are likely to discover by the middle of June that the precious relaxation which you have waited out the winter to enjoy is a mirage. The weekends during which you intended to commune with nature and your family are booked solid with weekend guests until after Labor Day. You have nothing but your own hospitable nature and your social conscientiousness to blame.

To those who are naturally hospitable, weekend guests in the abstract are nearly always attractive. They call to mind hospitality of a leisurely sort, and that in turn reminds us of pleasant hours we have spent in our own houses and the houses of friends—after-

* From *Guests,* by Russell Lynes, copyright, 1951, by Harper & Brothers.

126

noons active in the sun or dozing in the shade, amiable meals and comfortable beds, breakfasts out of doors with grasshoppers whirring in the nearby meadow, log fires on nights still with snow. It is a picture of enchantment, but when weekend guests become specific, and nostalgia is translated into problems of towels and food and personalities, we grow concerned. Even if our anticipation is happy, we are aware as our guests approach that one of the noblest things that a weekend has to recommend it is that sooner, rather than later, it is over.

If you are a part-time country dweller you have almost certainly managed during the winter to accumulate obligations that seemed easy to put off until summer when you could repay them with interest. Sometimes the invitations you dispense are your own idea; sometimes you are the victim of those who don't think it is worth their while to find themselves a haven in the country, so long as they have friends who have gone to that trouble for them. These are the people who are quick to inquire about your country place and to whom you mutter with general affability, "You must come out and see us sometime." Before you have clamped your lips shut on this treacherous cliché, they are thumbing through their engagement books, and you are committed for the third weekend in July—"or if that's not convenient, what about the first weekend in August?"

For the most part, however, you have acted of your own free will, and you have carved the image of your summer with your own hands. Not all weekend guests are problems, of course; otherwise they and the custom of inviting them would long ago have fallen into disuse. The odds, indeed, are well on the side of your urging only those you know you are going to enjoy to share your hospitality. What makes a good guest is a subtle complex of personality, manners, and delicacy of feeling, coupled with one's own state of forbearance at the moment when the guest appears. There are friends one can always depend on, but they are likely to be old friends for whom no amount of trouble is a burden and whose awareness of one's shortcomings is equaled by their readiness to accept them.

But not all guests can be old friends; they are merely the certain islands of calm and delight in a summer filled with potential catastrophe. Let us consider those other guests, most of whom we have invited in overexpansive moments to share our hospitality.

The standard weekend guests are a couple, but there the standard stops and the variations set in. We cannot discuss all of the variations, but let us take a few common ones, and their children, and face up to this problem before it is too late to do anything about it, which it almost surely will be.

Age makes less difference in guests than you would think; it is "habit patterns" (as the psychologists call the ruts of behavior) that are important to consider in dealing with guests. If, for example, you have invited what seemed to you on urban acquaintance a lively, active couple, you may as well resign yourself to their spending most of the weekend asleep. Being lively in the city is an extremely enervating business, and your couple will make up for it over the weekend. There is no use leaving the lawnmower conspicuously displayed; these are not the kind of people who are going to volunteer to push it. The chances are that they will arrive late for dinner on Friday completely equipped for tennis, golf, and swimming, and it will take the whole family to stow them and their tack in the guest room. By nine o'clock one of them will say: "Oh, this country air. I can hardly keep my eyes open." And by nine-thirty they'll both be asleep, or something, upstairs.

On Saturday morning it becomes obvious that these active urban types are country sluggards. They emerge dressed like manikins from a resort shop——the man in slacks and loafers and plaid shirt and his wife in shorts and sandals and halter——in the clothes, in other words, that people who spend much time in the country haven't time for——and they wear dark glasses. If you are sensible, you have been up for a good while yourself and got the lawn mowed (your guests love to lie in bed and listen to the reassuring whir of a lawnmower) and had your breakfast. You have made a list of the things you want to do without regard to what your friends want to do. If they feel like it they'll patter along when you go to town to shop; if they don't, they are perfectly happy sitting in reclining chairs, their faces lifted like platters to the sun. You need not worry about all the sports equipment they brought with them. That was a gesture. They won't begin to bustle until late afternoon when it is cocktail time. Then they will replace their shorts with something longer, and emerge after they have used up all the hot water, ready to use up all the gin.

The chances of what may then happen are about equally divided; they may drink so fast and furiously (they feel so full of health from a day in the sun) that they will again be ready for bed by nine-thirty. If this happens, Sunday's performance will echo Saturday's. If, however, they decide to make an evening of it, they won't appear until just before lunch on Sunday, by which time you can have had at least a half a day to yourself. The rest of the day you may as well throw away.

By contrast, let us look at a quite different sort of couple from the city. It would be risking too much to say that the opposite type, the kind of couple who reflect the cares and the harrying tempo of urban life and have a peaked air about them, are invariably the active ones over a weekend in the country, but there is some truth in it. They are likely to arrive somewhat bedraggled, usually by train, with the hot sooty look of people emerging from a couple of hours on a local in which the air conditioning has broken down. The first breath of clear country air brightens their gray faces; they stand on the platform and look around them as though refreshing their memories of what a tree looks like. They have a small suitcase each and carry no athletic equipment. If everything about the landscape enchants them as you drive them home, you should be warned that you are in for an active two days.

This sort of couple has a good deal in common with puppies. You throw out any kind of suggestion, and they scamper after it and bring it back and drop it at your feet. Everything is grist for their mill, but they have forgotten to bring the mill. If you suggest tennis, they'd just love tennis, but, of course, they have no rackets and no sneakers, and after you have ransacked the house and tried your own, your wife's, and your children's sneakers on them and have concluded that you are in for a game of pat-ball, they settle down to beat the pants off you with rackets that you have long since given up as warped and worthless.

129

You can save up the lawn for this type. One will surely cut it for you while the other weeds the flowers, or they may work in shifts. You will have difficulty keeping them out of the kitchen, if you are the sort who thinks of the kitchen as your private sanctum, because they will insist on helping with the dishes. The only real trouble you will encounter arises if you are so misguided as to leave them to their own devices to entertain themselves. Their puppy eyes will look at you as though you ought to be throwing a ball for them. You even have to suggest to them that it is time to go to bed. When you put them on the train on Sunday evening, you will notice that for all the healthful paces through which they have put you and themselves, they will have that same gray and harried look they had when they arrived.

These two kinds of couples are, of course, merely composites of many other species. But what of the couples who do not seem to make pairs and who go their separate ways? And what of those couples of which you like one member and can't abide the other? For our purposes they have to be considered as individuals. There are those who think that the state of being a guest relieves them of all responsibility and those who consider guesthood a perpetual challenge. In either case the extremes are difficult to cope with.

The range of individual guests is, of course, endless, and perforce we must confine ourselves to those whose eccentricities have some chance of seeming to be part of larger and more universally recognized patterns. You can make your own synthesis (nobody is anybody these days who doesn't at least try to make a synthesis) and match them as you please.

Some guests want to be left alone, and some say they want to ("Don't bother about me. Just go about your business. I'll find plenty to do.") and are miserable if they are.

The first of these lone wolves can be the pleasantest of all guests if they are resourceful, can take care of themselves happily, and at the same time pervade your household with the warm feeling that they enjoy just being in it. At their best they don't mind being interrupted in their own pursuits if there is some activity in which you want them to join. At their worst they make you feel that all they want out of you is a bed and three meals a day and a chance to ignore you. These are the men and women who come for the weekend to get away from people (including you) and to have a little quiet. They think they have discharged all of their responsibilities if they bring a box of chocolates that they have bought in the railroad station. They are so well able to take care of themselves that they make you feel as though you were in their employ.

A guest of the second type (who really does not want to be left alone but protests that he does) offers an acute problem of tact. He appears at breakfast with a small stack of books, a magazine, and some writing paper, bright-eyed and presumably equipped for the day. He quickly sets the books aside and takes your morning paper. (The sort of person who has a number of books from which to choose is rarely a reader. He is always looking for a chance to find some time to sit down with a good book, but curiously he never seems to find it. He won't find it over the weekend either.) After his third cup of coffee, you may get back the paper, and your friend will wander off to find a place to read one of the books. In half an hour or less he'll be hovering around again. "Too nice a day to sit and read," he'll say, and that is your signal to quit whatever you are doing and invent something to keep him busy. His resources and imagination were exhausted by picking out which books in your library he would fondle.

If this type stretches your tact, then you should be especially warned of the guest who makes an elaborate show of being tactful about you. He acts as though he knows that he is too much trouble and that everything you do for him is a great nuisance. He is constantly leaping out of his chair to perform some little service for you or for your wife, to get out the ice, to find the children's ball in the bushes, or to fetch the wood for the fireplace, all of which would be ingratiating if it weren't done half-apologetically. You soon find yourself wanting to tell him to sit down and relax, but instead you respond with an elaborate display of tact on your own part. He is wearisome because he is so hard to live up to.

Even so he is preferable to the intentionally tactless guest who thinks that to make light of your shortcomings as a host is a demonstration of easy fellowship and poise. He laughs at the way you lay a fire, and insists on taking your effort apart and stacking the kindling in his way. He reminds you that the leaky faucet in the bathroom could be fixed with a five-cent washer and fifteen minutes' work, and that you have put the wrong kind of composition shingles on your house; he could have got a much better brand for you wholesale at half the price you paid. He follows you wherever you go all weekend long; he stands in the kitchen door while you are getting drinks or a meal. If you play golf with him he tells you how to correct your slice, and if he sees you chopping wood he will observe that you are lucky you haven't cut your leg off long since, handling an axe the way you do. When he is not telling you how you ought to live, his conversation is almost entirely about the remarkable place at which he spent last weekend, with friends who did everything in such style. He is unaware that the walls of most country places are excellent conductors of sound, and you have no respite from him for some time after he has presumably gone to bed. If he is married, you can listen to him telling his wife that you would have a nice little place if you only knew how to take care of it.

Even the careless guest is preferable to the tactless type, though he too offers some minor aggravations. He strews the place with his belongings, he breaks a blade of the lawnmower on a rock anyone ought to be able to see, and he invariably is inspired to take a dip in the lake or river or ocean just as you are about to produce lunch or supper. When he does ultimately appear to be fed he will have deposited his wet bathing suit over the back of a piece of upholstered furniture. There is no malice in his soul though, and it is possible to love him.

It is impossible, on the other hand, to love the belligerently indolent guest who frustrates all attempts to make his visit pleasant or interesting. That is not to say that a host should force entertainment on anyone who doesn't want it, for a good host knows when to put enticements in his guest's way and when not to. But the belligerently indolent guest has a gift for making it quite obvious to his host that he expects to be entertained, yet displays a distinct distaste for any diversion that may be suggested to him. This is a common characteristic in children, and in adults it is, I believe, an indication of retarded maturity. I have often seen adults behave like a child I know who continually asks, "What'll I do now?" When a suggestion is made to him he has a pat reply. "Would you like to go swimming?" you ask him, and the reply is invariably, "Not particularly." "Well then," you say trying again, "how would you like to play catch?" "Not particularly," he says, and so it goes. When such guests, children or adults, do finally submit themselves to some plan you have suggested, they give you the uncomfortable sensation that they wish you had been bright enough to invent something really entertaining.

If this kind of guest is tiring because he is a constant challenge to your ingenuity, the opposite type, the ebullient guest, who sets out to give his host and hostess a rousing good time, takes the least planning and is the most exhausting. He arrives full of ideas, of projects for excursions, of resolve to get you out and give you some real exercise, and unless you want to be rude to him (which is necessary in extreme cases) it is best just to put yourself in his hands.

There are a number of common manifestations of the ebullient guest, each requiring a special defensive operation and its own system of logistics. I happen to have a house in the Berkshires. These gentle hills were at one time (especially in the environs of Stockbridge and Lenox) remarkable for the size and extravagance of the summer estates which graced their slopes. There is a legend in the Berkshires that a young man who was at Yale just before the turn of the century sent his mother a telegram in which he said, "BRINGING SOME '97 FRIENDS FOR WEEKEND," and his mother wired back, "TERRIBLY SORRY HAVE ROOM FOR ONLY SEVENTY-SIX." Most of the big estates are now hotels, or schools, or church institutions, and the Berkshires have become a hotbed of summer culture. We have music festivals at Tanglewood that rival Salzburg and Glyndebourne in fame. We have dance festivals at a placed called Jacob's Pillow, and we have enough summer theaters to give several platoons of Broadway stars their annual breath of fresh air. We used to frequent these places; in fact months before the music festival our friends could be seen conspicuously angling for invitations. We finally grew tired of running a lodging house for our music- and dance-minded ac-

133

quaintances, and we ourselves took to angling for invitations else-
where during that part of the summer. It was the ebullient guests
who wanted to be sure that we got our dosage of culture who
finally drove us to take umbrage.

Umbrage is one way to cope with the ebullient. Another way
is to lend your guests the family car, and if necessary your wife,
and let them go on an excursion of their own making. A third
method is to buy two tickets to the festival or the dance or the
theater and say that they are all you could get (which could easily
be true) and insist that the guests use them. This is both a generous gesture and assurance of a few hours' respite.

There is one kind of ebullience, however, which I have frequently encountered and have never been able to discover an
answer to. It is found in a single guest or in a couple who seem
to know a great many more people in the vicinity to which you
have invited them than you do. The minute they get in the house
they start calling up their friends. By the end of fifteen minutes
they have invited themselves and you to one house for lunch, another for drinks, and have possibly even got you committed to
appear at the Saturday night country club dance. You may, on
the other hand, find yourself giving a cocktail party for a lot of
people you scarcely know and have been successfully avoiding for
years. Short of cutting the telephone wires before your guests arrive, I know of no way to keep their socially manic behavior in
control.

There are, of course, many other types of weekend guests
than these few I have mentioned, especially the perfect guests, of
whom there are as many varieties as there are of imperfect ones,
but before we leave those of our contemporaries who strain the
muscles of our hospitality, and turn our attention to their offspring, I should like to mention a matter of utmost concern to
hostesses—food.

There is, for example, the problem of breakfast. What does a
hostess do about those guests who insist that she just leave a pot
of coffee on the stove and they'll have a cup whenever they get
up? They don't mean it of course; what they really want is a full
breakfast at the moment when they have drained away the last

bit of sleep, whether it is at nine or eleven-thirty, and they would really like it brought to them in bed.

One of the accepted conventions in this age of relaxed hospitality is the privilege of sleeping late on weekends, and while the guests sleep the routine of the household founders. The children have to be kept quiet, the kitchen can be only partly cleaned up, the day's plans must wait. If you could take your guests a tray at any specific hour, then planning would be possible, but no. You are much more likely to be faced with a guest who emerges just before lunch and to wonder whether you should offer him a martini or a soft-boiled egg.

People who go visiting in the country look forward to the casual life, and they assume that this means that meals just happen whenever it is convenient for them. They show up when and as they please just as surely for lunch or dinner as for breakfast, and expect that some magic will have produced a cold collation or a hot meal. If they are on elaborate diets, such as the salt-free or bland, then meals become to them the most important occasion of the day and also the most embarrassing. Diets are not nearly so hard for a hostess to deal with as the apologies with which they are accompanied. Some years ago I arrived at the house of a friend for the weekend with a case of cream soups and puréed vegetables which I produced with an elaborate apology for the unfortunate state of my viscera. "That's quite all right," my hostess reassured me, "but don't let me hear you apologize once more or I'll feed this pap to the cat."

The best measure of any guest is his attitude toward your children. It may be that they are brats, and you know it and momentarily you are not proud of them. You may be ashamed of their manners or their dirty faces or their fresh remarks, or of their shyness or cussedness, or of whatever phase they may presently be exhibiting. But the ways in which your guests react to them will tell you more about your friends than any other social litmus paper.

Children (it is hard for adults to remember) have their own kind of dignity, and they find many adults ridiculously childish, or perhaps I should say ridiculously grown-up. It is the guests who make your children feel younger than they are or not worth bothering with who should be avoided. The ones who treat them as people are rare. They are at least as rare as the children who behave themselves when you have guests around.

But what about children as guests? It is axiomatic that children when visiting without their parents behave better than they do either at home or when their parents go visiting with them. When they are on their own, there is nobody to whom they can shift the responsibility for their behavior; when they are visiting with their parents they take a special delight in being outrageous because they know they have the upper hand. From experience they have learned that a parent who will lose his temper at them at home can be counted on to make no such display in somebody else's house. They know too that a child who misbehaves in public is "the parents' fault." Where they get this idea, I do not know; but they get it early and use it for all it is worth.

Children who are usually obedient at home (or at least can be reasoned with) turn out to be little furies when they come visiting with their parents over a weekend. They show off; they sulk; they make a fuss about going to bed. Worst of all they get up at the crack of dawn and bounce a ball against the house just below your bedroom window. They don't like the food. They either are afraid of your dog and cringe whenever he appears, or they pull his tail and make him growl, so that either way you have no choice but to lock him in the cellar. Normally resourceful children when visiting can never think of anything to do, and like the child whose refrain was "Not particularly" they delight in straining your imagination and patience by finding all of your suggestions a stupendous bore. If you have children of your own, the juvenile sense of rivalry quickly sets up tensions which often burst into open warfare, and your children always get the blame because they are not being good little hosts and hostesses.

Possibly more difficult than young children are visiting teen-agers, who, unless you have prearranged a schedule of activities for them, hang around and are a constant and constantly bored rebuke. They have arrived at the age when they no longer think that adults are sophisticated and are beginning to wonder how anybody over thirty manages to drag his aging body around.

136

Weekend Guests

The games of childhood are behind them, and the games that adults enjoy are stuffy. They are always full of animal spirits and animal lethargy; they are always on their guard lest they should allow a telltale crack to appear in their façade of sophistication, mortally afraid that they may say or do something that might appear naïve. If, however, it is possible to arrange for them to join a group of their contemporaries, you are likely to be rid of them, so entirely rid of them that you may wonder whether you shouldn't be taking your responsibilities more seriously.

If you will refer to Stevenson's *Home Book of Quotations,* as I often do when I am looking for an epigram, you will find that an author named Laboulaye in a book called *Abdullah* said: "The first day a man is a guest, the second a burden, the third a pest."

The weekend is so devised that only a few guests stay around until they are pests.* Counting the day as twenty-four hours

---

* Not only Laboulaye had this time concept of guests. For those who like documentation for its own sake,† here are some variants on the theme, starting with the Roman playright Plautus (about 200 B.C.) who said: "No guest is so welcome that he will not become a nuisance after three days in a friend's house." ‡

Seventeen centuries later John Lyly made a fashionable switch by crediting the idea to the Greeks. He also added a gustatorial note, which stuck. In the *Euphues* (1580) he wrote: "As we say in Athens, fishe and gesse [guests] in three days are stale."

Other writers who have used this same figure of speech (and who probably thought they invented it) include Robert Herrick ("Two days y'ave landed here; a third yee know, Makes guests and fish smell strong; pray go." *Hesperides,* 1684) and Benjamin Franklin, who couldn't leave the idea alone. In 1733 he wrote: "After three days men grow weary of a wench, a guest, and rainy weather." Three years later he had boiled it down to "Fish and company smell in three days."

By the nineteenth century the phrase had been vulgarized to: "Fish and company stink in three days." And not longer ago than 1938 S. G. Champion in a book called *Racial Proverbs* cites a Japanese proverb: "Fish and guests are wearisome on the third day." There is no evidence that Benjamin Franklin had ever been to Japan.

Considering the chronological span of these quotations and their wide geographical distribution, they evidence a consistency of thought about guests which overrides the barriers of cultures and time. Modern refrigeration has licked the fish problem; it is unlikely that anyone will ever lick the guest problem.

† Lest anyone consider this an unwarranted display of scholarship on the part of the author, he is referred to page 1045 of the 1948 edition of Stevenson's compendium, where he will find all of these references.

‡ Freely translated this means: "Nam hospes nullus tam in amici hospitium devorti potest, Quin, ubi tridoum continuom fuerit, iam odiosus siet."

137

(though it may seem like more) and assuming that most weekend guests arrive on Friday evening, they usually sit out the "burden" period and leave just before the "pest" period sets in. The occasional extension of the weekend to 6:00 A.M. on Monday,* when those who want to avoid the Sunday night traffic tiptoe out of the house like a herd of buffalo, fortifies Laboulaye's aphorism, but there are some guests who leave when they are still only burdens and become pests *in absentia*.

I do not mean merely those who go off with the Sunday paper (at which you have not had a chance) in order to have something to read on the train, or those who have stowed in their suitcases the detective story that you (as well as they) have half read. I mean those who, snail-like, leave a sticky trail behind them. They are often the ones who say as they get on the train or pull out of the driveway, "If I've left anything behind, just throw it away."

What they have left behind is usually a tennis racket, putter, scooter, or other ungainly object that is impossible to throw away and defies being sent by parcel post or even by express without the most elaborate crating. Toothbrushes, razors, compacts, handkerchiefs, socks, lipsticks are easily forgotten by the departed guest, but if the object is really awkward, you will know at once that it will be badly missed. Monday night will bring a phone call full of self-accusation and urgency.

It is sometimes with a sense of loss, but more often with a sense of relief that one speeds the parting weekender, no matter how pleasant the visit may have been. If the weekend has been a success from everyone's point of view, it is just as well that enthusiasm cannot be stretched to the point where it diminishes to mere amicability, or amicability to the point where it becomes tolerance. If it was a good weekend, the quiet that the guests leave behind them is filled with pleasant echoes of the always unfinished business of friendship. If it has not been good, then they take away with them the burdensome business which has kept you struggling for the last forty-eight hours.

And this most surely explains the weekend as an institution.

* The *Vogue Book of Etiquette* says that it is to be taken for granted that the weekend lasts until Monday morning. Not at my house.

Its duration has been set by convention; the end is always in view and never very far away. The most dreary guests can be tolerated and coped with for forty-eight hours, and the most pleasant ones can be relished without fear that the pleasure of their presence will diminish. It was a wise host who invented the weekend, a host with a most sensitively balanced appreciation of the limits of man's social appetite and especially of his social endurance.

S. J. Perelman

A New Yorker by birth, training, and veteran contributor to the metropolitan weekly by that name, Sidney Joseph Perelman (born in 1904) is a critic in clown's clothing. He assembles the enormous nonsense of the big build-up, of inflated advertising copy and supercolossal slogans only to demolish them. This he accomplishes with an irresponsible logic in which clichés furnish their own satire and farce attains a kind of social force. There are, however, times when Perelman kicks up his Achilles' heels for the sheer fun of the thing; he hews to no one line of reasoning and lets the *non sequiturs* fall where they may. Such a time is the piece which follows, a piece in which Perelman gives all the good lines to his venerable if something less than venerated friend, Groucho Marx. Here, according to the magazine blurb, is "a hilarious proof that two madmen are three times as wacky as one."

In this connection it may be interesting to recall that several of the most incredible sequences in the early Marx Brothers films were invented by that expert in the higher lunacy, S. J. Perelman. It may also be interesting to note that the original title (later altered) for the following piece was "Punchinello with His Pants Down," and there was a subtitle which was an echo of Groucho's famous theme-song "Hurray for Captain Spaulding." It was "I'll Always Call You *Schnorrer*, My African Explorer."

Week End with Groucho Marx *

Borne on the northeast gale that had whipped Narragansett Bay into icy froth all through a February night in 1916, a freezing rain beat down relentlessly on Westminster Street, main artery and Rue de la Paix of Providence, Rhode Island. Inside the box office of the Keith-Albee Theater, the town's principal vaudeville stand, the house manager gnawed his nails and stared glumly at a rackful of unsold tickets. It was almost three o'clock; there were seventeen patrons out front, five of them cuffed in on Annie Oakley's and the curtain had been up half an hour on the most disastrous matinee in the history of show business. Just as he was preparing to issue forth to Farcher's drugstore and end it all

* Reprinted by special permission from *Holiday;* copyright, 1952, by The Curtis Publishing Company.

with two minims of prussic acid, a curious homuncule scurried into the lobby. He wore a reach-me-down mackinaw, a pair of mismated overshoes, and a yellow sou'wester by courtesy of Scott's Emulsion, and his twelve-year-old face—if, indeed, it could be so dignified—was beef-red with excitement.

"The holley had a trot-box!" he panted. "I mean, the trolley had a hatbox—I had to run all the way from Chalkstone Avenue! Are they on yet?"

"Is who on?" growled the manager, surreptitiously burning a pastille to neutralize any infection around his wicket.

"The head-hunters," the other babbled. "I mean, the headliners—the Four Marx Brothers in their sidesplitting extravaganza, *Home Again,* a funfest for young and old." Before the showman could produce his vouchsafer and vouchsafe a reply, the youth had fumbled a knotted bandanna from his jumper and spilled out a cache of greasy nickels. Then, snatching a ticket, he bounded up the stairs to the peanut gallery.

To recall with any degree of clarity the acts I saw on gaining my balcony perch would, of course, be impossible across the gulf of thirty-six years. Out of the haze of memory, however, I remember Fink's Trained Mules, Willie West & McGinty in their deathless housebuilding routine, Lieutenant Gitz-Rice declaiming *Mandalay* through a pharynx swollen with emotion and coryza, and that loveliest of nightingales, Grace Larue. All these, though, were mere appetizers for the roast. The *mise en scène* of the Marx Brothers piece was the Cunard docks in New York, an illusion conveyed by four battered satchels and a sleazy backdrop purportedly representing the gangway of the *Britannic.* Garbed in his time-honored claw-hammer coat, his eyes shifting lickerishly behind his specs and an unlit perfecto in his teeth, Groucho irrupted onstage accompanied by his presumptive wife, a scraggy termagant in a feather boa. Behind him came Gummo, impersonating his cocksure son, and Harpo and Chico, a pair of shipboard cronies. Groucho's initial speech set the flavor of the proceedings.

"Well, friends," he observed, stifling a belch, "next time I cross the ocean, I'll take a train. I'm certainly glad to set my feet on terra firma. Now I know that when I eat something, I won't

141

see it again." This earthy confidence, understandably, evoked a paroxysm from the audience (a small paroxysm, to be sure, in view of its size), and Groucho began expatiating on his trip abroad. Heckled at almost every turn by Gummo, he at length remarked waspishly, "Nowadays you don't know how much you know until your children grow up and tell you how much you don't know." According to Groucho, no pundit has ever been able to explain exactly what the foregoing meant or why it always elicited cheers and applause; apparently the customers sensed some deep undercurrent of folk wisdom he himself was unaware of. At any rate, after considerable horseplay in which Harpo disgorged the entire ship's cutlery from his sleeves and inspected the lingerie of several *zoftick* fellow-passengers, Chico approached Groucho with hand extended.

"I'd like-a to say goombye to your wife," he proposed, in what was unquestionably the paltriest dialect ever heard off Mulberry Street.

"Who wouldn't?" riposted his brother. This boflo ushered in the second scene, laid without any tiresome logical transition at Groucho's villa on the Hudson. The plot structure, to be candid, was sheerest gossamer; vague reference was made to a stolen chafing dish, necessitating a vigorous search by Harpo of the corsages of two showgirls drifting unaccountably about the premises, but on the whole there were few nuances. Following a rather soupy rendition of *The World is Waiting for the Sunrise* by Harpo, Chico played *Chopsticks* on the piano with grueling archness, and the pair exited rear stage left in a papier-mâché boat on wheels, knocking down three members of the troupe. Those who remained thereupon joined in a stylish chorale entitled *Over the Alpine Mountains E'er So Far Away,* and, as the orchestra segued into von Suppé's *Light Cavalry Overture* to herald the acrobats, I descended to Farcher's Drugstore for a double banana split with maxixe cherries.

The years slipped away in their usual fleet fashion, leaving an impressive residue of silver in the hair and none whatever in the pocket. I heard no more of Groucho and his tatterdemalion crew, and I assumed they had drifted into some other field where their inadequacies handicapped them less. What was my surprise, therefore, to receive a long distance call not long ago from Groucho in Hollywood.

"Well, well," I said encouragingly, "and what are you doing now? Working in some sort of restaurant or garage?"

"In a pig's eye," he sneered. "I'm on Main Street now. I'm making a flick with William Bendix and Marie Wilson, and what's more," he added boastfully, "I've got my own radio and televison show."

"Of course you have," I said soothingly. My experience with those afflicted with *folie de grandeur* has taught me that they must be humored. "What's afoot?"

"Well," he said. "I was just thinking it's time you came out of your shell. You're bored, restless, fed up with civilization and its hollow pretense—right?" I had to admit he had divined my mood. "Then why not fly out for a couple of days with me— at your own expense, of course? If you want to see unspoiled, primitive people, we've got some here who've just begun to walk erect."

"M-m-m," I said reflectively. "It does sound appealing, but I can't get away. There's my secretary, for one thing." I'd acquired an absolute whiz of a typist shortly before, kind of a younger Shelley Winters, and the problem of how to keep the child off my lap wrung my withers, word of honor.

"Couldn't you stand up and dump her off?" he suggested. It was typical of the man's audacious imagination, his refusal to bow to convention, that he should go straight to the core of things. Within forty-eight hours I had severed my obligations and was disembarking at the Los Angeles airport, and within another twenty-four, had reached the film colony. Slightly unsteadied by a cup of puréed avocado and a chickenfurter, I betook myself to R-K-O, where Marx was filming *A Girl in Every Port*. The set to which I was directed, a faithful replica of a battleship, hummed with activity; hordes of extras in navy blue were absorbed in scratch sheets, electricians on all sides feverishly worked to draw inside straights, and high on a camera parallel, two associate producers, arms clasped about each other, were busily examining their pelts for fleas. Groucho, as was his wont, was in the very thick of the melee. He was sprawled blissfully in a director's chair, having his vertebrae massaged by Marie Wilson, a young lady whose natural endowment caused a perceptible singing in the ears. I promptly drew up a chair next to her and confided that I too was suffering from a touch of sacroiliac, but the fair masseuse appeared to be hard of hearing.

"Did you bring any coffee with you?" demanded Groucho abruptly. I asked whether he realized that I had just flown across the country. He countered with a peevish snort. "That's neither here nor there," he snapped. "Anybody with a smidgen of decency would have brought me a cup of coffee from Lindy's. The stuff out here's pure slop."

"Then why do you stay here?"

"Where else can you get Marie Wilson to rub your back?" he asked. "A little lower down, dear—there, that's yummy."

"I haven't met the young lady yet," I remarked pointedly.

"No, and you're not likely to, you sneak," he retorted. "I know when I'm well off. Well, what's the chatter on Broadway?" In a few incisive phrases, I summed up recent developments there, such as Olga Nethersole's resounding success in *Sappho,* the razing of Hammerstein's Victoria, and the emergence of A. Toxen Worm as leading drama critic, and, to bolster his spirits, revealed that Milton Berle's TV show had a much larger following than his own. He was visibly pleased. "Let's get together before you leave town," he said, wringing my hand warmly. "I'd like you to poison some moles in my lawn." At this juncture, the lunch gong pealed, and leaving an effigy of himself with Miss Wilson to rub until his return, Groucho bore me off to the commissary. His outsize Corona and eyeglasses were somewhat at variance with his nautical dress, but he lent a salty tang to the meal by snarling out an occasional "Belay there, ye scut" and dancing a hornpipe with the waitress. Bendix, also clad in sailor suit, spent the lunch chewing meditatively on the foreleg of an Angus steer. He is a hearty trencherman, as befits a man of his girth, and has been known to consume a firkin of butter and a hectare of gherkins in less time than it takes to say "Bo" to a goose.

"You know, Mr. Bendix," I said enviously. "It must be hilarious, making a movie with a topflight comedian."

"Yeah," he agreed. "I'd love to do it some day."

"But I—I don't understand," I persisted. "You must roll on the floor when he gets off those repartees of his."

"Who's that?" he queried, detaching his eyes slowly from the steer. I indicated his costar. He masticated pensively for a moment. "It's a living," he grunted. During our colloquy, Groucho had seized the opportunity to couple his cheek with mine. On my expostulating, he unleashed such a torrent of sniveling and abuse that I finally paid in disgust. The mercurial temperament thrives on petty triumphs; at once he became ardent, solicitous of my welfare, determined to accord me every hospitality.

"Now listen," he said forcefully. "From here in, it's strictly my treat. What about dinner at my place and a night ball game afterward?" I agreed readily, and he pondered. "Where are your grips?"

"I left them with the cop at the main gate."

"Good," he said. "I've got a big, roomy house out in Beverly. Pick up the bags and take them to Schwabacher's used-car lot on Exposition Boulevard. You can sleep for nothing in one of their old jalopies."

"I have to clean up, take a shower," I protested feebly.

"Who takes a shower to go to a ball game?" he asked with irritation. "Lot of cheap swank." He scribbled on a card. "O.K., give this to my maid and she'll let you in the bathroom, but take it easy on the hot water—I'm not made of money. Did you bring a towel?"

"Only a fiber one I muckled from the plane."

"We-e-ll," he said grudgingly, "I guess we can loan you one, providing you sign for it. See you later, then; dinner at seven sharp." As I moved toward the door of the commissary, I felt myself the cynosure of countless envying eyes. A great star had bared his heart to me. What idiosyncrasies, what foibles I could divulge were I not bound by the journalist's sacred code. But my lips were sealed, and if Groucho's cuisine was as toxic as I anticipated, it would be worth my life to open them even a fraction.

At seven-thirty that evening, in the playroom of a repossessed Spanish hacienda on Hillcrest Drive, a couple of middle-aged gallants racked with sciatica descended painfully from their bar stools and linked arms with two statuesque actresses. The mood of the quartet was distinctly festive; tongues loosened by copious draughts of loganberry cocktails, their flushed cheeks and sparkling eyes marked them incontrovertibly as devotees of Bacchus.

"Shay, Groucho," I hiccoughed. "Thish a grea' party. Le'sh not go ball game; le'sh have s'more logleberry cocktails. Wha' shay, girls?" My host quickly snatched an aquarium from my path and threw open the door of the dining room.

"Bring him in here and we'll get some grub into him," he directed. "Watch out—he's scraping the piano."

"That's not all he's scraping," muttered my partner, disentangling my arm from her waist. "Where'd you find this creep, anyway?"

"On the old Fall River Line," said Groucho plausibly. "Used to be a washroom attendant. I gave him a lavish tip and he's been bleeding me ever since." He propped me up in a chair and retired to a side table to carve the roast. Inwardly I smiled a small, secret smile. My ruse was working perfectly; beneath a seemingly tipsy exterior, I was razor-keen, studying them as objectively as specimens under a microscope.

"You're too softhearted, Groucho," chided Queenie, the more buxom of the duo, thoughtfully crumbling her roll. "Silly boy, why do you leave grifters like this milk you? You need a woman to take care of you." Groucho was immediately all ears, so much so that he almost sliced one of them off.

"That's what I was just thinking," he said, swiftly circling the table. "What did you have in mind?"

"Oh, I don't know," she said coyly.

"You *don't?*" he demanded, rounding on her tigerishly. "Then what do you mean by teasing me to the brink of madness, mocking me with a mouth like a scarlet wound?" He flung aside his knife with a bitter laugh. "Do you know what it means to stand here night after night, sawing away at a cheap pot roast and thirsting for a coquette's kisses?"

"Hey, this meat is awful dry," complained Chiquita, our other dryad. "Isn't there any gravy?"

"Gravy, gravy!" shouted Groucho. "Everybody wants gravy! Did those six poor slobs on the *Kon-Tiki* have any gravy? Did

146

Scipio's legions, deep in the burning African waste, have gravy? Did Fanny Hill?"

"Did Fanny Hill what?" I asked.

"Never mind, you cad," he threw at me. "I'm sick to death of innuendo, brittle small talk, the sly, silken rustle of feminine underthings. I want to sit in a ball park with the wind in my hair and breathe cold, clean popcorn into my lungs. I want to hear the crack of seasoned ash on horsehide, the roar of the hydra-headed crowd, the umpire's deep-throated 'Play ball!' " So graphically had he limned the color and excitement of the game that the three of us hung there with shining eyes, too rapt even to spurn the paper-thin, parsimonious slices of meat he had served us.

"Golly!" breathed Chiquita. "I feel like as though I had really witnessed the game!"

"So do I," said Groucho, yawning, "and I'm pooped. I'll thank you two harpies to clear out and take that lush with you. I've got to be on the set at eight." Courtly as one of George Cable's antebellum planters, he stood in the doorway and waved us farewell. I turned from the curb for a last glimpse of him, and somehow it seemed to me his gesture of parting had a peculiar tremulous quality. I looked again; yes, he was scratching himself. I called to him, but already his thoughts were far away, intent on the copy of *Smokehouse Monthly* with which he invariably concluded his day. Softly I tiptoed out into the smog.

"All right, settle down, everybody—this is a take!" bawled the director. "Hit the wind machine, and remember, Groucho, bend down into his ear and plead with him." A hush fell over the turbulent sound stage, technicians exchanged a last crisp monosyllable, and the transparency screen behind the set lit up to reveal half a dozen race horses plunging toward us. In front of them, in jockey's silks, sat Marx and Bendix on two amazingly lifelike steeds molded of rubber. As the machinery underneath them began churning, the horses came alive; their necks elongated, manes and tails streamed in the breeze, muscles rippled in their flanks and bellies. The riders plied their mounts with whip and endearments, straining forward into the camera to steal the scene from each other.

"Cost twenty-five grand to build those bang-tails," the producer confided to me in the darkness. "We rent the pair of 'em for
five hundred a day. But it's worth it. When they go to see the picture, they'll swear it's a real horse race."

"What happens if they don't go to see the picture?" I asked,
fascinated. He turned deathly pale, and excusing himself, stum-
bled off to the studio psychiatrist. A few minutes afterward, rid of
his make-up and in jaunty spirits, Groucho met me at the door
of his dressing room. The picture was finished, and he was at last
free to resume his passionate avocation, the collecting and cross-
fertilization of various kinds of money. To celebrate its comple-
tion, he had suggested a final lunch at Romanoff's. Over our ri-
sotto, I inquired about his future plans.

"Who knows?" His smile was charming, and seeing his teeth,
one would have sworn they were real. "I shall, of course, travel;
I do think travel tends to broaden, don't you? Marriage? No, I
hardly think so. Babies? No, I hardly think so."

"Chutney?" put in the waiter.

"No, I hardly think so," said Groucho. "Wait a minute—that
comes with the *plat du jour*. Give me a double portion, and I'll
take some home in a bag."

"What advice would you give a young person just starting out
in the theater?" I asked.

He ruminated awhile, and his face softened.

"You know what I'd say?" he mused. "I'd take that young girl
by the shoulders, I honestly would, and I'd say, 'Honey——' " He
looked up alertly as Marilyn Monroe, in a diaphanous pink
blouse, passed the table bound for a rear booth. There was a
sudden uprush of air beside me, and a scant fifty minutes later he
returned, wry bewilderment on his countenance. "Talk about
coincidence," he marveled. "It seems that kid was just starting out
in the theater, too, and she asked me the very same thing."

"What did you tell her?"

"Oh, just trivialities." He coughed. "Naturally, in so brief an
encounter, I didn't get a chance to grapple with her particular
problems. We're meeting at the Mocambo tonight to discuss them
further."

"Well, Groucho," I said huskily, reaching for my hat, "it may

148

sound fulsome, but I can testify you've got a heart as big as all outdoors. If you ever come to Bucks County, there'll always be an extra bed for you at the George S. Kaufmans'."

"My boy," he said, and his voice shook slightly, "a very wise old man once said that there are two things money cannot buy— nostalgia and friendship. He died in the poorhouse. Don't forget to square that tab on the way out." He gripped my hand hard and was gone, a gallant freebooter who had made his rendezvous with Destiny. As his skulking, predatory figure faded from view, wreathed in chicanery, I bowed my head in tribute. "Adieu, Quackenbush," I whispered. "Adieu, Captain Spaulding. No man ever buckled a better swash." Then, through a mist of tears, I soberly signed his name to the check and went forth to a workaday world.

Victoria Lincoln

The mill town of Fall River, Massachusetts, was the background of Victoria Lincoln's early life and works. She was born (October 23, 1904) definitely on the right side of the tracks, for her lineage was pure New England Colonial and her father's family had been wealthy manufacturers of textile machinery for generations. The less aristocratic side of her hometown furnished the setting for the half-romantic, half-rowdy *February Hill,* an emasculated version of which became a film "vehicle" for Ginger Rogers. After the depression and the closing down of many New England plants, Victoria Lincoln left the Northeast Corner for England, Germany, and much of the southern and western United States. Her marriage to a teacher of philosophy brought her to Cambridge, Columbus, and, most recently, to a sprawling early American ex-farmhouse outside of Baltimore where her husband, Victor Lowe, is on the faculty of Johns Hopkins University.

After *February Hill* Victoria Lincoln's writing grew steadily deeper, full of flashing insights into the minds and motives of men, women, and especially children. *Grandmother and the Comet* is both whimsical and compassionate; *The Wind at My Back* is made up of three highly sensitive short novels, one of which, "Before the Swallow Dares," is a poignant evocation of young girlhood trembling on young womanhood. Few American writers have accomplished so successful a fusion of tenderness and humor, of patent absurdity and sheer poetry.

A Flag for the General *

Since the days of the Roosevelt-Landon election, when Laurie Wilbur and I were quite newly acquainted, I have never ceased to be fascinated by my friend's political mind. At the start I carelessly assumed that she had none. Charlie Wilbur was a Republican in those days, and his bride was so feminine, so vague, and so devoted that when I asked her how she was voting, the question was a pure social routine, like inquiries for her health or remarks about the weather. However, she surprised me.

"Well, now, don't you tell Charlie," she said. "It would just upset him, and I can't argue, forgetting names and dates and stuff the way I do. But that Landon looks just like Mr. Barker, who was so horrid when I backed into his car. And he keeps Mrs. Barker on a budget, too. Poor woman, I watch her, out sweeping her front walk. You only have to compare the look on her face with the look on Mrs. Roosevelt's."

That was the year Laurie was a fellow-traveler for three weeks, too. She said it was because Stalin always looked so relaxed. I was feeling a little guilty and reactionary in those days, and I was much relieved one afternoon when Laurie set down her teacup and remarked that she didn't like Stalin any more.

"I just happened to think who he looks like," she said. *"Hunter."*

Hunter, a large Persian tom, was at that moment asleep before the fire, and she regarded him darkly.

"You see?" she said. "Exactly the same expression. And I'll no sooner have let him put away half a can of salmon then he'll be rubbing on Charlie's legs and leading him to the refrigerator, and Charlie saying, 'Don't you ever remember to feed this poor cat?' " She lit a cigarette and set it in the ashtray before her. She leaned over it and toward me, her eyes remote. "Naturally," she said, "naturally I thought a man who looked like that—so relaxed, I mean—must have a conscience that was at rest. And then I looked at Hunter. Your conscience doesn't have to be at rest to look like that. You can feel just as fine if you never had any. Not that I'm one bit sorry I subscribed for an ambulance —those poor Spaniards—but from now on I'm *watching* that man." She paused, turning the lighted cigarette slowly on the edge of the tray. "Not that I like that Franco, either," she said. "There's a man near us in Hingham, summers, and he's always doing stuff for St. Stephen's Church—the way they say Franco does for those nuns and all—and the way he treats his wife is too ghastly to think about. No, if the Pope himself was to come into this room this minute, I'd still say, 'Well, look at Mr. Whitford.' "

It would be inaccurate to say that my mind has ever been clarified by Laurie Wilbur's pronouncements, but there is a quality of Delphic intoxication in them that half persuades me, even when I darned well know better, that they come from a source more than human. Maybe what I feel is no more than an atavistic remnant of that awe in which primitive people have always held the mad; heaven knows I'd be the last to deny that Laurie is crazy as a coot. But the sensation—call it that—has always been there, like a faith and solace, and I must say that it was unsettling to come up her walk on the day MacArthur returned to Washington and find the Stars and Stripes flowing out upon the air from the front porch.

It was particularly unsettling because General Marshall is the living spit of Mrs. Wilbur's late father, a saint of God if there ever was one, and Harry Truman looks just like her grocer, Mr. Rowley, who is so honest and obliging that it's well worth the difference over the A. & P.

So I walked into the house wondering who MacArthur looked like to her, and almost afraid to find out. Her first remark, however, left me both relieved and confounded.

"Aren't you thrilled about Truman?" she said. "I never would have thought he had it in him if it hadn't been for Duke."

Duke is a Gordon setter, and for once I felt that I didn't have the strength to take it the hard way.

"Look, dear," I said, "if Truman acts like Duke and looks like Mr. Rowley, why are you flying the flag for MacArthur?"

She stared at me, her large eyes flooding with astonishment and horror. "For *MacArthur!*" she exclaimed. "Are you out of your mind? Why, I'm flying it for General Endicott!"

"General Endicott?"

"Of course, of course. General Endicott. Right over there."

She waved her hand impatiently toward the open door. In the garden across the street, another flag flew, from a flagpole in the center of the lawn.

I could only look dim.

Laurie interpreted my silence in her own way. "Oh, Vicky," she said, "how can you be so intolerant? Think how he was brought up, West Point and everything. And retired, and arthritis, and his wife dead, and how nice he was when Duke got into his tuberous begonias, and you know how those fleshy stems snap if you barely *look* at them! I'll never forget his face the day MacArthur was recalled. Like death, just forcing himself to stand up straight, and his only son a Democrat in the State Department!"

There are times when you realize that you might just as well roll with the punches. "Oh," I said. "Oh, I see!" Like a sleepwalker, I turned and followed her across the hall and into the living room.

"Oh, I knew you would!" she exclaimed happily. She sat down and lit a cigarette. She laid it in the ashtray and let its smoke rise before her, the vapors from the sacred tripod. "You do see," she said, "don't you? That dear old man. You do see that it's the best way someone with my convictions can hit at people like Colonel McCormick and Senator McCarthy, and at the Communists, too, right at the same time, don't you?"

For once, the Delphic look was mingled with something unfamiliar, an anxious, almost childlike appeal. I hoped that my own face did not look as blank as it felt.

"Well, perhaps not *exactly*," I said gently.

She leaned forward. "Think about General Endicott first," she said, "and West Point, and the way he grew up—William Howard Taft, I mean, and girls in long piqué skirts, and all that."

"Some anachronisms can be pretty expensive," I heard myself say sharply.

She bowed her head. "I know," she said. "You don't have to tell me. And of course the scariest thing about MacArthur is the way he just looks like MacArthur, even old, I mean, and especially in his toupee. But what I started to say was, General Endicott—Well, nothing I could do would change his vote anyway, would it? And his sweet old face, and all those chrysanthemums and things he gives us when he thins out his borders. And how could it make one bit of difference to Truman or Acheson, now or ever, whether there's one flag or two—right in the same neighborhood, I mean?" She broke off, her chin lifted, looking past me now. "So I got to thinking about that man Molière—no, Voltaire—and how he said, 'You're crazy, but I'll die for your chance to say what you think.' And then I thought about people—just one by one, I mean—and how they're all that really matters, and what governments are *for*. And how that's the thing that McCarthy and the Communists both just don't believe. And the next minute I had it right down out of the attic and in the stand on the porch rail, don't you see?"

Suddenly I laughed. "Laurie," I said, "do you know you're an anarchist?"

At once she had relaxed in my laughter, taking the words for nonsense. "I knew you'd understand," she said. "Now I'm going to get you a glass of sherry, and you just stick around until Charlie comes home. It all hit me after he left, you know, and you're so good at explaining things. And when he comes up the walk, he'll be wild. Just wild."

I drew a long, slow breath. "If it's just the same with you, dear," I said, "I'd rather have a Martini. A good one."

B. M. Atkinson, Jr.

At the age of thirty-four B. M. Atkinson, Jr., has been successful in leading a literary double life. His regular stint is a daily column for the Louisville *Times,* which he has been doing since 1946; his extracurricular activities are fictional only in a technical sense—they have resulted in some of the most adroit short stories to be found in the current magazines. Atkinson's account of his progress is modest. "Before the war," he says, "I wrote a sports column for the *Times,* did stunts, and made an ass of myself wrestling bears, driving cars through flaming walls, etc. I am now married, have three children, and am one of the country's foremost experts on domestic relations and wives in general, despite what some 100,000 wives in the city here will tell you. I started writing fiction two years ago when my third child was born, more or less as a command performance for the doctor and the treasury department at the hospital." It is apparent that Atkinson's children—abetted by the treasury department—will encourage him to keep on writing.

The Soul of Joe Forsythe*

I still say the twenty bucks had nothing to do with it. It was strictly for the sake of Brother Joe Forsythe's soul. Of course, where sophomores and their souls are concerned you have to take drastic steps, and that's what I did. It was just unfortunate that he took it the way he did.

What got me interested in Brother Forsythe's soul was a letter from his fifteen-year-old sister, Sally, who was madly in love with me and every other brother in the chapter who'd ever gone home with Brother Forsythe for a week end.

The letter started out:

Dearest Wretch: When I am the sweetheart of Sigma Chi, SAE, Deke, KA, etc., you Chi Phi stinkers will rue the day you didn't invite me up for those crummy spring dances.

It wound up:

Even though you don't have the decency to rescue a maiden fair from the vile clutches of a bunch of high-school creeps maybe

* Reprinted from *Collier's* Magazine.

155

you will at least stoop to helping one of your own filthy kind. My idiot brother Joe wrote Mother that unless she sent him twenty dollars before the dances he was going to destroy himself. Father told her that he was going to destroy them both if she did, so she didn't. That sounds like high tragedy but it's really a panic.

Joe has twenty dollars right in his room at school but he doesn't know it. You know what a great churchwoman Mother is. Well, she sent Joe a Bible back in the fall and told him to be sure and read it. In the Bible at the place where it says the Lord will provide, she tucked a nice, crisp twenty-dollar bill. Every time she writes him she asks if he is reading the Bible. Every time he writes he says he is learning whole chapters by heart. She knows it's a lie because he has never mentioned the twenty dollars and if Joe ever found twenty dollars you could hear him mentioning it all over the county.

So, if it's not asking too much of you, kind sir, please get him to read his Bible. Just hint at it because I promised Mother that I would never tell him about it. Good night, Stinker.

Your Handmaiden,
Sally

Well, when I read that, I closed my door and had a long heart-to-heart talk with myself. "Pete," I said, "the fact that you desperately need twenty dollars to go with that poor lonely ten of yours has nothing whatsoever to do with the decision you're about to make, does it?"

"Perish the thought!" I said.

"You are going to buy that Bible from him just to teach him a lesson, aren't you? Any boy who will lie to his mother about reading the holy book deserves just what he gets, doesn't he? You're doing it for the good of his soul, aren't you?"

"Yes! Yes! Yes!"

"Besides," I said, "it will teach him some respect for his elders. A sophomore should not win all the brothers' money playing poker and then spend it all wining and dining the brothers' girls, should he?"

"Horrors, no!" I replied. "Go buy that Bible immediately. Make all the world your debtor."

Well, I went into his room and there he was stretched out on his bed. That's another one of his failings. He studies one hour a night and he's got the highest grades in the lodge.

"Brother Forsythe," I said, "you don't happen to have a Bible, do you?"

"Why, certainly I've got a Bible!" he said. "What do you think I am?"

"I know what you are, Brother Forsythe," I said. "That's the reason I want to buy it from you. Your way of life calls more for a voodoo manual."

He sat up and stared at me. "You want to buy my Bible?" he gasped. "You, Godless John Upshaw, want to buy a—?"

"All right!" I told him. "I'm on a spot. My uncle, the Reverend Philip Upshaw, is in town and he just called and said he was coming out to see me. He gave me a Bible last Christmas. I sold it and I've got to have another one because I know he will be looking for the—"

"Oh, you wretch!" he said. "Your uncle gives you a nice Bible and you sell it. How low, how degraded, how mercenary can a—? How much money you got?"

"Don't talk that way, Brother Forsythe," I said. "You can buy a fine Bible any place for a buck, so—"

"A buck!" he screamed. He reached up on the top of his bureau, got this oblong cardboard box down, blew the dust off, opened it up, and pulled out this brand-new Bible. It had never been opened.

"Brother Upshaw," he said, "my dear old mother sent me this Bible. There's a million dollars' worth of love and hope and sentiment behind this book. However, as we are brothers in the bond, pledged to one another even unto death, I'm gonna let you have it for only five bucks."

"Five bucks!" I gasped.

"Brother Upshaw," he said, "this is a horrible thing I do. I must have funds enough to drown my shame in the proper fashion."

"You're a loathsome leech on the body fraternal, Brother Forsythe," I said bitterly, "but here. Take it." I fished one of the two fives out of my wallet and handed it to him.

157

He snatched the Bible back. "Just what the hell is this? It just ain't right you paying me five bucks for *my* Bible when you could borrow one around the house someplace for—" He started to thumb through it. I grabbed it from him.

"There's my Uncle Philip," I gasped. "Just heard him come in downstairs. I've got to have this."

"Ten bucks," he snarled. "It's some kind of low, dirty trick but you're going to pay for it."

"Damn you, Brother Forsythe," I said, "you'll regret this!" I gave him my other five and dashed down the hall. "Coming, Uncle Philip." . . .

A half hour later I was down in the library, thumbing through the Bible for the fifty-third time. There just wasn't any nice crisp twenty-dollar bill in it. I gave it one more shake and headed upstairs for his room. He wasn't there, but this letter of his was lying on his table.

Dear Sally, it said, *Please send more Bibles. Just hooked Brother Upshaw. That makes seven dear brothers this week. A funny thing but not one of them has said anything to me or to anybody else about it. I wonder why? Write Ed and Roger next. Enclosed is twenty bucks. Ten is for you. Put the other ten in the collection plate Sunday. The Lord's work must go forward.*
                                                                    Joe

P.S. Yes, I've already written Mary Jane that although I love her above all the creatures of this earth I can't have her up for the spring dances as I have to take my dear little sister. It is hard for me to believe that such a straightforward, upstanding young man as myself could have a blackmailing sister who would threaten to expose him to his father.

John Collier

In late 1951 John Collier collected his fifty most imaginative short stories in a volume entitled *Fancies and Goodnights*. All but seventeen of these surprising tales had appeared in previous books variously and teasingly entitled *Presenting Moonshine* and *The Touch of Nutmeg*. (Another equally unlikely piece of fiction was a novel called *His Monkey Wife*.) In all his writings Collier had dealt jauntily with themes that were maliciously erotic, coldly sardonic, acidly grotesque, or just downright outrageous. His concern with devils, ghosts, jinn, and genies was no less disturbing—and no less stylistically polished—than his fantastic portrayal of people, people who were seemingly plain but actually monstrous . . . in a commonplace way. His new collection displayed his genius for the odd, the bizarre, and the macabre—the Real Macabre.

Born in London, England, on May 3, 1901, John Collier (no relation to the English portrait painter by the same name) followed up his early writing of poetry with a history of England after World War I, and came to America about eighteen years ago. During most of these years Collier has been in Hollywood where his first-rate talent for the extraordinary has been spent on third-rate treatments of the obvious. His best stories are, as Clifton Fadiman wrote, "acetic, unexpected, wild, and lightly diabolic." Orville Prescott concluded that his stories combine "a dry and sophisticated wit with exuberant fantasy and cruelly ironic results . . . In the imaginary world of John Collier the supernatural is almost natural."

All of which places Collier in the company of Poe, "Saki," and Ambrose Bierce. Like his mordant predecessors, Collier alternates between a bland horror and a biting humor; his stories range casually from the almost intolerable to the altogether incredible.

Season of Mists*

I was ready for anything when I came to the town of T——. It was already late in the year. Dead leaves crawled like crabs over the asphalt of the deserted esplanade. Winds raced along the corridors of the larger hotels, barging into the wrong rooms.

It is at such a place, and at such a season, that one finds the desperate grass widow, or young things whose natural credulity snaps starvingly at the grossest counterfeit. The illusion of teeming possibilities has gone with the licentious carnival of summer, the masks of coarse sunburn, and he who may be sitting alone among the sand dunes. Ravenous dreams pace the unvisited sitting rooms of villas or stalk between rising waves and falling leaves.

The concealed smile in my smile, and the concealed meaning in my words, would have made me seem a sort of scheme-riddled Machiavelli in the ephemeral mating dance of July. I should have been condemned as heavy going, would-be clever, even unpleasant or dangerous. Now, on the other hand, my slightly involved personality would be as welcome as a jig-saw puzzle in hands already fidgety with boredom. Nevertheless, I had gone so far as to purchase a ready-made sports jacket, and had my black mustache had any objective existence I should have taken the precaution of shaving it off.

I still had a little money. I was not after profit, but pleasure. I desired to intoxicate myself on a real emotion, and I wondered in which of the still-occupied villas, in what sort of absurd drawing room, treading softly in fear of what husband or what aunt, I should perform what drunken antics my chosen potion would inspire in me.

Meticulous in my observance of protective mimicry, I could not of course omit the *snorter* or *quick one* before dinner on my first evening in the hotel. I entered the bar in jaunty style, my mouth already writhing with a classy catch-phrase, like the eye socket of a provincial actor (but all actors are provincial) in travail with his waggish monocle.

This witticism was never uttered. I thought I saw a golden fish. It was the honey head of the barmaid, bent over a love story, but, as the place had the appearance of the tourist cocktail lounge of a liner sunk two years previously in a hundred fathoms of gray-green ocean, I thought it was a golden fish. I was sharply corrected when she raised a face so dappled with flush and sun gleam that I looked instinctively for the orchard boughs above her head.

160

All this was disconcerting, and effective in shattering my pose. It happens that these fresh and almost eatable faces have a peculiar effect on me. "Farewell before hail," I thought, "to the sailor's languishing wife, and to the ardent anemia at the Vicarage! I am off."

I ordered one of the far inferior intoxicants that stood ranked behind her, and retired a pace, changing my name to Bert, a young man already doing well, at once cheeky and shy, but probably capable of being serious. One never knew what I could come out with next.

I was wondering about that myself when I saw that she, affecting to take no particular notice of me, had retired into the flowery thicket of her reverie. I realized that this must have grown very wild and tangly in the last month or two, because, before she could turn and peep out from it, it swallowed her up entirely, like a prospective sleeping beauty, and indeed she yawned.

I analyzed this yawn with the aloof precision of one of those scientists who are always helping Scotland Yard. I discovered it to be heavy with a supersaturation of sigh, its origin a plaintive protest against the difference between dreams and reality. Though this was only the middle of November, I diagnosed it as a premature December yawn, *and in December they settle for reality.* This emboldened me to act at once.

Affecting to consult my heart, exactly as if it had been a pocket watch, I gasped, bit my lip, and stared at her in wild surmise. You could never tell when I was joking. "Do you believe," I said fervently, "in love at first sight?"

"No, sir," she said severely. "That sort of thing doesn't appeal, thank you."

It was clear she had not been a barmaid more than seven or eight weeks. From behind her professional hauteur she peeped out to watch for its effect, as bewitchingly as if she were a child wearing her mother's terrible hat.

"I'm not fooling," I said (taken down a peg or two, you understand). "The fact is, believe it or not, I'm a bit psychic." On this word, the most useful though not the most beautiful in our language, she raised her eyes to mine, which I had baited with pieces

161

of an old sincerity which I carry about for just such purposes. I put a little in my voice too, as I added, "Do you know what I thought, the minute I saw you?"

"What?" said she.

"I'll tell you," said I. " 'That girl's tragic,' I thought. 'She's being wasted. There's a sort of bar between her and all sorts of delightful surprises. I wish it could be melted away.' "

"Not really!"

"I did," said I. "Give me your hand. I can read it like a book, probably by your favorite author. Oh, I'm psychic all right. I had a sort of premonition when I came here. I knew I was going to fall desperately in love."

"I know you're kidding," said she, but she offered me her open hand, which proved to be quite illegible.

Nevertheless I spoke with confidence. "You've been thinking of love today. You've been dreaming of a stranger. Now don't deny it, because it's written in your hand. And that's not all."

"What else does it say?" said she.

"Call it Fate," said I solemnly. "Call it Kismet if you like; I can deny you nothing. Or, look here, let's call it Destiny. You can't go back on Destiny, you know. It would absolutely ruin it. It says . . . Guess what!"

"I can't," she said. "Do tell me."

I couldn't guess either. Dumbly I scrutinized her palm. She leaned a little farther over the bar, joining me in the study. Our foreheads touched. I remained conscious, but the shock had dislocated all connection between awareness and volition. With a divine shudder I heard myself reply, "It says we are going to be married."

"Oh," said she. "I don't know about that."

"What?" I cried, hurt to the quick, all caution forgotten. "Is this mutual understanding? Is this two hearts beating as one? Don't let's start off with a rift like this between us."

"I didn't mean it that way," she replied remorsefully.

"Splendid," I said. "Our first little quarrel healed already. And don't we sort of know one another better for it? Aren't we somehow closer? If not, we ought to be. Lean over a little farther."

Fate had evidently triumphed. Her kiss was like cowslips and cream. I was unquestionably in love and felt no longer responsible for my actions.

At that moment, however, a gong sounded in the echoing depths of the hotel. "Better go," she said, already wifely. "Go and get your dinner. I'll be here later on."

I bowed before the importance of Bert's dinner, and went. When I returned the bar was still empty of intruders, and she was still there. I rushed forward, I flung my arms about her, and resumed the kiss that had been so coarsely interrupted.

I had just been struck by the nice thought that perhaps after all it tasted of cream and honeysuckle, rather than cowslips, when I was also struck by a tremendous blow in the face.

"What?" I said, staggering back. "Are you tired of me already? You might at least have broken it more gently."

"I'll call the manager," said she.

"Do so," said I. "Call the boots, too. Call the waiters. Call all the principal residents of T——— on Sea. Let them hear how you promised to marry me before dinner and socked me in the puss for a kiss immediately afterwards."

"Promised to marry you?" she cried. "Before dinner. Oooh! It must have been Bella. Fancy! Bella!"

"What is your name?" said I.

"Nellie," said she.

"That's who it was," said I. "Nellie. You. To the devil with this interfering, designing Bella, who . . ." But, as I spoke, she turned and darted through the door behind her.

I heard some delicious squeals and giggles. "I hope," I thought, "she is giving that abominable Bella a good pinch. Pretending to be her! She had the poor girl all confused." At that moment the door opened again, and out they came, hand in hand.

"I'm Nellie."

"I'm Bella."

"Keep quite still," said I, clowning astonishment. "I must think for a little while about this."

"Look! He's all bowled over."

"Isn't he sweet?"

"Yes, he's a duck. Bella, you *are* lucky."

163

"Your turn next."

That was the rub. My mind darkened at the thought of a brother-in-law. You know what beasts men are. A thousand intricate jealousies tangled themselves before me. The girls were so exactly alike; they *went together,* as we say. Besides, who can choose between cowslips and honeysuckle?

It was time I said something. "Well!" said I. "By all that's wonderful! I wish old Fred were here tonight!"

"Who's Fred?"

"Fred? You'll like Fred. He's a splendid fellow. We're twins."

"No!"

"Yes, identical twins. More alike than you are. Same looks. Same tastes. Same thoughts. I always know what he's thinking. Listen! He's sort of trying to get through to me now. I bet he knows I'm happy. He does. He's sending congratulations. In waves. He's asking something. What is it, Fred, old boy? Is there what? Oh, *Is there one for me, Bert?* That's what he's trying to say. What shall I tell him, Nellie?"

"Don't know, I'm sure."

"Why don't you bring him along one day?" said Bella.

"I can't," said I. "We're on a very special job. It's just half the time off for each of us. But I'll tell you what; I'll *send* him along."

This was agreed upon. I spent the rest of the evening delightfully, and in the morning bought a new sports coat, brushed my hair differently, and returned as Fred.

I entered the bar peering through my fingers. "Which are you?" I cried. "I don't want to look at you properly till I know. I might fall in love with the wrong one."

"I'm Nellie."

"Good! To make it absolutely perfect, I'm Fred." With that I dropped my hand. "Good old Bert!" I cried. "Wonderful taste he's got! Wonderful fellow!"

"He's nice. But you're nice, too."

"Do you really think so?"

In short, we were happy. Soon afterwards Bella came in. There was nothing but giggles, comparisons, talk of future joys.

"It really ought to be a double wedding," they said.

"Can't be done," I replied. "Truly. Ask Bert if you don't believe me. He'll tell you it's out of the question."

The next few days passed like lightning. All went twice as merrily as the ordinary marriage bell. I rented two bungalows, semidetached, furnished them from the same store, took a week off for my honeymoon as Bert, and the next week for my honeymoon as Fred.

I then settled down to lives of singular contentment and regularity. One evening Nellie and I would have Bella to dinner, and spend the time saying what a grand fellow Bert was, and the next evening Bella and I would entertain Nellie and do the same for Fred.

It was a full month before I asked myself, which is the happier of the two, Fred or Bert? I was unable to answer. The doubt persisted until it tortured me.

I became a little moody, and sometimes would retire to the next room, under the pretense of a headache, in order to ponder the question over again. On one of these occasions, I went into the hallway to get cigarettes from my overcoat and I heard the girls' voices through the flimsy door of the drawing room. "The darlings!" I thought. "They are discussing their husbands again. This may shed some light on my problem. Bella thinks Bert has the nicer voice. Nellie claims that Fred knows more songs. What is this? Really, Bella! Come, come, Nellie, you flatter me! Bella, what an exaggeration! Nellie, that is a downright lie!"

Soon afterward I heard Nellie go home. I rejoined Bella, who was obviously much exercised in her mind. "Bert," she said, "who is the best swimmer, you or Fred?"

"We never compete, darling, we are so sure we are equal."

"I wonder if you would be if you tried," said Bella, still looking extremely thoughtful.

When I returned to the other bungalow next evening, I found Nellie equally ill at ease. "Tell me something," said she. "Of course I know Bella's my sister, my twin. Nobody could love her more than I do. But tell me, Fred, would you say she was absolutely truthful?"

"Absolutely," said I. "I'd stake my life on it. Bert's life, too. She is incapable of a lie."

"Oh!" said Nellie, lapsing into a deeper reverie than before.

It was with a sardonic pleasure that I watched the increasing wistfulness of both my wives. "I have an idea," said I to myself, "that I shall soon learn whether Bert or Fred is the happier."

Sure enough, it was not long before Nellie sent round one evening to ask if Bert would help her move some heavy furniture. I went to her aid, and afterward we sat talking for a while on twins, likenesses, differences, marriage, conventions, love, and what would have happened if Fred had met Bella before I had, and whether what hurts nobody can really be said to be wrong.

It took a long time to resolve all these problems to our complete satisfaction, and I was deprived of a good deal of Bella's company that evening. But this was made up to me on the following day, for she came round to ask if Fred would help her with a leaky tap, and we had an almost identical discussion which took just as long for its complete resolution.

I was now in a state of extreme and complicated bliss. It was clear that Bert had no reason to envy Fred, and that Fred's happiness was in all respects equal to Bert's. Not only had I two charming wives, but my double domestic happiness was multiplied by a dual and delicious infidelity.

But I was one day in the character of Bert, sitting before the fire enjoying the more legal of my happinesses with Bella, charmed by her prattle and pleased by the complete restoration of her good spirits, when suddenly I was struck, as if by a thunderbolt, by the thought: "This woman is deceiving me!"

I leapt up with a muttered excuse, and rushed out of the now hateful house. I walked on the shore till late that night, a prey to the most bitter reflections. I had to admit that I was largely responsible, but I at least knew that it made no difference. She had no such excuse; it was she who had blighted our Eden.

I went home long after midnight, slept uneasily, and hurried off in the morning, eager to exchange the pitiful personality of the deceived husband for the roguish character of his betrayer.

As Fred, I returned with a jaunty sneer. Nellie greeted me. "How was Bert," said she, "when you left him?"

"Bert?" said I. "Bert!"

Without another word I went heavily upstairs, and looked at

myself in the mirror. The sight maddened me. I itched to get my fingers round my throat. I longed to rush next door and pour out my troubles to my adorable mistress, but I knew in my heart that she was as false as her sister below.

I thought of divorce, working out the actions and counteractions on my fingers, and badly spraining two of them in the process. Besides, there was the unsavory publicity.

At last I made up my mind. I hurried off to catch the last train to the town. Arrived there, I wrote two notes, as follows:

"Dear Nellie, I have found you out. I am asking Bert to come for a swim. He will never return. Fred."

"Dear Bella, I know all. Am persuading Fred to take a midnight bathe. He will not come back. Bert."

Having posted my letters, I took my two sports coats to the beach, where I left them side by side.

There was just time to get the train for B——, and it was there that I met Mrs. Wilkinson.

Parke Cummings

Although Parke Cummings was born (October 8, 1902) in Massachusetts, he joined many of his fellow writers in their migration to Connecticut. Before going from West Medford to Westport, Cummings went to Harvard. Immediately after graduating in 1925 he began writing the humorous pieces which added up not only to a living but to a reputation. In spite of the difficulties, he has remained a free-lance writer for more than a quarter of a century, a light essayist whose sense of comedy emanates from common sense. He has, basically, a feeling for human values, especially when the humans happen to be children. His own children led him to write a book on the young of the species, *I'm Telling You Kids for the Last Time*. It was published in late 1951 and provoked from the critics a series of uncritical chuckles.

Too Many Saints *

Parents must do more than supply food, clothing, and shelter for their offspring. They must also administer justice, and this takes some doing. Try as you may to be a combination of Solon, Blackstone, and Oliver Wendell Holmes, there will be occasions when you find yourself regarded like a baseball umpire who has made a bad call. And, although an umpire can throw protesting players out of the game, you cannot throw your youngsters out of the house.

Children are exceedingly vocal in stating their rights, and are particularly astute when it comes to citing precedence in their favor. Is Junior refused an ice-cream stick? Quickly he points out that Cynthy had one yesterday, and begins hinting strongly of favoritism, an accusation which makes the parent—the modern parent especially—freeze up with terror. Don't all the psychiatrists constantly warn us that favoritism, in rearing children, is one of the cardinal sins?

The chances are that Junior gets his ice-cream stick, which is just what Cynthy wants. She promptly demands one for herself. When it is pointed out that she had one yesterday, she cites an instance last week where Junior got to go to the carnival while she

* From *I'm Telling You Kids for the Last Time,* by Parke Cummings; copyright, 1951, by Henry Schuman, Inc.

168

stayed home. If Cynthy wins her point, and there are other children in the family, they will put in their own demands and usually realize them. There is a widespread belief that an only child gets a disproportionate amount of playthings and favors, but I have my doubts. My suspicion is that children in large families do better by the time-honored expedient of playing off one against the other.

But even an only child can utilize precedence to his advantage. He may not have other brothers or sisters, but there is always the Other Parent. This is illustrated by the age-old argument which goes: "But, gee, Sandy Taylor's mother lets *him* do it!" It would seem that there are, in this world, untold millions of Other Parents who give in to every demand of their children without the semblance of an objection. Unfortunately, they are hard to track down. When you interview one, you are apt to get a different view of things. This may be illustrated by a brief chat I had with an Other Parent recently:

I: I understand you let Freddy go to the movies three times a week.
OTHER PARENT: Huh? What gave you that idea?
I: That's what our John said.
OTHER PARENT: Matter of fact, Freddy's only been twice in the past six months—and they were educational films.
I: Oh.
OTHER PARENT: Of course it's none of my business, but I was surprised to hear that you let John smoke.
I: *WHAT!*

From this something additional may be deduced: While you are fuming at the laxity of Other Parents, there exists the possibility that you yourself are being billed in the neighborhood as an Other Parent. Once I heard of a refinement on the process. For a long time a boy kept citing the privileges of another lad whose parents were apparently incapable of uttering the monosyllable "No." Finally, his own parents decided to investigate. What they discovered was that their offspring had invented both the Other Child and the Other Parents. This lad will go far.

169

In view of the constant pressure exerted by children for getting favors, a good many parents eventually acquire a certain craftiness when it comes to answering requests.

If they can avoid it, they do not reply with a direct "Yes" or "No." An affirmative answer, too readily given, establishes the parent as an easy mark who can be consistently bilked in the future. "No," on the other hand, is apt to result in an argument in which the child cites privileges accorded other brothers or sisters, or the Other Child of the Other Parent.

To meet this dilemma, something more evasive is in order. Perhaps child-guidance experts would frown on this, but I am acting strictly in a reportorial capacity, attempting to draw no morals. Some of the more effective (or least ineffective) answers follow:

"Aren't you too old for that?" By appealing to his maturity, it is sometimes possible to talk a child out of a demand with this challenge, although not with its opposite: "Aren't you too young?" (A child is never too young for anything.)

"If they aren't sold out." This is a precautionary measure following a demand for a new gadget or a trip to the circus or rodeo. It gives the parent an excuse, but also shows that he is willing. Warning: the child frequently checks up on this ahead of time, however.

"I'll think about it." This establishes you as a level-headed and judicious adult, not to be rushed into some rash decision. You aren't just putting your foot down; you're giving the matter every consideration. This is especially useful for such miscellaneous requests as permission for an overnight hike, new skates, or a later bedtime hour. A shorter and equally effective version of "I'll think about it" is "We'll see."

"If I can find the time." One of the best. On the surface it appears to be a cheerful assent, but it has a hidden reservation like a fine-print clause. It is then up to the parent to keep his calendar filled until things blow over.

"Who's going to pay for it?" Usually this is purely a rhetorical question (any father knows perfectly well who is), but occasionally it has been known to help in getting a request trimmed down, say, from a motor boat to an air rifle. And once in a while, if boldly put, it may elicit the information that the child has saved up four or five dollars of his own, and if Dad would just make up the difference . . . In other words, money in the bank.

"You misunderstood me." An excellent cover-up for a rash promise made when in an expansive mood, as after getting a raise or imbibing too much. If politicians can use the "I-was-misquoted" excuse, there is no reason why the parent cannot do likewise. It is up to him, however, to make up his own story to cover the situation.

"When I was your age—" These five words should be followed up with a heart-rending description of the hardships the parent endured and the denials he faced in his formative years, as "When I was your age, I was lucky if I got a soda twice a year." Don't hesitate to exaggerate here. They can seldom check up on you.

"Ask your mother." This is the last gasp, when all other answers have been tried in vain, and the parent is now faced with coming out with that irrevocable and costly "Yes," or that certain-to-be-protested "No." There should be no hesitation. The head of the family should put the bit firmly in his spouse's teeth and do the cowardly thing. It follows as a corollary that the female parent should avail herself of the same privileges and answer calmly: "Ask your father."

Hannibal Coons

Hannibal Coons took an old but difficult fiction-writing formula and gave it a new liveliness. Using the device of a plot propelled by misunderstandings and complicated through a series of crossing (or double-crossing) letters, Coons gave the back-and-forth technique a breathless tempo and a series of madcap twists. His hero, George Seibert, is always in trouble. Plunged into a morass of publicity stunts, George sinks deeper with every struggle to extricate himself but, just as he seems about to go down for the third time, he gives one more desperate plunge and, somehow, flounders free. The battle between George and his boss, Richard L. Reed, has become something of a saga in *Collier's*, and readers hope that the conflict will go on as long as Hollywood manufactures topsupercolossals or similarly unreasonable facsimiles.

No childhood prodigy, Coons was well over thirty before he found a way to adapt the familiar formula. He educated himself strenuously, attending seven grade schools and three high schools in various states. After finally graduating from Chicago's Oak Park High School in 1926, Coons went through what he calls his "storm and distress" period. He was publicity man for a dance academy, sold mailing machines, gave violin lessons, promoted a Shakespearian stock company, composed greeting-card rhymes, wrote lyrics for night clubs, and, during World War II, was a lieutenant in the Navy's Training Literature Section, "the most unliterary group in naval history." Coons emerged looking like a larger (and healthier) version of the late Alexander Woollcott, although Coons insists that any resemblance is purely libelous. He is actually six feet tall, weights two hundred and fifteen pounds, and loves any sport "at which the chairs are at all comfortable."

Chicago Safari*

FEDERAL PICTURES
Hollywood, California

From RICHARD L. REED
Director of Publicity

July 6, 1951
Air Mail

Mr. George Seibert
Special Representative, Federal Pictures
Hotel Mayflower
Washington, D.C.

Dear George:

Well, George, you can call a halt to that fool gumshoe activity there. We've shelved the Alaskan deal, so just rub noses all around, tell everybody we'll see them later, and thanks a lot.

As is not unusual in this business, we are off in another direction. Do you own anything decent in the way of a pith helmet? Anything you'd want to go out in? If not, purchase one immediately; they are becoming an absolute necessity in the movie business. Any studio today that isn't making at least one picture in darkest Africa just isn't in it at all. There's one sport at which we're undisputed world's champions out here, and that's follow-the-leader. King Solomon's Mines makes money, and boom! Africa is so crowded with actors there is hardly any space left for the animals. From now on if a lion isn't in the picture he can't get a room, and that's that. If you and I had any sense we'd quit this publicity dodge, open a branch of the Brown Derby at Nairobi, and make a fortune.

At any rate, till this travel epidemic blows over, just think of us as Burton Holmes. If people want a look at some of these foreign lands they're reading about, Heaven knows we're willing to oblige. So willing we'd almost take home movies of people's children if the people would promise to attend.

But at the moment we're all of course busy in Africa. And with a cartload of African epics either already playing or about due to open, who has had the only original idea in the proceedings? Me.

The problem, as usual, has been how to give our own horn the loudest toot. Our thing, Nairobi Nights, is not a bad African travelogue at all, but most of the others, from what we hear, are just as genuine. So how to stand out?

Then I got it. The other day our elegant Mr. Conrad J. Thorne, who directed the epic, was showing us some of the crates of souvenirs and relics he brought back with him to impress his Palm Springs house guests. And the stuff was really interesting. At least I'd never seen a lot of the things, and I'm not exactly a stay-at-home. And suddenly I thought: If this stuff is interesting to me it ought to be to others. And in no time we whipped up the plans.

We are going to start the picture off with what we hope will be quite a bang by taking a fast road tour of the big cities, with Director Thorne and several of the stars going along to show the audiences all the actual stuff they brought back and telling some of their interesting and very genuine experiences during the making of the picture. And the kicker will be when Thorne brings out six genuine African cannibals, or head hunters, or whatever they call those native jokers over there, who will proceed to scare everybody half to death with some tribal dances and very real spear tossing.

Which is where you come in.

Because at this very moment our six African head-hunters are approaching New York from Nairobi on the SS Spitsbergen. And somebody has to meet them, welcome them to our shores, and see that they get to Chicago by Friday. We've done the main rehearsing here, and Thorne and the others will go direct to Chicago, where the thing opens Sunday.

Beautiful Rebecca Lane, the blonde lady star of the picture, is in New York, but she'll fly directly out by herself, also getting there Friday.

So as you can see there's really no problem at all, except for somebody to meet these fun-loving head-hunters—six thirty Monday morning, Pier 6—and get the safari started for Chicago. I'd love to do it myself, as you know, but I'm needed here.

So guess who has drawn this plum of an assignment? Right.

I'm leaving everything to you, including the mode of transportation. There are floods all over that end of the country, so go by canoe if you want to, just so you're in Chicago by Friday. Do whatever you think best after you meet them and size up the situation.

There's nothing to it. You shouldn't have any trouble at all locating them. Unless it's a cruise ship, they'll be the only people getting off the boat naked and carrying spears.

Love,
Dick

RICHARD L. REED
FEDERAL PICTURES HOLLYWOOD
CALIF

THANKS, BUT DON'T NEED ANY HEAD-HUNTERS TO HUNT MINE. I KNOW RIGHT WHERE IT IS. AND RIGHT WHERE I INTEND TO KEEP IT.

GEORGE SEIBERT   GEORGE
HOTEL MAYFLOWER WASH DC

OH, GEORGE, DON'T GET DRAMATIC. THESE GUYS WORK FOR US. PROBABLY ALL GRADUATES OF OXFORD. AUTHORITIES ON NATIVE ARTS AND CRAFTS. THE ONLY POSSIBLE DANGER IS THAT YOU MIGHT HAVE TO BUY A BASKET.

DICK

RICHARD L. REED
FEDERAL PICTURES HOLLYWOOD
CALIF

THAT'S WHAT I'M AFRAID OF—TO CARRY MY HEAD IN. LOOK, DICK, I'M ALWAYS HAPPY TO SERVE IN ANY REASONABLE WAY, BUT WHEN YOU GET INTO THE CANNIBAL DEPARTMENT I SAY YOU'RE CARRYING GENUINENESS TOO FAR. SUPPOSE I JUST TURN THIS WHOLE PROJECT OVER TO THE NATIONAL GEOGRAPHIC—THEIR OFFICE IS NOT OVER TWO BLOCKS FROM THIS HOTEL—AND THEN GET BACK TO MY WORK. OKAY?

GEORGE SEIBERT   GEORGE
HOTEL MAYFLOWER WASH DC

WHY CAN'T THIS PLACE GET ME ONE DECENT ASSISTANT? GEORGE, THESE GUYS WERE PERSONALLY PICKED FOR US BY OLD BILL JENKINS AT NAIROBI, WHO HIRED ALL THE NATIVES WE USED IN THE PICTURE, AND WHO WOULDN'T DARE LET US DOWN. AND YOU KNOW IT. AND IF YOU SEND ME ONE MORE SUPPOSEDLY WITTY TELEGRAM YOU'LL HAVE SOMETHING WORSE THAN CANNIBALS TO DEAL WITH. MEANING ME. NOW GET GOING, GEORGE.

RICHARD L. REED

RICHARD L. REED
FEDERAL PICTURES HOLLYWOOD
CALIF
    YES SIR.   GEORGE

HOTEL STATLER
New York, New York

July 9, 1951
Air Mail Special

Mr. Richard L. Reed
Director of Publicity, Federal Pictures
Hollywood, California

Dear Dick:

Well, if anyone had asked me, I would have said no, Hollywood could no longer surprise me. Mine eyes had seen the glory, twenty years of it, and there was just nothing else to be seen.

Well, let me be the first to say that I was wrong. This time you have really blown the cork.

Dick, I can't take this collection of savages on a road tour any more than I could take an active volcano on a road tour. It's an interesting idea, but it just won't work. You may be kidding, but these guys aren't. They've got very mean expressions. And every time they look at me the look says, H'mm, long pig. They don't speak a word of any language that anybody ever heard of, and their entire costume consists of four medium-size feathers, located not at all strategically. And their armament consists not only of spears, but huge knives, heavy enough, I would say, to cut the average bungalow in two. And when anybody approaches them they swing them as though doing dumbbell exercises. Sa-wish!

Somebody, lad, has just sent us the wrong merchandise. When you start dealing with the African Sears, Roebuck, you'll just have to start typing the orders, instead of scribbling them in longhand this way. The captain of the Spitsbergen, an old Norwegian named Sorensen, and a man not noticeably nervous, brought these characters over in the brig. Sorensen said, yes, he knew that we'd paid first-class passage for them, but he yoost felt more comfortable that way. And they evidently didn't mind.

176

But having crossed, what now? Phineas T. Barnum, even as a young man, would have refused to accept this shipment. They're still in Captain Sorensen's cozy brig, and it's a *status quo* I see no reason to disturb. The Spitsbergen will be here several days loading, and the only thing I see to do is to leave them right there, pay Captain Sorensen their return passage—whatever the brig costs—and have him take them back where they came from.

I say have a care. And let's start now.

As ever,
George

GEORGE SEIBERT
HOTEL STATLER NEW YORK NY

GEORGE, WHY DON'T YOU HIRE A BABY SITTER FOR A COUPLE OF NIGHTS? TILL YOU GET OVER THIS ATTACK OF THE VAPORS. IN OTHER WORDS, LITTLE RED RIDINGHOOD, LET'S GET THOSE POOR GUYS OUT OF THAT BRIG AND GET GOING. INCIDENTALLY, WHEN WE NEED YOUR ADVICE ON POLICY MATTERS, WE'LL WIRE YOU. DON'T CALL US. WE'LL CALL YOU. AND NOW LET'S GET THIS SHOW ON THE ROAD. EH? DICK

HOTEL STATLER
New York, New York

July 10, 1951
Air Mail

Mr. Richard L. Reed,
Director of Publicity, Federal Pictures
Hollywood, California

Dear Dick:

Have you ever been a prize-fight manager? You remind me so much of one. "They can't lick us. Now get out there and punch that guy." Three thousand miles from danger you are one of the bravest men I have ever known.

But, so be it. I guess any Army needs both generals and corporals.

And realizing that you would no doubt take your usual deep interest in my personal safety, I decided that the only thing to do was to try somehow to get acquainted with these pantless Thespians, and see if there was any chance at all of getting them to

177

Chicago alive. Of getting them to Chicago with me alive, that is.

So, laying in certain supplies, I fastened my safety belt and took off for Pier 6. Squatting down in front of the brig door, I uncovered a large platter of fried chicken legs and said, "Me white man. Me like you. Me got lots fried chicken. You like?"

Well, what they should have done of course was to answer in perfect English, with a request for finger bowls. But unfortunately this wasn't vaudeville. What they actually did was to give me a particularly frightening glare, grab the chicken without a word, and gulp it down.

Well.

Next I tried bananas and assorted fruit. Then more chicken. Then more bananas. And when I was definitely sure that they couldn't eat another bite of anything I said, "Me George. Me George Seibert. Sigh-bert. Me friend. Me coming in to give you nice presents."

Well, I didn't know that I was known even in Africa but evidently I am. Because they at least stopped swinging their blasted cutlasses. And unlocking the brig door—dropping the key only four times in the process—I entered. Passing out gifts. Hurriedly. I had stopped at a costume house on the way over, and secured an armload of old musical comedy costumes. And they loved them. I don't believe that I have reported that they're all men—there's little doubt of that—which simplified my shopping greatly. "You like?" I said, handing out my treasures with a broad, if somewhat tight, smile.

And suddenly they started grinning back, and the battle was won. In fifteen minutes we were the best of friends, grinning, slapping each other on the back, comparing wrist watches and spears, and having a very dickens of a time. Captain Sorensen was standing outside, looking as though at any moment he might slap the door shut on all of us.

At any rate, you can forget this one. We're off to Chicago.

Relieved regards,
George

Chicago Safari

GEORGE SEIBERT

HOTEL STATLER NEW YORK NY

GEORGE BOY, GET OUT OF THERE. YOU WERE RIGHT IN THE FIRST PLACE. THOSE CHARACTERS ARE FAR TOO UNCIVILIZED TO ATTEMPT TO TAKE ON A ROAD TOUR. LEAVE THEM RIGHT IN THAT BRIG AND WAIT FOR IMPORTANT AIR-MAIL LETTER.   DICK

FEDERAL PICTURES
Hollywood, California

From RICHARD L. REED
Director of Publicity

July 10, 1951
Air Mail Special

Mr. George Seibert
Special Representative, Federal Pictures
Hotel Statler,
New York, New York

Dear George:

George, how glad I am that I caught you before you started out with those anteaters.

That blowhard Thorne almost got us in a terrific jam. That's the trouble with good directors—they keep getting themselves confused with Superman. When Conrad J. Thorne is directing an aviation picture, he once taught the Wright Brothers all they knew. On a cowboy epic he was once the world's greatest bulldogger; tells everybody in sight just how to board their horses. FBI picture—he singlehanded captured most of the early day desperadoes. Also, as you know, he started everybody in show business who's ever been in show business, and in general he just blows it at all times like a bassoon.

Well, it seems that while they were over there making this African thing he had a brand-new audience, and accordingly outdid himself. I'm told he wore an old threadbare bush jacket at all times, carried a loaded elephant gun draped across his arm, and around the campfire nights he talked for hours about how he had put down native revolts in New Zealand, and killed tigers in India armed only with a willow switch.

And now it appears that his busy larynx has finally backfired.

179

Not on him, as unfair fate would have it, but on us. I've just had a letter from Bill Jenkins at Nairobi asking if the natives he sent us were genuine enough. He said that he knew that any such noted explorer as Mr. Thorne would want only grade-A savages, so he'd gone out of his way to find us some; he'd gone clear up into the back country and got us half a dozen of the most completely uncivilized savages in all Africa. He said when these guys ate an explorer they ate boots and all. He said that actually we shouldn't have any real trouble with them, but that he would advise us to keep Mr. Thorne in direct charge at all times, as otherwise they might have somebody's head on a pole.

Well, that naturally tears it. Due to gabby Mr. Thorne, the great Poo-Bah of everything, we've spent a lot of time and money bringing over six such completely genuine savages that we don't dare even open the box. The cannibal business is of course silly, as we can certainly keep them supplied with food. And after all we usually have cops available in this country. But if those six big guys should suddenly get mad at something and start swinging those neck choppers, we could still find ourselves in quite a mess.

It certainly is lucky I caught you. If you'd started out alone with those characters, things could very easily have got out of hand. In ways that stagger the mind. We could have got into some damage suits that would have made legal history. In addition to the possible nuisance of burying what was left of you.

Whew! There are times when I think that I'm underpaid.

As ever,
Dick

HOTEL STATLER
New York, New York

July 11, 1951
Air Mail

Mr. Richard L. Reed
Director of Publicity, Federal Pictures
Hollywood, California

Dear Dick:

Just a fast note to say that I haven't got time to wait for your letter, whatever it is. I'll just have to hope that it isn't anything important. Because we have to leave for Chicago this afternoon. The Spitsbergen is loaded and ready to pull out for the return trip to Africa, and I've got to get our laughing boys out of the brig and off by three o'clock.

I've decided to make the trip by car because I've got a wonderful idea. Now that I know that these guys aren't really dangerous, just that they look fierce, all we have to do is hold out our hand to get about forty million dollars' worth of publicity.

Here's the deal. We are on our way to Chicago to join a stage show in conjunction with the great Federal Pictures epic of darkest Africa, Nairobi Nights—right? We definitely have to be there by Friday, so we wouldn't logically dawdle—right? We are taking them by car because they are so completely uncivilized that we don't dare take them by train or plane—right? And between us and Chicago at this moment, particularly in Ohio, there are at least two dozen rivers of assorted sizes, all overflowing like a child's sand bucket—right?

Well, just before we leave this afternoon I will call the Weather Bureau and find out just where along our route I can expect a really rousing flood. We will then proceed there at full speed, splash as far into same as the car will go, and become thoroughly marooned. We'll be lost for days. While you and the nation's reporters scour the countryside to much huzza and headline. With you pretending great alarm. Everybody will accept the gag as genuine because the big opening at Chicago will actually be delayed, and who would be fool enough to do that?

Then, say late on the second day, I will fight my way through to a rescue station, nearer dead than alive, and just before losing consciousness gasp out the news that in a desperate effort to save our lives we all took off in different directions in search of help, and thus half a dozen genuine African cannibals are loose on the land, oh, Heaven help the state of Ohio. I will then faint. So, if I am any judge of people, will most of the citizens of Ohio. Because with that you will have to admit reluctantly the whole chilling story, and the headlines will balloon as though printed on yeast cakes.

Did you ever hear a better idea in your life?

It's foolproof. I'll have a big hamper of fried chicken along and, properly fed, these boys wouldn't hurt a flea. And it can't be any

181

trouble finding them later and rounding them up. Believe me, they don't look at all like anyone else in Ohio. And there's no danger of drowning them—any native I've ever heard of can swim like a fish.

So what could go wrong? It's the chance of a lifetime. If they make anybody along the way or at a motel nervous, I'll just say they're a bunch of wrestlers I'm driving to Des Moines.

All you have to do is quit worrying and make a tremendous uproar when we don't arrive in Chicago on time. Try to seem genuinely concerned.

And leave the rest to me.

Hasty regards,
George

P.S. Oh, one other thing. I just called Rebecca Lane and talked her into riding along with us instead of taking the plane. On a deal like this a beautiful girl can be useful in so many ways. She can't do anything in Chicago till the rest of us get there anyway, and I've just thought of a wonderful way to work her into the publicity.

When we become marooned, instead of all of us scattering in search of aid, I, brave George, shall go forth alone through the raging waters, leaving Rebecca behind with our trusty head-hunters. Because why? Because in getting out of the flooded car she will have cruelly injured her ankle, making further travel on her part impossible. And the reason I will also have to leave our fun-loving savages behind is because they are very valuable, at least to us, and I don't want any excited citizen sighting one and possibly shooting him deader than a mackerel. Which, as I now realize, could easily happen if they just all took off across country willy-nilly. Far better, if possible, to keep them in a group. Just as upsetting to the populace and safer for all.

And believe me, Rebecca will be in no danger whatever. All she'll have to do is pass out the sandwiches and bananas at frequent intervals and sort of chaperon everything till I can get back with the constables and photographers.

I haven't told her the full details of the plan as yet; I thought it best to explain it to her as we go along.

At any rate, being forced to leave beautiful blonde Rebecca Lane alone with them, even for a few hours, might be all we'd

182

need to turn this thing into a truly front-page smash. And all so logical. I understand that in the picture she manages thousands of natives on her huge zebra ranch, so how perfectly natural for her to manage six of them while I go for help. Thus saving the countryside.

What a jackpot we have come upon. Just try to act excited and leave everything else to me.

CHIEF, OHIO HIGHWAY PATROL
COLUMBUS O

QUICK. MATTER OF LIFE OR DEATH. AT ANY COST APPREHEND CAR NOW OR SHORTLY TRAVERSING YOUR STATE CONTAINING FILM STAR REBECCA LANE, A DEMENTED PUBLICITY EMPLOYEE OF OURS NAMED GEORGE SEIBERT, AND SIX AFRICAN SAVAGES. USE DUE CAUTION AND WIRE ME IMMEDIATELY UPON APPREHENSION. I'LL EXPLAIN LATER. I'D EXPLAIN NOW BUT YOU WOULDN'T BELIEVE IT.

> RICHARD L. REED
> DIRECTOR OF PUBLICITY
> FEDERAL PICTURES
> HOLLYWOOD CALIF

RICHARD L. REED
FEDERAL PICTURES HOLLYWOOD
CALIF

WHAT TYPE CAR ARE SUSPECTS DRIVING?

> H. L. TWINE, SUPERINTENDENT
> OHIO STATE HIGHWAY PATROL

H. L. TWINE, SUPERINTENDENT
OHIO STATE HIGHWAY PATROL
COLUMBUS O

HOW DO I KNOW? JUST FIND IT. RICHARD L. REED

RICHARD L. REED
FEDERAL PICTURES HOLLYWOOD
CALIF

YOU DON'T KNOW WHAT TYPE CAR YOUR OWN EMPLOYEES ARE DRIVING?

> H. L. TWINE

H. L. TWINE, SUPERINTENDENT
OHIO STATE HIGHWAY PATROL
COLUMBUS O

NO, AND NEITHER WOULD YOU IF YOU KNEW GEORGE. HE COULD
BE DRIVING A STUTZ BEARCAT OR A STANLEY STEAMER CONVERT-
IBLE. WHAT DOES IT MATTER WHAT HE'S DRIVING? HOW MANY
CARS ARE THERE ON YOUR ROADS CONTAINING SIX NAKED SAVAGES?

RICHARD L. REED

RICHARD L. REED
FEDERAL PICTURES HOLLYWOOD
CALIF

IF YOU PERSIST IN JOKING I SIMPLY CAN'T HELP YOU. WHY DON'T
YOU TRY IT AGAIN TOMORROW?   H. L. TWINE

H. L. TWINE, SUPERINTENDENT
OHIO STATE HIGHWAY PATROL
COLUMBUS O

OKAY, DROP DEAD. I'LL CALL THE AP.   RICHARD L. REED

CANNIBALS INVADE OHIO

COLUMBUS, O., July 13 (AP)—Tonight the beleaguered citizens of flood-stricken Ohio were faced with a new and fantastic
danger—an influx of African cannibals! . . .

RICHARD L. REED
FEDERAL PICTURES HOLLYWOOD
CALIF

ATTABOY, DICK, YOU SOLD IT. AND ON THE FRONT PAGE! YOU
MUST HAVE GIVEN A TRULY STIRRING PERFORMANCE. HAS A PUB-
LICITY MAN EVER WON AN OSCAR? BY THE WAY, WE'RE OF COURSE
DOING FINE. ALL WELL HERE. I'M KEEPING THESE CHARACTERS SO
FULL OF VITTLES THEY CAN HARDLY BEAR TO LOOK AT FOOD OF
ANY SORT. YOU COULD LEAVE THEM ALONE IN A DELICATESSEN,
AND THEY WOULDN'T TOUCH A THING. I DO WISH THOUGH THAT
THEY'D STOP SHARPENING THOSE BIG KNIVES FOR A FEW MINUTES.
I SHOULD NEVER HAVE BOUGHT THEM THE WHETSTONES. BUT I
THOUGHT IT WOULD KEEP THEM OCCUPIED, WHICH I MAY SAY IT
HAS. ANYWAY, IT WON'T BE LONG NOW. I EXPECT TO GET US MA-

ROONED SOMETIME TOMORROW MORNING. BETTER YOU NOT KNOW EXACTLY WHERE. JUST KEEP UP THE ALARM. YOU'RE DOING FINE.

GEORGE

H. L. TWINE, SUPERINTENDENT
OHIO STATE HIGHWAY PATROL
COLUMBUS O

QUICK, TWINE, JUST HAD WIRE FROM MISSING PARTY SENT FROM EAST LIVERPOOL, OHIO. THEY'RE JUST ENTERING YOUR STATE ON WAY TO CHICAGO. NOW LET'S GET GOING AND FIND THEM. SEND OUT ALL CARS. IN FLOODED AREAS GET ROWBOATS. GET THE QUEEN MARY. ONLY I BEG OF YOU FIND OLD GEORGE. OH, THE HORROR OF IT ALL. TO BE EATEN BY CANNIBALS AT EAST LIVERPOOL, OHIO.

RICHARD L. REED

RICHARD L. REED
FEDERAL PICTURES HOLLYWOOD
CALIF

ALL NIGHT SEARCH CONTINUING INTO THIS MORNING DISCLOSES NO TRACE OF SUSPECTS. THEY CAN'T POSSIBLY BE IN OHIO. HAVE YOU TRIED INDIANA?

H. L. TWINE

H. L. TWINE, SUPERINTENDENT
OHIO STATE HIGHWAY PATROL
COLUMBUS O

NO, AND NEITHER HAVE I TRIED WYOMING. THEY HAVE TO BE THERE SOMEWHERE. LOOK UNDER YOUR DESK.

RICHARD L. REED

SEARCH NARROWS FOR OHIO CANNIBALS

COLUMBUS, O., July 15 (AP)—This afternoon H. L. Twine, Superintendent of the Ohio State Highway Patrol, said that the search for the six missing African head-hunters and film star Rebecca Lane now centers on the area just north of East Liverpool, Ohio, where early this morning hundreds of motorists were marooned when a dam on the upper Ohio River gave way at Sanders Mill. Rescue parties are working desperately to get boats through to the affected area, as the stranded motorists are without food, and no doubt unaware that African cannibals are possibly loose among them . . .

185

STUDIO OFFERS $50,000 REWARD TO FINDER OF
MISSING FILM PARTY—(AP)

MISSING CANNIBALS FOUND

SANDERS MILL, O., July 15 (AP)—Tonight the attention of
an entire nation was centered on this tiny flood-bound Ohio hamlet,
where not over an hour ago the grisly search ended for the six
missing African head-hunters. The search ended when George Seibert, veteran Federal Pictures publicity man, staggered into a rescue
station, nearer dead than alive, and gasped out the fantastic tale
of his flood adventures with film star Rebecca Lane and the six
cannibals . . .

HOTEL TAFT
Sanders Mill, Ohio

July 15, 1951
Air Mail Special

Mr. Richard L. Reed
Director of Publicity, Federal Pictures
Hollywood, California

Dear Dick:
Well, it's been a busy day. But, although a little tired, I hasten
to get off this report to fill in a few added details on the wondrous
news in the public prints. Even on the front page they often miss a
few things, for which praise be.
In the first place, don't be too harsh on Mr. Twine. The reason he
couldn't find us in Ohio was because we weren't in Ohio. We were
for a few minutes yesterday afternoon, when I sent the wire from
East Liverpool, but as soon as we had another sandwich and some
more bananas all around we doubled back into Pennsylvania. Cast-
ing about on the road map for a good spot to get marooned, I
noticed that we had come right past Johnstown, Pennsylvania,
where they had quite a flood in 1889, and the car radio said that
the Conemaugh River there was again rising. Well, where could
there be a more newsy place to enjoy a flood than at Johnstown?
So bending on all sail, we hastened back there. It was raining

186

cats and dogs, so there were very few people out to wonder who we were. Also, I had fortunately hired a station wagon for the trip, not only for the needed seating room, but because nobody ever wonders at anything they see in a station wagon. In addition, I had purchased rain hats and slickers for all, and actually we looked not unlike any other surveying party.

But to business. What a dirty trick that Johnstown played on us. When we finally arrived I discovered that they've done a lot of sneaky flood-control work around there, and they're out of the flood business completely. So, since it was apparent that with all the stuff in the papers the hounds must be closing in, we had another sandwich and a handful of bananas at a dim drive-in, and headed back toward Ohio at great speed. The laughing boys enjoying everything immensely, but Miss Lane beginning to look a little wan.

But I pushed on. Ever westward.

Just before we hit the Ohio border we stopped and took over most of the rooms at a ratty little motel where the owners looked as though they couldn't read, and while the others slumbered I planned our next move. I knew that we couldn't get very far into Ohio without the enraged Mr. Twine putting the finger on us, so we needed a flood as near the eastern border as possible. Additional calls to various weather bureaus, in my role of Arthur Snead, anxious parent, disclosed that the most likely spot was that upper Ohio region around Sanders Mill.

So, sloshing into town in the station wagon, I found an all-night restaurant, got a tremendous hamper of food, centering on fried chicken and bananas, and shortly after dawn we were off. Still raining.

Crossing into Ohio at the smallest town I could find on the map, Metropolis, we raced north directly for Sanders Mill.

And to tell you the truth, I almost overdid it. Because just as we got in sight of Sanders Mill, the dam blew.

Dick, have you ever been in a flood? A real flood? Let me tell you that before you know it you can be in more water than you've figured on. In a matter of seconds we were looking not for lowlands, but for highlands.

I will never again criticize the Empire State Building; it is the only sensible form of architecture.

187

By eight o'clock we had churned our way through to a little rise in the road, where maybe fifty other cars were marooned in an otherwise endless sea of muddy, swirling, tumbling water, which was rapidly rising.

In about two minutes more we were on top of the station wagon, all my bright plans forgotten, and Rebecca was pushing up against me saying, "George, I'm scared." She was probably cold. Before we'd left in the morning, since I fondly thought that this would be the day for photographs, I had had her don one of the little tattered-britches costumes she wears in Nairobi Nights and, while attractive, it undoubtedly wasn't overly warm. The boys, however, didn't give her a second glance. By their views of clothing, she was dressed to the teeth.

And it was at this point, with the endless muddy river swirling rapidly up around us, making further maneuvers of any sort impossible, that I had the first feeling that I had maybe oversold myself on my own brilliance. Because at this moment two things occurred. I suddenly remembered that in our hasty departure I had left the big hamper of food back at the motel. And second, our African friends, evidently tiring of my management, suddenly dived down into the flooded station wagon, retrieved their well-sharpened knives, and came up, ringing the station wagon top like grinning sharks. For a minute I thought we were goners. They couldn't possibly be hungry already, I thought desperately. But then some people just naturally like an early breakfast.

Also at this point, the situation was not helped by the people on the tops of the other cars suddenly sighting them, realizing that they were actually the missing cannibals, and all starting to scream like utter fools.

So what happened? Well, you wouldn't believe it. Never let it be said that everybody in this world doesn't have his purposes.

With all us civilized citizens perched on the tops of our cars, waiting helplessly to be drowned, those six African savages, happy as larks, simply swam over to a group of trees still sticking out of the water, and began building rafts like Henry Kaiser! In no time they had made several dandy rafts, cut pusher poles, and established bus lines to higher ground. Not only for our covey of scared motorists, but for various damp citizens on the surrounding house-tops.

And by late afternoon, when one of my beloved head-hunters could pause in his work long enough to pole me over to where I could splash on to the rescue station, I was able to report that due largely to the aid of six African cannibals, not one life was lost at Sanders Mill, Ohio, in the terrible flood of 1951. And tonight, as you certainly know, they are the heroes of the land, and Nairobi Nights is off to a start such as a picture has seldom had. And didn't Rebecca look nice in the newspapers, in her little torn britches, and with her honor guard of cannibals?

Oh, one other thing. A few minutes ago, as I was putting the boys and Rebecca on a chartered plane for Chicago, one of them drew me aside and said, in just dandy English, "Pardon me, Mr. Seibert, but when we get to Chicago how will we know who is Mr. Thorne? We're supposed to give him a little scare for Mr. Jenkins at Nairobi. He talked so much down there that Mr. Jenkins decided somebody ought to give him his comeuppuance, as he put it. That's why we acted so foolish when you first came on the boat—we thought you were Mr. Thorne. As soon as you said you were Mr. Seibert we naturally mended our manners.

"But please don't give us away till we have just a few days to scare Mr. Thorne, because Mr. Jenkins made us promise to do it. And could you do us one more favor, and see that nobody buys us any more bananas for a while? We're all very tired of bananas."

Civilized? They're the glee club from Nairobi Tech!

And now what was that about a $50,000 reward?

As ever,
George

Stephen Potter

Cherished by a few *aficianados,* but unknown to most Americans, Stephen Potter, Special Features director of the B. B. C., suddenly found an audience on both sides of the Atlantic in 1950 with the publication of *The Theory and Practice of Gamesmanship.* This rather academic title was plainly a deception, for it was followed by a wicked subtitle: "The Art of Winning Games without Actually Cheating." Readers were variously alarmed and astonished, shocked, tickled, outraged and, in some cases, benefited. Following the success of the little volume which taught the unscrupulous second-rater how to outwit his superior, Potter visited America and brought out *Lifemanship, or The Art of Getting Away with It without Being an Absolute Plonk.* This sequel was an even more devastating manual of "conversation by intimidation." Here, even more frighteningly than in the first volume, Potter lays down Machiavellian approaches, plots the methods, and plans the campaigns by which the confident ignoramus can take the field and triumph over the bewildered expert. Bob Considine voiced the opinion of some critics when he called Potter's work "a shadowy endeavor somewhere between sportsmanship and downright crookedness." But the true Potterite knew that the Master had turned social discomfiture into an art, a parody of good conduct, and a series of pretension-piercing jokes.

*How to Be a Counter Expert**

I always believe that some kind of ABC of counter expert play is the best grounding for the young Lifeman. Without any special knowledge, without indeed any education whatever, it is possible not only to keep going in conversation, but, sometimes, to throw grave doubts on the value of expert knowledge in general.* There

* From *Lifemanship,* by Stephen Potter. Copyright, 1950, 1951, by Henry Holt and Company, Inc. Used by permission of the publishers.
** There is no need to stress the failure, here, of the sloppy expertship of the old school. The man who depended on mugging up the subjects of his week-end fellow guests never went very far. The classical example of this was, I always thought, G. Protheroe. On one occasion, for instance, hearing that Dr. Lowes, the expert on Coleridge, was to be present during a week-end holiday, he spent the previous month (he was a very slow reader) trying to memorize the facts of a small, mass-produced life of S. T. Coleridge printed in the These Men Have Made Their Mark series. (*Note continued on p. 191.*)

is no finer spectacle than the sight of a good Lifeman, so ignorant that he can scarcely spell the simplest word, making an expert look like a fool in his own subject, or at any rate interrupting him in that stupefying *flow,* breaking the deadly *one upness* of the man who, say, has really been to Russia, has genuinely taken a course in psychiatry, has actually read history at Oxford, or has written a book on something.

A few simple rules, then, for a start.

The Canterbury Block. We always encourage youngsters to *practice as they learn.* Why not an easy exercise to warm up? The expert on international relations is talking. He is in full spate. How can he be jolted? (R. Bennett's variant).

EXPERT: There can be no relationship based on a mutual dependency of neutral markets. Otto Hüsch would not have allowed that. He was in Vienna at the time. . . .

LIFEMAN (*As if explaining to the rest of the audience*): It was Hüsch who prevented the Archbishop from taking office in Sofia.

A suggestion only. But no matter how wild Lifeman's quiet insertion may be, it is enough to create a pause, even a tiny sensation.

Nor is the typical Block necessarily complex. The beauty of the best Canterbury is its deadly simplicity, in the hands of an expert. Six words will suffice.

EXPERT (*Who has just come back from a fortnight in Florence*): And I was glad to see with my own eyes that this Left-wing Catholicism is definitely on the increase in Tuscany.

By the Sunday evening, when the visit was coming to an end, he realised only too well that as yet *no reference to Coleridge had been made.* During a pause in the conversation he decided to speak.

PROTHEROE: I am right in saying, I believe, that there are two versions of the "Ancient Mariner," and they are not the same.
LOWES: 1798 and 1800?
PROTHEROE: 1798 and 1800. . . .
LOWES: Yes—they are not the same.
PROTHEROE: Not the same.

And here the conversation ended. Easy to find fault with Protheroe. Not so easy to formulate the basic rules which turn failure into success.

THE CANTERBURY: Yes, but not in the South.*

"Yes, but not in the South," with slight adjustments, will do for any argument about any place, if not about any person. It is an impossible comment to answer. And for maximum irritation, remember, the tone of voice must be "plonking."

Here, then, we have two forms of what is known as the Canterbury Block. For "plonking," see next paragraph.

If you have nothing to say, or, rather, something extremely stupid and obvious, say it, but in a "plonking" tone of voice—i.e. roundly, but hollowly and dogmatically. It is possible, for instance, to take up and repeat with slight variation, in this tone of voice, the last phrase of the speaker. Thus:

TYPOGRAPHY EXPERT: . . . and roman lower-case letters of Scotch and Baskerville have two or three thou. more *breadth,* which gives a more generous tone, an easier and more spacious colour, to the full page—
YOURSELF: The letters "have width."
T. E.: Exactly, exactly, exactly—and then if—
YOURSELF: It is a widening.
T. E.: What?—Oh yes, yes.

This is the lightest of trips, yet, if properly managed, the tone of voice will suggest that you can afford to say the obvious thing, because you have approached your conclusion the hard way, through a long apprenticeship of study.

"Plonking" of a kind can be made by the right use of quotation or pretended quotation. Here is the rough format:

MILITARY EXPERT (*Beginning to get into his stride, and talking now really well*): There is, of course, no precise common denominator between the type of mind which, in matters of military science, thinks tactically, and the man who is just an ordinary pugnacious devil with a bit of battlefield instinct about him.
YOURSELF (*Quietly plonking*): Yes, . . . "Where equal mind and contest equal go."

* I am required to state that World Copyright of this phrase is owned by its brilliant originator, Mr. Pound.

192

This is correct quotation plonking (*a*) because it is not a genuine quotation and (*b*) because it is meaningless. The Military Expert must either pass it over, smile vaguely, say "yes," or in the last resort, "I don't quite get . . ." In any case, it *stops flow,* and suggests that whatever he is saying, you got there first.

These early gambits mastered, the student can begin his study of more advanced expertship. Here is a slightly more complex ploy against the man, always dangerous, who has actually been there.

This expert can only be attacked on his own ground. And the basis of attack is to take if possible *one foreign place* where you have *actually been.* A convenient one for young British Draftees who have spent their army year in Germany is Munster Lager, transit and demobilization camp, well known to them, but entirely unknown to anybody over the age of twenty-one. Munster Lager is good, because it can be pronounced, by variation, as if it was a place-name of any country. The conversation goes like this. Subject, say, Fishing Rights on Russia's Eastern Seaboard. The expert coming in to the attack:

TRAVEL EXPERT: Well, I don't know, but when I was in Vladivostock, I knew there was going to be trouble. Nyelinsky was on the warpath even then, and I was fortunate enough to meet his staff with the Korean Councillor.

AUDIENCE: Really?

TRAVEL EXPERT: The local papers were front-paging it day after day. I soon *sensed* a very nasty situation, even if it didn't blow up then. It wasn't a very *comfortable* visit, but I was glad I'd been, afterwards.

SELF: Yes.

TRAVEL EXPERT: You see—

SELF: I was going to say—I'm sorry.

TRAVEL EXPERT: I'm sorry?

SELF: I was only going to say that though I was never in Vladivostock, I *did* spend some months in Munster Lager, not a million miles away. (*The pronunciation can be slurred into something like Man Stalagin.*)

TRAVEL EXPERT: Oh, yes?

193

SELF: Of course, I was working as a stevedore among the dockers and porters . . . I didn't see much of the high-ups, I'm afraid. But, Lord, I feel I understood the *people*—the cutters and the quay-cleaners, the dossmen and the workers on the factory fringe. The wives waiting on the quayside, waiting with their children. I needn't say where my sympathies lay.

Often the Travel Expert is completely shut up by this kind of talk; but it is *not for beginners*. The clever Lifeman can continue in this vein indefinitely, without ever having to say, or not, that he has been in Asia, or that, in fact, he has not.

A very small probe, which yet is not ineffective, has been used by Cogg-Willoughby, who has been fairly successful with a series of counterings from the psychiatrist's angle.

The expert holds the floor. His audience is submissive. Cogg waits, attentive. Sooner or later the expert will say, "But I'm talking too much"—always a prelude to talking still more. Or, "What do you think," he may even say, simply.

EXPERT: But you say. What do you think?
COGG-WILLOUGHBY: No, go on.
EXPERT: But I have been going on!
COGG-WILLOUGHBY: I know. But it's good. It's right. I knew as soon as I came in you were happy. You—you look so natural. . . .
EXPERT: Natural?
COGG-WILLOUGHBY: Yes, it's all right: don't take any notice of what I say. It's good.
EXPERT: Good?
COGG-WILLOUGHBY: It means that you're what we call happy. Go ahead. We're all listening to you.

Cogg was extraordinarily successful with this sequence for a time, and it led him to explore, curiously enough, the field of counter psychiatry. Cogg's Anti Psyke, as it came to be called, is not well known, and I have been asked to publish a note on it here. He had two principal tactics, and trained himself to make a spontaneous choice of either.

Tactic One, his favorite, was used against direct attack by an

194

accredited psychoanalyst. This would be the shape of the dialogue —or at any rate there were the words I noted down when he was set against Krautz Ebenfeld. Imagine, if you can, the thick Slovene accent of the one and the quiet Cambridge tones of Cogg for contrast:

COGG: I expect you are always observing and analyzing, Dr. Ebenfeld.

EBENFELD: It is my job.

COGG: You will make me self-conscious.

EBENFELD: Why is that? It is what you do when you are not conscious that interests me. Do you know that you caress the back of your neck with your left hand when you speak to me?

COGG (*who has been doing this on purpose*): No. Really?

EBENFELD: Do you know why that is?

COGG: Well—you mean . . .

EBENFELD: You had a brother or young cousin who was a fine swimmer, yes?

COGG: Rather!

EBENFELD: And you perhaps were not much of a swimmer. Yes?

COGG (*very warmly*): How glad I am to hear you say that.

EBENFELD: Glad?

COGG: The doctrine of '95, supported by you of all people.

EBENFELD: Ninety-five what?

COGG: Back to the founder of all founders—and how rightly. Hardt's doctrine, as my own father taught it to me.

EBENFELD: Yes—Hardt . . .

COGG: How well did Freud say, in his queer English, "He is my look up to. I stand to him—pupil."

"That is very interesting," says Ebenfeld. But he realized he was gambited. Later Cogg even reduced Sophie Harmon, the great lay psychiatrist, to silence.

In this case (*Tactic Two*) Sophie as usual began it.

SOPHIE: You have a limp?

COGG: No.

SOPHIE: You were dragging your foot as you crossed the room.

COGG (*smelling a rat*): Was I?

195

SOPHIE: You are not satisfied, fulfilled, today?

COGG: Ah.

SOPHIE: You have *two motives* pulling different ways.

COGG: My limp, you mean?

SOPHIE: Perhaps.

COGG (*lowering his voice yet speaking more distinctly*): Perhaps.
Or just an old weakness of the paradeltoid?

SOPHIE: Perhaps.

Sophie keeps her head, but she is ployed, and Cogg knows it, knowing that she never took anatomy.

It is easy to bungle Counter Psychiatry, which is, of course, a huge subject. But it is essential, we now believe, to work at these opening exercises before the more intricate problems are attempted —before dealing, that is to say, with the experts in painting and music, politics and philosophy.

To murmur "exhibitionist" or "Œdipus" or just to whisper the one word "aunt" when any rival is in full flow is a fine ploy, equaling Lifemanship at its best.

NOTE.—For "incest" read "aunt" throughout.

Frank Sullivan

Although Frank Sullivan has devoted himself to a lifetime war against platitudes—he is the country's most intrepid hunter of clichés—it is a platitude that Sullivan is one of the best-known and most anthologized of American humorists. He was born Francis John Sullivan, September 22, 1892, in Saratoga Springs, which, in spite of metropolitan temptations, has always been his home. He has learned to steel himself against the gag that he was born on the wrong side of the race track and, in consequence, has become a foe of the stereotyped wisecrack.

Sullivan's life has been that of a roving gentleman-journalist. After graduating from Cornell University with a B. A. degree in 1914, Sullivan became a second lieutenant in World War I, and, thereafter, got himself a job on the old New York *World*, where his desk companions were such famous writers as Walter Lippmann, Alexander Woollcott, Franklin P. Adams, Deems Taylor, and others. His first volume, nostalgically entitled *The Life and Times of Martha Hepplethwaite*, was followed by a succession of books which were both gay and satirical, absurd and probing. Sullivan delights in balancing contradictions and juggling opposites—his paradoxes are at their brilliant best in such books as *Broccoli and Old Lace, A Pearl in Every Oyster,* and *Sullivan at Bay.*

Perverse News Items *

SHEEPSHEAD BAY, N. Y.—Bustabonico's famous old restaurant here was burned to the ground last night in a fire of undetermined origin. The restaurant was famous because, although it had been in existence for seventy-five years and always served excellent broiled lobsters, it had never once been patronized by Lillian Russell or Diamond Jim Brady.

NEW YORK, N. Y.—Among arrivals at LaGuardia Field yesterday on the Clipper from Eire was Mrs. Delia Machree, 90, of Ballaghaderreen, County Roscommon.

Reporters were disconsolate when they learned that it wasn't by any means her first airplane trip.

* By permission. Copyright, 1952, *The New Yorker* Magazine, Inc.

DAMARISCOTTA, MAINE—All her life Grandma Hester Tooley, 72, has yearned to go to college, but circumstances hitherto have foiled her. As a girl, after she had saved enough to enter Radcliffe, her father and two brothers decided not to work any more, so she had to abandon her dream and support the family. Later she married and had to bring up a family of six children and one husband. Now, at last, Grandma Tooley is alone, and a week ago, on winning a cash prize of $14,000 on a radio quiz program, she found herself with means and leisure to achieve her lifelong goal.

But she isn't going to college. Too silly, she says.

FOND DU LAC, WISCONSIN—Quentin Durward III, of Ishpeming, Michigan, was driving toward this city from Milwaukee yesterday when he had two experiences which will astound the American Newspaper Publishers Association. A bee flew into Mr. Durward's car, but it didn't sting him, thereby causing him to lose control of the car and crash into a tree. Durward slowed down instantly, shooed the bee out of the car, and then resumed speed. Ten miles farther on, a partridge flew across the road in front of Mr. Durward's car. Got safely to the other side, too. Missed his windshield by a mile.

NEW YORK, N. Y.—There was no happier man in New York City today than Phumiphon Puccini—at least not among taxicab drivers. Yesterday morning, according to his custom, Puccini searched his cab before turning it in and on the rear seat found a handbag containing a three-strand pearl necklace, a bracelet, and several rings. He remembered that his last fare was a richly dressed woman whom he had driven from a night club to the Waldorf-Astoria, and he reported this clue to the police.

The owner of the jewelry was soon established as Mrs. Frederick M. Hagemeister, widow of the wealthy steel tycoon. Mrs. Hagemeister expressed her cordial gratitude to Puccini, congratulated him on his honesty, and presented him with a reward of $10,000.

GLASS FACTORY MOUNTAIN, N. Y.—Verne Playfeather, 81, who for years had made his home in an abandoned trolley car with only his dog, Spot, as companion, was found dead in his humble lodgings yesterday by state troopers. The troopers did not find Spot standing faithful guard over the body of his dead master and snarling at anyone who came nigh. They found Spot at a nearby farmhouse, where he had trotted when mealtime came around and Mr. Playfeather did not stir to feed him.

SPOKANE, WASHINGTON—Two years ago Deems Balboa, a spawn director for the Spokane Salmon Guild, fell madly in love with pretty Louisa Grimp, a fellow-employee. They kept steady company until two months ago, when Miss Grimp fell in love with another young man. She explained the situation frankly to Mr. Balboa, suggested that it might be better if they ceased to see each other, and gave him back his ring.

Balboa did not blow his top and slay the girl who had spurned him, or even attempt the slightest mayhem on her. He just took the ring and said, "O.K., if that's the way you feel, there's just as good fish in the sea."

LITTLE ROCK, ARKANSAS—One night in late May of 1935, Colley T. Cibber, who had built up a prosperous business manufacturing elastic dibbles to fit any size hole in a garden bed, put the leash on his English bull, Prognathous, and took the dog out, as was his nightly custom. An hour later Mrs. Cibber heard a scratching at the door and on opening it found Prognathous back with his leash trailing. There was no sign of his master.

Mrs. Cibber notified the police. Years of investigation failed to reveal a trace of the missing dibble manufacturer. After seven years had elapsed Mrs. Cibber had her husband declared legally dead and married an old high-school sweetheart, Alexander Pope.

Last night as Mr. and Mrs. Pope were seated at dinner the doorbell rang. Mrs. Pope opened the door to discover a bearded man standing before her. She gave a scream and fell in a faint, but quite unnecessarily. The man was not her long-lost first husband; he was just a character distributing tracts for a cult.

PHILADELPHIA, PA.—"It was the goldangdest fire I ever see in my fifty-six years as a fire laddie!" exclaimed Chief Rawdon Crawley today in discussing the blaze which swept a North Philadelphia warehouse yesterday, destroying 10,000 rare old 1939 Philadelphia telephone directories.

199

"Can't understand it," said Chief Crawley. "There wasn't a single suspicious character lurking in the vicinity of the blaze!"

CHICAGO, ILLINOIS—Before turning in last night, four-year-old Hilary Carscadden, of 43 Michigan Avenue, sauntered down to the corner candy store for his usual evening lollipop. On his way home he encountered a policeman wandering along disconsolately. Young Carscadden questioned the officer, who said that his name was Theodore Bucket, and that he was thirty-five years old. He confessed that he was lost. Samaritan Carscadden took the officer to the candy store, comforted him with an ice-cream cone, and telephoned headquarters. It was a somewhat exasperated lieutenant who drove up shortly to claim Officer Bucket.

WEST TISBURY, MARTHA'S VINEYARD—On April 28, 1945, at Penzance, Cornwall, a retired blacksmith named Joseph Gargery wrote on a piece of paper the following message: "Will whoever finds this please communicate with me? Hope all are well. All well here. Love. Joseph Gargery." Mr. Gargery placed the message, with his address, in an ordinary bottle, sealed the bottle, and cast it into the Atlantic.

Last Tuesday just after dawn Abner Starbuck, of West Tisbury, was bass fishing in the surf when his eye was caught by a glistening object bobbing in the water. "Looks like a bottle," he muttered and, wading in, he retrieved it. It was a bottle, sure enough, but it was not the bottle Mr. Gargery had cast upon the waters in 1945.

NEW YORK, N. Y.—Mrs. Audrey Fragonard, 22, of 18 Merriweather Terrace, is passionately fond of children and has often been heard to lament the fact that she and her husband, Wolfgang, have never been blessed with any.

Yesterday afternoon, Mrs. Fragonard was shopping on West 125th Street when she came upon chubby, year-old Oliver Wertenbaker, sitting in the baby carriage where his mother had left him when she entered a store. The baby smiled up at Mrs. Fragonard and a great surge of frustrated mother love swept her. But she didn't kidnap the baby. She merely smiled back at little Oliver, said "Ooza booza googalums, yezzoo *iz*" (baby talk for "You are a beautiful baby, yes you *are*"), then went her way.

200

Joseph Carroll

A true son of the old sod—the soil being that of northern Illinois—Joseph Carroll was born in Chicago in 1911. Adhering to the tradition, he was educated in parochial high schools, Notre Dame University and Loyola University. After he received his B. A. degree from Loyola he entered the army and found himself in the cavalry as well as in the Division of Information and Education. At about this time his short stories began to appear in the magazines. Carroll was featured in the *Saturday Evening Post, Cosmopolitan,* and most notably in *Collier's.* It was in *Collier's* that the voluble Matthew Cleary made his debut and began a series which promises to become an ever-extending saga of an extensively complicated family.

Matthew Meets His Peer*

Matthew Cleary swiveled on his bar stool in Mulry's Dark Rosaleen Bar and Grill at the sound of a voice familiar enough, but not in these surroundings. He gaped at the man who stood uncomfortably beside him: Packy Kinsella, dressed as he had never been dressed before except at his wedding, some months ago, to Matthew's sister Meg. Packy hardly ever went into Mulry's; he rarely drank, and when he did it was the occasion for alerting entire police precincts.

"Whatever at all are you got up like that for in the height of an afternoon in the middle of the week? If you'll forgive me as one man to another—and ourselves being related through the holy bonds of matrimony—you look like one of the wax figures in the mens' clothes stores on Madison Street. I never thought to see that suit again until we laid you out in it, may it be a far day."

Packy smiled feebly. He was a squarely built man, heavy in the waist, pleasant-faced without by any means having Matthew's nobly handsome features. He was of late middle age, a dozen or so years younger than Matthew—it was hard to tell exactly because Matthew's lies about his age were extremely inconsistent. Packy

* Reprinted from *Collier's* Magazine. Copyright, 1952, by The Crowell-Collier Publishing Company.

201

wore a swallow-tailed coat and gray striped trousers; his shirt was snowy and starched and his necktie was gloomily conservative.

"I'll tell you the lengths and breadths of it as soon as I have a drink," Packy said, climbing onto the stool next to Matthew's and pulling his pants legs up at the knees in that futile gesture intended to preserve the crease.

Mulry, the proprietor, served them drinks as grudgingly as if they were on the house; he was notorious throughout the neighborhood for his mean disposition, and people crowded his squalid little saloon as they might go to the panther's cage at the zoo, simply to hear him snarl.

Neither Matthew nor Packy had any time for Mulry now, however, and Matthew rudely told him to go away before he got the earache from straining to listen to a private conversation. Mulry told him to gas away and be damned, and then went to the other end of the bar. Such exchanges were a commonplace of their relationship and there were no real hard feelings on either side.

Packy had a pull at his drink and said: "I must have only one, Matt, so don't be tempting me to more, there's a dear man. One I must have or I can't go through with it at all. And if I have more than one, the whole of my resolution will drain away on me and I won't go through with it."

"Go through with what, man?" Matthew asked. "Why aren't you working? By rights you should be guiding a Garfield Park L through the hazards of the Loop, like the fearless motorman you are, instead of sitting here with your backside bursting out of those clergyman's pants."

"I took the day off," Packy said. "It's a favor I'm doing for Meg."

"Mightn't I have known?" said Matthew, running his hand through his shiny white hair. He had quite approved of his sister's marriage to Packy. He was fond of them both and their relative ages were suitable, but he had always known that psychologically Packy was overmatched. Meg, who had been a widow for years, was an incontinent meddler, a compulsive manager of other people's affairs; she was good-humored and intelligent, but never really happy unless she was goading the idle from key posts in a score of committees and organizations. The gentle

Packy loved her, though their attraction was like that of Othello and Desdemona in reverse. Meg had all the adventures and Packy did the admiring.

"Mightn't I have known?" Matthew repeated. "Packy, amn't I telling you many's the time never to promise to do a favor for Meg, fine figure of a woman though she is, until you learn what it is and in the presence of witnesses? Where her committees are concerned, you wouldn't find her like for treachery and cunning in the annals of Dublin Castle. Once she inveigled me into being the judge of a baby contest at a picnic out in the Forest Preserve. The babies were all gargoyles, and when I picked the least hideous I barely escaped with my life from the harpies that spawned the others. One of them screamed that I'd been bribed. Bribed indeed. The foul little nipper that won bit me twice with the two teeth he had in his head, and committed unspeakable indignities on my person.

"Another time, owing to the stratagems of Meg, my life was made a living hell by a broomstick of a woman who kept coming to the newspaper where I work to put flowers on my desk—with the whole city room gazing at her—and leaving poetry would bring a blush to the cheeks of a burlesque queen."

Packy looked up, interested. "Do you tell me, Matt? A poet? It's one of them Meg is sending me after now."

Matthew turned to him gravely. "If it's the same one, Packy, take it from me: better a quick merciful death by leaping into the river from the Link Bridge. What's her name?"

"It's a man. Name of Cathal Breffny. I'm to meet him at the La Salle Street station very soon."

"I never heard of him," Matthew said. "He must be a minor poet. What's he to do with Meg?"

Packy sighed. "He's to be the guest of honor at a brannigan the Daughters of Innisfail are throwing tonight over at a hotel near Columbus Park. He's to read them his poems and tell them about poetry, and then afterwards there'll be eating and drinking."

"Drinking?"

Packy shook his head. "Nothing you'd care about, Matt. Punch!"

Matthew quivered. "I know the kind. Bits of orange peel and assorted refuse floating on top as if it was the drainage canal.

What's all this to do with you? You're not a Daughter of Innisfail?"

"I'm telling you," Packy said. "I've to meet this poet at the train. Meg has a committee meeting, so I'm to stay with this fellow till it's time for the shindy tonight. Whatever am I to say to him?"

"You won't need to say much," Matthew said. "Poets are devils to talk, mostly about themselves."

Packy said dejectedly, "Meg wants me to talk with him, ask him questions. She says I'm not very poetic. The only poem I know is 'The Deserted Village,' which I was forced once to learn in school, because of some piece of misbehavior. I don't even remember that much any more, except when I've a drop in me, and then I'm likely to stand on tables and recite it."

"I never heard you," Matthew said.

"Then you're the lucky one. Mostly it's hard to stop me, and it's a terrible long poem."

He stood up. "It's time for me to go, Matt. I wouldn't want this poor streeshahaun standing in the wilderness of a railway station, being knocked down by commuters bound home for the suburbs, and himself without a friendly face to turn to."

"How will you know him? There's no certain way of telling a poet by the looks of him. In these times, a poet might look like a stockbroker or an insurance salesman. Will this lad be wearing a bay wreath?"

"His name is on his valise," Packy said, "and I'm to meet him at the information booth. Would you come with me, Matt? You know all about poetry, or so you're forever telling everybody."

"I can't," said Matthew. "I'm here to meet Denny Lynch. He's something on his mind, for he phoned saying he had to see me. But I'll likely as not see you tonight, Packy; I've a great curiosity to see the Daughters of Innisfail in action with a live poet."

Packy went somberly on his way.

Some time later Denny Lynch arrived and greeted Matthew listlessly. "It's the women of the Cleary family that keep their husbands frisking like kittens for the sheer joy of living," said Matthew. "First Packy, and now you. What the hell is ailing you?"

Denny was married to Matthew's daughter and only child, Imelda. They were a splendid couple, Matthew had always thought, for all that Denny had the body of an overtrained wrestler and Imelda was a slight girl, dark and pretty.

"Ask your daughter what's ailing me," Denny said. "It would take her hours to tell you. I think she keeps a list so she won't forget any little flaw or shortcoming."

"Bitter, Denny, bitter," Matthew said. "Is it some trifle of a family quarrel? The gravy was lumpy maybe, and you told her it was like eating wet flannel. These things happen—"

Denny made the noise that is called snorting. Matthew hit him on the back and asked: "Drink go down the wrong way?"

"Stop beating me," Denny said irritably. "I've taken all I can from the Cleary family."

"Do you mean to tell me Imelda raised her hand to you?" Matthew said. "I'd not have thought it. A tongue like a scythe, yes, when the bad mood is on her, but open violence—"

"Oh, shut up, Matt," Denny said, "and let me tell you. She was sweet as anything up till the day before yesterday. I don't know what I did or didn't do, but there's no pleasing her now. She looks at me as if I were an oaf and a fat-wit. She practically says I am, when she says anything at all. She told me I have no poetry in me."

"You too?" Matthew said. "Whatever is coming over these women? I never knew either Meg or Imelda to pass the time learning poetry by heart. Meg's more likely to be out suborning chairladies to make rulings in her favor, and Imelda to be home trying out a new recipe. And now both of them are carrying on like they were Phoebe Cary or Adelaide Crapsey."

He told Denny about Packy's ordeal.

"Poor Packy," Denny said. "I have to go to that thing tonight too, Matt—with Imelda, though I wonder she'll let me take her. This Cathal What'shisname is one of her favorites. She says he has elfin qualities that of course will be lost on me."

"Much she knows about elfin qualities," Matthew said. "Small danger she'll go wandering palely in the Celtic Twilight, living on dreams. Not with *her* appetite. She makes a god of her stomach, and I've seen her put away meals a hard-working truck driver like yourself would find hard to manage."

"Now wait a minute, Matt," Denny said indignantly. "Stick to the subject. Why shouldn't she eat decently? I like to see her eat, she's such a little thing."

Matthew looked at him pleasantly. "I make the most innocent remark about the girl's grosser habits and you begin raging at me. Am I to take it that you're not thinking of breaking your home and going for a soldier?"

"You know damn well I'm not," Denny said emphatically. "I didn't mean to be bitter. The girl's probably right: she's too sensitive for a clod like me. But my opportunities are so limited, Matt. I drive that truck daytimes, and at night I study law. You ever try to get poetry out of a tort or an escheat, Matt? I thought you could help me out. You're always blowing about your own poetic nature."

Matthew turned on him imperiously. "Blowing? Now I come to think of it, that's almost the same thing Packy implied. Let me tell you, my lad—"

The telephone had been ringing, and Mulry called grouchily: "It's for you, Matt."

Matthew went to the phone booth. A voice roared into the receiver: "Is that you, Matt? It's me—Packy."

Matthew winced. "Stand back and lower your voice, Packy. You're an insult to the memory of Alexander Graham Bell. What the hell's the matter?"

"I need your help, Matt," Packy yelled. "I can't handle this poet all by myself. Sure, I never knew poets were like this."

"Like what?"

"Like this one. He was capering like a goat when I met him at the train, and the goats won't be in it with him if he keeps up the way he's going now. Matt, I've lived among rough and uncouth characters in my time, but I never heard the like of this one for coarseness."

"Where are you?"

"We're in a place on the near North Side, but we won't be for long, for I think the manager has sent for the police. This dreadful poet has lined up all the waitresses and is teaching them what

206

he says is an Irish dance, though *I* never saw an Irish dance like that before. He only now got through singing a song about how the French are peculiar because they call their daughters fillies and their mothers mares. The manager is French and he challenged Cathal to a duel."

"Did he accept?" Matthew asked, fascinated.

"No. He says dueling is contrary to the teachings of his religion. But he offered to fight bare-knuckle any time or any place, the silly little bantam."

"Is he little?"

"He looks like the Pooka," Packy said. "You know, the little sprite that goes around curdling milk. If he took his hat off— and he ought to: wait till you see it, Matt—he could run under a low table and never muss a hair."

Matthew had already made up his mind, even without these allurements. "Where is this place?" he asked, and when Packy told him he said: "Stay where you are. Denny Lynch is with me, and he has a vested interest in this poet too. We'll be there in no time. If the cops come, tell them I'm on my way. They all know me as a prominent newspaperman, or at least as an unbeatable poker player—I have IOU's from half the force."

He hung up and called to Denny as he strode toward the door: "Come on now, Denny. There's man's work to be done."

Denny followed him to the street. "Where are we going, Matt?"

Matthew flagged a taxi and they climbed in. "You want to find out about poetry, don't you?" Matthew answered. "This is your chance. Packy has a live poet by the tail, and we're on our way to rescue him."

"The poet?"

"Certainly not. Packy."

They found the near North Side restaurant easily, but in it nothing like the scene of carnage Matthew had been prepared for. The only rowdiness seemed to be coming from Packy, who rose unsteadily from his chair at a table far in the rear and shouted: "Come on now, Matt, and join us. Denny, you're welcome, but it's Matt we're waiting for, he having the devil's own memory for words. It's a song I'm trying to think of, Matt, and

207

the words are gone on me entirely." He hummed hoarsely. "You know the one I mean: Mrs. Mulligan the Pride of the Coombe."

Matthew looked at him closely, and then at the rest of the party. A husky young policeman sat at one end of the table, his hat pushed back and smiling a rather loopy smile. At the other end of the table sat a large man with magnificent mustaches, whom Matthew rightly took to be the manager. And seated between them was a figure that could only be Cathal Breffny, the poet.

All three rose to shake hands when Packy made the introductions.

"Ah," said Cathal Breffny, "this is an exquisite pleasure that the dashing Packy there has been holding before us with a generous eloquence must have had your ears burning red fire. Sit down now, Matt, and that snowy-breasted pearl yonder will bring you and Denny a drink."

Matthew glanced at the giggling waitress to whom Cathal was pointing; he could only suppose that the epithet was mere inference, for the girl was chastely covered by her dark uniform. She went for the drinks, and Matthew turned again to examine Cathal.

He was an odd little valentine, with hair the color and luster of gingerbread; his body was skinny in tweedy clothes of outrageous pattern; his face was engagingly homely, and his bright eyes had a clever look.

"I had it in mind you said trouble was stirring," Matthew said to Packy.

"Trouble?" said Packy as though he had never heard of it. "Sure, there's no trouble at all, Matt. Cathal straightened everything out. The officer there did come in some such anticipation, it's true, but he arrived to the very cooing of doves. And as he was going off duty anyway, he agreed to join us in a drink."

The policeman grinned at Matthew and tilted his glass.

"You see, Matt," Cathal said, rising like a toastmaster, "our host there"—he nodded toward the proprietor—"thought I intended a slur on the nation of his birth by a little song I sang, and in the heat of the drink high words passed between us. But then, as my native wisdom asserted itself over my quick temper,

208

I realized that the dispute need never go so far as the United Nations."

Packy, who had got himself another drink, tossed it off and said: "Hear, hear!" The proprietor beamed internationally.

"Now then," Cathal continued, pointing at Matthew, "can it be gainsaid that the Irish and the French have bonds of friendship forged in the very smithy of history?"

"It cannot," Matthew said. He was already fond of Cathal Breffny, recognizing in him a fellow spellbinder and self-hypnotizer.

"It cannot," said Cathal, "and so I told this honest native of fair France. I told him of the Wild Geese that went from Ireland to France in the seventeenth century."

"I didn't understand that part of it," the policeman said suddenly. "Didn't they have any geese of their own?"

Cathal leaned toward him majestically, or as nearly so as his stature allowed. "Officer," he said, "you should spend less time harassing society's unhappy outcasts and more in reading the history of the country of your forebears. It's a figure, a metaphor."

The policeman looked as though that only made it worse.

"The Wild Geese were soldiers and patriots who fled from the tyranny that oppressed Ireland and took refuge on the continent. Some of the bravest fought in the armies of France—"

Denny decided to interrupt. Like Matthew, he was pleased by Cathal Breffny, but he was damned if he was going to sit still for a course in Irish history, however abridged.

Not for nothing was Denny the son-in-law of Matthew Cleary. "I think we all need another drink," Denny said.

Cathal turned to Denny approvingly. "Now here's a man with a head on his shoulders," he said. "Another drink he's calling for, and a wiser word never was spoken, not by the sages of old or the druids or the prophets."

The proprietor by this time was far gone in good will and his own wares; with a generous flailing of arms and a burst of language that raped English idiom with every word, he made it plain that this one was on him, that, in fact, the sky was the limit and their money was no good in his establishment.

209

All the others gestured back, and in French even weirder than the proprietor's English Matthew told him that of course they would accept a drink. When his skimpy French—and it was even skimpier than his Gaelic—ran out he resorted to the English of the stage Frenchman. "We—how shall I say?—we are not insensible to—what is it, the word?—the munificence—"

"What he means," Denny told the propietor, "is that we aren't throwing anything over our shoulders."

Matthew at first scowled and then went back into his act. "So well you explain it, my old: over our shoulders nothing are we throwing."

And so for hours they threw nothing over their shoulders.

The time for the meeting of the daughters of Innisfail was drawing near. Packy clearly had forgotten his responsibilities and was reciting "The Deserted Village" to a waitress; he had to recite very loud to make himself heard over the juke box, into which Denny kept putting quarters in order to hear "Galway Bay" over and over again.

Matthew saw that it was up to him. "Cathal," he said, "we must be off. The Daughters of Innisfail will be waiting for you to edify them with the music of your voice and the sweetness of your understanding of poetry."

Cathal had drowsed off, but he stirred himself and said, "True for you. I'd be charmed to meet your daughters any time, and—I being a man punctilious in the decencies—you could trust me with them anywhere."

"Only one of them is mine. The rest are Daughters of Innisfail—about a hundred of them in all."

The cop whistled. "A hundred! Is this Innisfail a friend of yours?" The cop had been drowsing too.

Matthew smiled uncharitably. "Now is the time to meet him. I've known him for years. Let us all go together."

"Galway Bay" died out, and Denny heard Matthew's proposal; Packy's memory had flagged somewhere in the middle of "The Deserted Village" and he heard it too. They both expressed enthusiastic approval.

"You see, Cathal," Matthew said, "there's an idea at large

among some of these Daughters that there is a dearth of poetry among their men. It doesn't apply to me, of course, for no woman—not one as brazen as my sister Meg or as calloused in conceit as my daughter Imelda—would be bold-faced enough to deny my learning in poetry. But there's more than a little feeling that Packy here is a poor earthbound bosthoon—"

Packy, warmed by Goldsmith's lines, looked indignant.

"—and that Denny, though a man with formidable biceps, knows nothing more about poetry except that sometimes the lines sound the same at the end."

Denny looked indignant too; he remembered that he had been deeply moved by "Galway Bay" all twenty times he had played it.

Cathal's drowsiness was all gone. He was interested by the challenge of Matthew's words, and was all on the side of Denny and Packy. "Let the policeman come too," he said. "He may be needed to keep the peace."

The cop, in a condition of parboiled amiability, moved his hand vaguely in a gesture of assent, as though he were waving a motorist through an intersection. The proprietor, who had with belated prudence changed his drink to black coffee, refused their invitation on the grounds that he must stay to make the evening trade feel at home.

"Let's be on our way then," Cathal said. "These ladies of intellect will be given such an evening that I've more than half a mind to up my price."

At the hotel near Columbus Park, Meg Cleary Garvey Kinsella—who had acquired her surnames in that order—stood at the entrance to the Tara Room, graciously greeting the incoming Daughters of Innisfail, who were out to pay homage to literature if it killed them; the husbands and swains they drove before them had the gloomy faces of men who were certain that it would do exactly that.

Imelda Lynch stood next to her aunt and watched the door from the street, half anxiously, half impatiently. "Denny should be here by now, Meg," she said. And then she added with bitterness: "If he's coming at all. The very thought of poetry may have frightened him away."

Meg said, "I hope it hasn't frightened Packy, for the guest of the evening is in his keeping. They should be here too—it's only a few minutes till starting time. I hope Packy is learning something from the conversation of a genuinely sensitive man like Cathal Breffny. Packy has splendid qualities, but—"

She stopped, startled by the look on Imelda's face, a look of astonishment. Meg turned in the direction in which Imelda was staring. Across the lobby a tipsy procession was approaching, Indian file, led by Matthew with Denny towering at the rear.

"Are they being arrested, Meg?" Imelda asked.

"Not by the looks of that cop. In his condition he couldn't arrest a truant from the fourth grade. Wouldn't you know Matt would be with them? My poor Packy has obviously been sniffing corks—that's all it takes with him. Dear girl, we're in for a time of it."

Imelda nodded, numbly.

"The little fellow must be Cathal Breffny," Meg continued, "and I must say I expected something different, considering the price we're paying. I hope he *talks* well."

The procession arrived, and Matthew greeted Meg with shameless self-assurance. "Tennyson, anyone?" he said in the posh accents of a stage juvenile making an entrance. "You'll have poetry and to spare before this evening is over, my high-chested sibling and friend of the arts."

Meg's reserves of poise were fathomless, and she held out a queenly hand to Cathal. "Ah, Mr. Breffny," she said, "I cannot tell you how deeply honored we are to have you with us."

She had said the same thing to hundreds of guests of honor, and there was lots more to the speech; but Cathal squinted at her so impudently that Meg was almost disconcerted and broke off.

Cathal removed his extraordinary cookie-shaped hat and took her hand courteously. "I should like you to meet a dear friend of mine," he said. "A man of remarkable intellect, with the most profound poetic insights. Mr. Packy Kinsella."

He threw an arm around Packy's shoulders, standing on tiptoe in order to accomplish this.

"Mr. Kinsella and I," said Meg, "are already acquainted."

Packy, grinning foolishly, lunged at her as though she were one of the Sabine women and flung his arms around her waist. " 'Sweet Auburn, loveliest village of the plain, where health and plenty cheered the laboring swain,' " said Packy, the best friend Oliver Goldsmith ever had.

Meg, whose dignity was often in danger of being betrayed by her humor, choked back a giggle. "Pull yourself together, for heaven's sake, Packy," she said. "People are looking."

And so they were, raptly, some of the men beginning to feel that the evening might not be such a bore after all.

" 'Where smiling spring its earliest visit paid, and parting summer's lingering blooms delayed,' " Packy went on, still clasping Meg ardently.

Cathal Breffny and Matthew looked on with delight, but Matthew said: "Not all of it, Packy: we've a full evening ahead of us."

Meg, without actually struggling, managed to break away from Packy's grip. "It's well past time for the meeting to begin, Mr. Breffny," she said, "and people will be getting impatient. If you're quite ready, I'll lead you to the dais. I'm in the chair, you know."

"And well you'll fill it," said Cathal, with a glance at her person. Meg decided to take the kinder meaning of his remark and smiled. "This way then," she said. He followed her up the aisle.

Denny's magnificent glow, meanwhile, had worn completely off. Imelda had taken one look at him and walked away to take a seat far up front; this had the same effect as black coffee, and Denny disconsolately sat down in a chair in the last row, next to the policeman, whose head was nodding. Matthew sat down with them and nudged the policeman.

"The show's beginning," Matthew said.

The cop sat upright and yelled, "Take it off."

Matthew hushed him, but the damage was already done; and

213

Meg, on the dais, faced an audience that was having a hard time avoiding laughter. The policeman went back to sleep. Packy's glow was as good as ever, but he kept it in order and sat down quietly and gazed lovingly at his wife up on the dais.

Meg kept her introduction short and simple. The name of Cathal Breffny, she indicated, was too well known to make it necessary for her to elaborate on his achievements in the world of poetry. Hardly anyone in the audience had ever heard of him before, but Meg's platitudes gave them no sense of inferiority: they had listened to too many introductions of speakers who were well known to everybody but themselves.

Meg stepped away from the rostrum and Cathal approached it. This was disastrous to the solemnity of the occasion, for Cathal's gingery head barely rose above the rostrum; and again there was the restlessness of laughter held back.

Cathal was incapable of being abashed by any kind of laughter; he stepped from behind the rostrum and, seizing a chair, drew it up to the very edge of the dais and sat down cozily.

"I like to see the people I'm talking to," he said, and now there was no need to hold back the laughter. The audience—at least the male half of it—was beginning to take Cathal to its heart.

"D'ye know," he said, as intimately as if he were chatting with a friend in a bar, "I've a notion in my head, from what I've heard from some splendid gentlemen I met when I arrived this afternoon, that this evening oughtn't to take quite the course the good ladies of your organization planned.

"It is true surely that I am supposed to be a poet, but d'ye know, people have the damnedest ideas about poets and poetry alike, and I'd be the fool of the world if I were to sit here and connive with an attitude of mind which, it seems to me, gives poetry a black eye with many an honest soul. Y'see, I happen to *like* poetry: the written kind, the formal kind, the kind you find in books. But that isn't the only kind of poetry—or better I should say books aren't the only places to look for poetry.

"It finds its way into the books in ways you wouldn't expect. My great compatriot, John Millington Synge, once told how he

214

got some of the loveliest lines in one of his plays from listening through the chink of a cottage wall to the conversation of two servant girls in Wicklow. The girls would have been astonished if anyone told them they were talking poetry. And that happens all the time for anyone with the ear to hear it.

"Now, I know better than to think that among these ladies of intellect and charm there could be that most pitiable of creatures, a snob. I have it on the word of a distinguished member of your audience, Mr. Matthew Cleary, who is a sound man on everything except perhaps Gaelic. I should hate to ask my way around Connacht with the Gaelic Matt has, for between you and me, the man doesn't know his Erse from his elbow."

Meg, at her chairlady's table, had been looking her most puzzled: a haughty kind of puzzlement. Now, before she could stifle it, a laugh escaped her. It was always pleasant to see Matthew done one in the eye. The other ladies of the audience laughed too, reasoning that they were no more obliged to keep a dignified silence than their chairlady. Besides, they were warming to Cathal from moment to moment. He had praised their brains and their womanly graces, and explicitly exonerated them of any charge of snobbery, which had been pressed at many a dinner table that evening.

In the back of the hall Matthew at first bridled when Cathal paid his dubious tribute. Then he smiled, knowing that the poet was using policy, and a very wily policy too, that would have done credit to Matthew himself. It was plain to see that Meg, though still grappling with indignation, was looking more good-natured than she had since the meeting started.

Cathal threw out his arms as though to embrace everyone in the hall and squinted blandishingly.

"But, d'ye know, nothing can kill poetry quicker for any man or woman of spirit than to be told that you're *obliged* to like it —in the book way, I mean. And that is what I do hope doesn't happen here. It *won't* happen here, unless someone else is prepared to give a lecture, for I'm not."

The audience leaned forward expectantly. They weren't sure exactly what Cathal had in mind but it was sure to be interesting.

215

Cathal went on: "I notice," he said, "having a quick eye for such things, that there is a piano in the back of this hall."

The audience stirred, with a restless turning of heads.

"Now why the hell," said Cathal, "why the hell shouldn't we push all those undertaker chairs to the walls and dance?"

An instant of silence followed, and then a thunder of applause, led by the men but soon joined in by the women. When it died down, Cathal, who was now standing, said:

"If no one else can play the piano, I can, and sing like a thrush on top of it. In the interest of my profession, I won't have it said that a poet ever stood in the way of a good time." He clapped his hands. "Let's be on with it then. And for gallantry's sake, let the men move the chairs. Put your shoulders into it, boys."

The hall was lively with laughter and the noise of chairs being dragged across the floor. Cathal turned to Meg and said: "Of course, I won't be taking the fee."

She stared at him steadily a moment and then began to laugh, a loud and pleasant laugh. "Indeed you will take your fee, Mr. Breffny," she said, when she could manage to talk. "I'd pay twice the money out of my own pocket to be told so tactfully to stop acting like a fool."

She stood up and extended her hands to Cathal. "I'm going to Packy now," she said. "I never did hear how 'The Deserted Village' turns out."

They went down the steps from the dais and Cathal asked: "Tell me now, which of the lovely girls is Imelda?"

Meg pointed to her niece, stony-faced in a corner of the hall. Cathal skipped swiftly over to the girl and began to talk to her earnestly.

Meg joined Packy, Matthew, and Denny at the back of the hall. The policeman was still sleeping in the one chair that had not been moved. Meg smiled at Packy, but held up a hand when he set out to make another of his violent lunges. "Later," she said. "We've all the time in the world."

"Poetry, is it?" said Matthew.

Meg turned to him. "I know it was your doing, Matt. You

216

have your points, charlatan though you are. The punch bowl is over there. And Packy, dear, I do think you've had enough."

Someone was playing the piano, and the floor was crowded with dancers.

Cathal Breffny edged his way along the wall and joined the group at the punch bowl. Of the lot of them, only Denny was looking sad.

"Look here, my lad," said Cathal to Denny, "you are a fine fellow and a handsome one, with the look of one of the fighting heroes out of the old legends. But you are an ass."

Denny lifted his head indignantly.

"Now don't get into a rage," Cathal said. "I'm telling you this for your own good. Don't you ever read books, you lumbering innocent? Surely you know why your wife is acting the way she is."

Matthew, Meg, and Packy leaned toward Cathal expectantly; you never knew about Cathal. Denny's indignation gave way to bewilderment.

"What *is* the matter with Imelda?" he asked. "Did she tell you?"

Cathal nodded smugly. "I'm the lad that can always get the girls to talk. But Denny, you juggins, you should have guessed. Some women wake up in the night and want olives or blue cheese or artichokes, or anything else that's not available at the precise moment. Most women want something all the time, when they're in that condition. An eminent psychiatrist, who is a dear friend of mine, explained it all to me once, but I forget the explanation. Anyway, it doesn't matter. Imelda thought she wanted poetry, but she knows better now."

A smile of brilliant happiness was rending Denny's face. Matthew, Meg, and Packy also were smiling, especially Matthew.

"What does she want?" Denny asked.

Cathal looked at Matthew and squinted charmingly. "Being the daughter of Matthew Cleary, she wants the moon. Go and give it to her, boy."

Denny ran.

The music and the vigor of the dancing suddenly awakened

the policeman, and he made his way uncertainly to the little group around the punch bowl. "Sorry I missed your act, sister," he said to Meg courteously, "but I had a lousy seat and you never can see anything anyway, without there's a runway."

Meg's forces were spent: it had been a strenuous evening and she felt she was entitled to collapse in laughter. "Packy, my angel," she spluttered, "I believe this is your dance."

They waltzed away, light of foot and light of heart.

"The dame's batty," the cop said to Cathal and Matthew, but they were too far gone in laughter to manage any speech.

"You're all batty," the policeman said, and then, always the philosopher, helped himself to some punch.

Charles W. Morton

Charles W. Morton freely confesses that he belongs to the Couldn't-Stand-It school. He left Omaha because he couldn't stand the hardware business he was in, and he left Nebraska because he couldn't stand the ragweed. He couldn't stand Morristown School in Morristown, New Jersey, and couldn't stand Williams College either. After he bought a typewriter and received his first check for a piece on the follies of American advertising, he thought of many other things he couldn't stand. It became a kind of career.

Discovering that he could not only write his grievances but edit them, he got a job on the old Boston *Transcript* and, after the demise of that venerable journal, was employed by the U. S. government for "five years of complete concealment." Ten years ago he became Associate Editor of *The Atlantic Monthly,* where he conducts the Accent on Living pages, and is publisher-editor-promoter of the *Atlantic Bulletin,* a throwaway which the magazine sends to advertisers, friends, and a few selected (or hostile) strangers. All these experiences equipped Morton to gather a hundred and one of his little essays and publish them in a sort of I-Can't-Stand-It volume entitled *How to Protect Yourself against Women and Other Vicissitudes.* The result was a tart collection of half-amiable, half-prickly pieces, concerned, wrote Bergen Evans, "with his own pleasures and aversions, with stylistic pomposities, with absurdities, vagaries, and curious recollections." The concluding causerie, "Can Husbands Be Taught?" is typical of Morton's querulous charm and quizzical gusto.

Can Husbands Be Taught? *

Would it be of any use to start a technical school for husbands? The school, as I envision it, would instruct the husband in the techniques of his wife. That is, it would show him that some of the things that happen to him—mysterious yet powerful forces no one has ever explained to him—are in fact techniques, of human and not metaphysical origin. He would learn that other wives, of course with certain variations of their own, customarily apply similar techniques to their husbands.

Might this not make the husband feel better? Reassure him that he is not the only man in the world who doesn't quite understand what is going on and that he can't stop it anyhow?

There are, offhand, two or three major techniques worth understanding, worth a catalogue-listing in such a school. For instance: The Impossible Situation—Why Wives Create It, How They Solve It; The Technique of the Narrow Escape or The Uses of the Not-so-bad-as-I-thought-it-was Principle; The Quick Shift or How to Terminate the Husband's Argument.

Without information about these matters, yet playing the No. 2 role in them daily, the husband is likely to become morose. He begins to wonder about his own effectiveness: it seems all right in the office where he works, but at home—well, somehow at home his orders and his ideas don't seem to land always where he intended, just don't pan out so neatly.

The strange thing is that the husband has absolutely no place to go for advice about all this. He certainly can't expect his wife to explain it to him. That would be much like expecting Notre Dame to explain to Michigan what the next play would be. No, his wife would be kind, affectionate, even worried—tell him, no doubt, to get a medical checkup or not to work so hard—but I don't think she would give away much technical information. A psychiatrist would want to know if he hadn't perhaps started the whole thing with a nightmare at age four. Other husbands could tell him no more than he himself knows, and besides, no husband would ever hint to other husbands that he didn't understand everything about women. The need for such a school as I have mentioned is really urgent.

Consider the effect on husbands of the Impossible Situation. Every husband has burned his fingers on this time and again, always with loss of confidence in himself. A technical course about the subject wouldn't try to prevent the wife's creating an Impossible Situation, but it might keep the husband from insisting every time that she won't be able to bring it off successfully. (I know only one man who ever got so far as actually proving that an Impossible Situation had indeed failed to work. He was right, and his seventeen-year-old daughter was wrong. Yet the innocent child came through with a last-ditch victory simply by looking woebegone and saying to her father in a voice near tears, "I think you're mean." He was in bad shape for days.) As it now stands, a wife can arrange an Impossible Situation, breeze through it on her own schedule, and prove her husband's warnings—his most reasoned and mature judgment—to be bosh. This sort of thing is hard on a man—very hard.

Example: Husband, at breakfast, suggests that wife meet him at twelve-thirty p.m. Wife says she can't because she has a twelve-thirty dentist's appointment, a twelve-thirty luncheon engagement with Emma Haycox in another part of town, and another twelve-thirty engagement at home with old Mr. Gabboulian, the upholsterer.

Without benefit of technical classwork on an exercise of this kind, the husband is scandalized. Three engagements in different places all at the same time? Outrageous. Fantastic. Inconsiderate. Bad. Awful. Downright rude. It arouses his preachy vein: what would people think if he, in his business, were to make, etc., etc.

Yet what comes of it all, the class would learn, documents every one of his objections as absurd.

The wife keeps the dentist's appointment punctually, because she knows it will cost her money to be late.

She arrives for the twelve-thirty luncheon engagement at one-thirty-five, the very moment Emma Haycox gets there. Emma is an old Impossible-Situation expert herself. They lunch in a leisurely way.

The wife returns home at three-forty, to keep the twelve-thirty date with Mr. Gabboulian. Mr. Gabboulian arrives at three-forty-five with apologies: his truck has broken down or his shop has just caught fire. The wife graciously forgives Mr. Gabboulian his tardiness under the circumstances, gives him some chairs to upholster, and he goes his way rejoicing.—Q.E.D.

A good technical school should simply show the husband the realities of an Impossible Situation and why he must stop wandering in with negative forecasts on its outcome. For her part, the wife will keep right on creating and overcoming Impossible Situations simply because she enjoys them; it puts zip into many doings that would otherwise prove to be intolerably dull.

The reader must keep clearly in mind the purpose of the technical course: *not* to teach a defense against the wife's techniques, a quest that has baffled the keenest scientific minds, but simply to teach a husband to identify them and adapt himself to them. He should know more than he does, for example, about the Narrow Escape.

If a man can be kept slightly rattled, he is much less likely to insist on having his own way. Using exaggerative language is an easy way of rattling a man: he does not know how much of it to discount or how much to accept at face value. Thus a wife may say, "Helen gave us the *most sumptuous* egg salad—I never tasted anything so delicious *in my life*," or, "I found the *loveliest* string-bean slicer at Gumpelmann's the other day." Such remarks do not stamp the speaker as a woman of limited experience or vocabulary. Their florid quality is merely the hard-driving style that rattles the husband and fits so readily into the device of the Narrow Escape.

A typical problem: The husband has vowed never again to set foot in the household of George and Ethel Grudge, because he detests them. The wife wants him to go with her to the Grudges', perhaps to show him the loot Ethel made George buy in New York, or perhaps to break up a precedent in which the husband would be having his own way too permanently. How can the husband be induced to take his wife to the Grudges'?

A brisk application of the Narrow-Escape technique is indicated. It consists of whizzing the husband through a kind of mental tour of disasters, scaring him good and hard, and then signing him up while he is still groggy. It works best by telephone.

Picture the husband in his office. He is somewhat worried—in fact, he is always somewhat worried. Most men are perfectionists, and they have never learned women's knack of not worrying in an imperfect world. At the moment, in addition to this, the husband has just finished an exhausting bit of play-acting over the phone, buttering up his bank on the prospect that the company needs a bigger loan than the company thought it did. He is really quite jittery.

Can Husbands Be Taught?

His wife telephones: "Oh, Jack, I'm *so* glad I was able to find you. I've been *simply terrified* that you might have gone out to lunch. But the most *awful* thing has happened. *I don't know what to do.*"

"What is it? What's wrong?" The wife's exaggerative language is paying off.

"Well, I took the children and got out the car and started off to the Wilsons'—you know they asked the children over to play this morning, and I do so want them to see as much as possible of the Wilson children. *Such* nice children."

"Yes, yes. Yes, yes."

"Well, I finally got them all settled in the car and was just on my way down Elm Street—you know that bad corner by the Hayworths' place—when *fortunately* I remembered that I hadn't brought along the books I was going to give to Henrietta Schermerhorn—" harrowing pause—"so I had to go back to the house, *and when I got there—*"

By this time the husband has imagined in fast succession (a) terrible accident to wife; (B) terrible accident to children; (c) total destruction of house by fire. He is responding normally. "Yes-yes-yes. *What is it?*"

"Well, while I was in the house—just for a minute, too—the telephone rang, and it was that awful Ethel Grudge—where we had such a *frightful* time that Sunday and-she-asked-us-for-dinner-tomorrow-night-and-I-didn't-have-the-energy-to-say-no-and-I-said-we'd-come-and-I-know-you-won't—" wail *"what shall-I-do?"*

"Don't worry about it. Don't worry about it. I'll do whatever you want—g'bye." Hm-m-m, his subconscious tells him as he puts down the phone, not so bad as it sounded for a while there.

Ordinarily, as he mounts the Grudges' steps the next evening, a husband would be tormented by self-doubt. What madness has brought him here again? Has he lost his mind? No will power? Yet his wife *had* asked him and he had said yes. It shocks him to remember that he said yes even with some eagerness. Why in the world did he ever say yes?

Here again, technical instruction and classwork with other husbands, a chalk-talk by the teacher, would enlighten a husband on the facts. He has gone to the Grudges' not because he is a mental defective, but in a perfectly natural response to the Narrow-Escape Technique.

The Quick-Shift Treatment has great shocking power and will bring a man back to earth in a hurry no matter how high he is flying at the moment.

The problem: Assume that the husband, for days or even weeks, has been brooding about bills the wife should have paid. They begin turning up, instead, beside his breakfast plate, in his pockets, on his hat, etc. He finds that, contrary to all budget agreements, he is being jockeyed into a $316.41 bail-out. How can the wife give the husband a hearing and be sure at the same time that he will end up $316.41 in the red?

The husband himself sets the scene for the Quick-Shift Treatment. With the documents spread before him, he harangues his wife long and earnestly one evening after dinner. He talks on and on, reminding her of budget promises, previous failures, other obligations.

Just as he feels that she is getting the point, his wife suddenly interrupts: "You don't mean to say that you haven't paid poor old Mr. Gabboulian yet for upholstering that chair?"

The value of the situation has taken a new turn. Instead of an argument between husband and wife, the issue is now one of slow starvation for poor old Mr. Gabboulian.

The wife follows it up. "Why, it must be *two weeks ago* that I gave you that bill," she goes on, "and you know he's putting his daughter through medical school and his father has been ill. Jack, how *could* you?"

Regardless of who should actually have paid Mr. Gabboulian, the husband has lost the initiative. He is off balance again. Shall he trade Mr. Gabboulian for a restoration of the family finances? Very well, he will send Mr. Gabboulian a check instantly. But what about the other bills? The husband resumes his mournful summary, delivering a monologue that lasts another twenty-five minutes.

His wife waits it out, then demands abruptly, "What did you think of those veal birds I made Sunday?"

The shift is on.

"Well, I don't see—" the husband begins, but he is wary of a new argument in the making so he side-steps it. "I thought they were wonderful," he replies.

"Well, you know we're having the Morgans over Friday, and I thought it would be nice if we tried the veal again," the wife continues. "We could have that leeks soup and the *gnocchi* and a salad. I really ought to be making out my list." The wife gets up, goes to the desk, and begins writing furiously, talking half-aloud. "Parmesan cheese, leeks, black cherries—telephone Mrs. Hayes and ask her to help—I do hope I'll be able to get her."

This time, the shift keeps on shifting. No more trivia about bills for porch paints and snow tires. Shifts of every sort are in the making. The silver needs polishing. "It looks simply yellow," says the wife. "I'm *appalled* at how faded the paper in the hall is getting. Amy Follansbee has just done over her *whole house.*"

The husband exits hastily.

Now, why should this vanquished husband brood vainly over what he fully believes was a failure of his own? He played errorless ball; his argument was correct in every word and attitude. Even his wife—although she could not afford to tell him so—thought his summing up a model of eloquence, good sense, and good manners; a shame to shut him off. But the minute the wife saw him with the bills spread out before him, she decided that nothing short of the Quick Shift would save the day. It was only a question of when to pull the switch. He never had a chance. He was scheduled, well in advance, not only to lose that particular argument but also to accept for payment, and without wincing, all future bills from old Mr. Gabboulian.

If a new kind of technical school can once get started teaching this kind of thing to husbands, it would expand rapidly. In no time it would have a ball team and a school song. Where it would get the teachers, I haven't figured out.

Bob Elliott and Ray Goulding

"They take you unawares, this pair of deadpan New Englanders," concluded John Crosby, writing about the Bob and Ray shows in his Radio and Television column in the New York *Herald Tribune*. "You find them sitting at a desk, exchanging *non sequiturs,* at which they're pastmasters, when a news ticker starts to tick away. Bob leaps up, grabs the tape, and exclaims: 'Will the mother who left the little boy in a blue suit in the laundromat, please take him out? The colors are running and ruining the other tenants' clothes.'

"From there they go immediately into a commercial for Sturdley's anchovies 'the only anchovies which smell like anchovies, feel like anchovies and, I understand, taste like anchovies.' One of the recent impartial surveys was concerned with whether one barrel of monkeys was having more fun than another barrel of monkeys. From there they plunge into a sort of continuing soap opera 'The Lives and Loves of Linda Lovely,' which contains my favorite television actress, an empty-faced young lady who for no reason at all bursts into song or the Charleston but never, never utters a word of dialogue. Bob and Ray play all the parts in this soap opera—an explorer who has just returned from eight years in Africa where he was searching for a Dr. Murchison (he didn't find him), kindly old Dr. John who has been just a little too kindly to the explorer's wife, an idiot cousin who incessantly makes peanut butter sandwiches and currently owns a collection of 375 of them."

Bob (Elliott) was born March 26, 1923, in Boston; Ray (Goulding), also a Massachusetts boy, was born a year earlier, March 20, 1922, and raised in Lowell. Both were staff announcers at a local Boston station where they learned so much about radio that they learned to kick it around for a living. Never before had the commercials, the spot news, the serials, and the pretentious programs received such a healthy deflation as the half hour devoted to "Inside Bob and Ray" and other satirical skits whipped up by this pair of seemingly aimless sharp-shooters from Boston. Their characteristic quality is indicated by the announcement which introduces their daily network show: "Bob and Ray take great pleasure in presenting The National Broadcasting Company."

Amanda of Mental Therapy *

Man and boy, we have been listening to daytime serials now for a decade and a half—a decade for the man, and a half for the boy. And only recently we have been thrilled to see them appear on the television screen, with all the tragic overtones so familiar to radio audiences portrayed in simple black and white.

Wending our way through the corridors en route to do our radio program, we sometimes forget it's almost air time as we are halted by the sharp cry of a newborn baby in an adjacent studio. And as we prepare to slink before the cameras for our television stint, we somehow can't escape the realization that other cameras are even then focusing on a broken heart in Amnesiaville, U.S.A.

We have come to love the click of heels along a hospital corridor, the *t-w-a-n-g* of a personality as it splits, the low moan of a wife as her husband leaves her for the Other Woman, and the sound effect of crushed moiré as, contrite, he returns and falls into her arms.

From thus keeping our ears to the ground antennas, we have evolved a formula for writing daytime dramas, and are proud at this time to announce that our own program, Amanda of Mental Therapy, is now available to sponsors from coast to coast. (It is not available to sponsors from border to border, since we write only horizontally.) But before we tell you about Amanda, as we affectionately call her, a few words about this art form.

A woman listening to The Sin of Nell Bloodstrong, while tears run down her cheeks, finds it a revivifying experience. It also helps wash away the dust and soot smudges she has gathered from vacuuming or bending over a hot stove. The same applies to the followers of Young Dr. Fentriss, Boy Psychiatrist; Mary Backstage, Noble Wife; Stella Callous; Life Can Be Contagious, or the American Album of Familiar Maladies. (Note: These last two are not heard in the East, but are released to independent stations in the Surgical Belt west of the Mississippi.)

We trust that our new program, Amanda of Mental Therapy, will have all the attributes of the tried-and-true dramas just mentioned.

And what are these attributes? We hoped you would ask that question, because we have the answer for you.

* Reprinted from *Collier's* Magazine.

In the first place, "Amanda" follows the established rules, with its cast of typically intense characters, who, typically, are beating their way through life in the typical town of Centerville. Like everyone else, Amanda not only has an Absent Husband, she also has a New Man in Her Life, a Mother, a Father, a Sister, and an Old, Old Friend.

To keep the action typical, our own little play incorporates several absolute "musts." The first of these is medical emphasis—the antiseptic haze which surrounds the daily serial. Every such program is clothed, so to speak, in a hospital gown.

That is the reason why we will not write "Amanda" alone. We will be guided by a board of advisers consisting of three famous New York doctors—a brain surgeon, a psychiatrist, and a plastic surgeon, plus a simple country doctor from the Old Smoky region who helps us out with simple fractures, backaches, contusions, and general run-down conditions. He'd be a specialist in situations like this:

AMANDA: "Doctor Charley, do—you—think Mother—will—get—well?"

DR. CHARLEY (*Chuckling*): "Never yet heard of no ornery mountain woman like your maw yet died of a li'l ole broken back."
(*Note:* All illustrative speeches are taken from Amanda of Mental Therapy, by Bob Elliott and Ray Goulding, and may not be reproduced in any way except for money.)

Some listeners may assume that the illnesses which occur in daytime dramas are the unhappy result of mere chance. This is not true. They are carefully planned. And we have two methods by which our characters wind up in a hospital bed, wheel chair, or double traction.

One is called Creative Diagnosis. When we use this method, we simply describe a character going about her usual daily routine—taking her own temperature, watching the ambulances gliding past her window, putting wet compresses on Mother's forehead when she is down with brain fever, all the little things normal human beings do every day. As the action progresses, our medical board will listen to the program for symptoms and from them diagnose what

228

is wrong with the character. In other words, the medical board will carry the ball we have passed them. Then *we* take over again on a lateral pass and carry the diagnosis to a logical, successful illness, over the Goal Line of the Future.

Study this bittersweet extract, for example. Amanda's mother, who is eighty-eight years old, suffers from a strange disease that defies diagnosis. Young Dr. Thurston Forbush, who is keen on Amanda, has admitted defeat; mystified by the old woman's symptoms, he has suggested sending her to the Frisby Clinic for examination by the only doctor in the world who possesses the skill and knowledge to effect a cure. The fee is $112,000, but, unknown to Amanda, Thurston has quietly arranged to pay for the treatments by hocking his instruments:

Sound: Purr of car wheels on asphalt driveway as private ambulance fades into distance.
THURSTON: "She'll be in good hands now, Amanda."
AMANDA: "Yes, Thurston." (*Pause*) "Pull back the draperies, and let the sun in . . ."
THURSTON: "Amanda, it's good to see you smile again!"

The second method we call Planned Mortality. Here, with the aid of our medical board, we decide beforehand, arbitrarily, what the character is going to suffer from and proceed accordingly—with only an occasional assist from the doctors. Thus:

AMANDA: "But what *is* a headache, Professor Kalbfleisch?"
PROF. K. (*Smiling gently*): "To use the scientific term would only confuse you, *Liebchen.*"
AMANDA: "But can't you explain it in *little* words?"
PROF. K. (*Kindly*): "I never use little words, *Kleinchen.*"

Both of these methods achieve the desired result: a program which is good, clean, wholesome, and yet gives off the faint, impressive odor of ether. Subtle treatment of dialogue helps in this respect:

AMANDA: "Good-by, Thurston. I'm off to the Good Government meeting to vote for hot lunches for the school children."

229

THURSTON: "On the way, my darling, will you stop at the chemist's and have this digitalis bottle filled?"

Incidentally, it is not true, as some say, that special training is necessary for a writer of daytime serials. Any man or woman over twelve years of age, who has had a mother or father and who has lived in a large city, a small town, or a rural section is qualified.

What *is* necessary is that the writer have a certain attitude toward life. He must realize that where there is good health, there must also be bad health. If people laugh, they must also cry:

AMANDA (*Laughing*): "Ha ha ha."
THURSTON: "What's the matter, Amanda?"
AMANDA (*Crying*): "I don't know."

We have found, too, that it is necessary for the writer to live in a proper environment in order to create the right atmosphere for his listeners. For instance, in our little circle of intimate friends there is only one man out of six who is not receiving total disability compensation.

Then again, we had to move from our last apartment, which overlooked a children's playground, because the joyous laughter of the youngsters threw our perspective off. Now we live over a drugstore, whence the faint odor of oil of wintergreen and the subdued rustle of prescriptions being wrapped put us in a creative frame of mind as we sit down at the typewriter. Further, our programs are performed with a doctor and nurse always in attendance.

And now we come to the next important must—go slow. Remember always that on the coat of arms of every serial writer appear these symbols: a run-down clock and a century plant. Dialogue must be written in a literary form of slow motion. In fact, if you can give the impression that the speeches are progressing backward, you're a cinch to be a successful daytime drama writer. An exchange from one of our own scripts is a perfect example:

AMANDA: "—Thurston—"
THURSTON: "Yes, Amanda?"
AMANDA: "Thurston, I have—"
THURSTON (*Urging*): "Yes, Amanda, you—have—?"
AMANDA (*After long pause*): "—Never mind—"

230

To keep a sequence going, only one thing should happen on any given program. For instance, we are planning a very dramatic operating-room scene. First, we intend to devote several weeks to making the situation plausible: Amanda becomes indispensable around the Centerville hospital by taking time off from her job in Mental Therapy to assist in Surgery. Finally, comes the day of the Big Operation and that's when we really turn the heat on and leave it there. It should take at least four days for Amanda to hand old Doctor Charley a scalpel. The first day he asks for the scalpel. In the next episode she asks, "Scalpel?" The following afternoon he says, "Yes." And the fourth day Amanda hands him the instrument.

This type of retarded dialogue is also beautifully illustrated in a scene which involves two of the incidental characters in our little epic—a friend of Amanda's who is in love with a married woman whose husband beats her. The lady is covered with black and blue marks, has welts on her back, a broken leg, and a mouse on her left eye. The man wants to ask if her husband beats her, but his sense of delicacy prevents him from hinting that his old Harvard classmate may be less than a gentleman:

WETHERELL: "Your husband . . ."
MAVIS (*Through puffed lips*): "Mmgh?"
WETHERELL: "Your husband . . . Philip . . ."
MAVIS: "Mmgh?"
WETHERELL: "Does Philip . . ."
   Music Cue: (Orchestra plays Fair Harvard faintly in background.)
WETHERELL: "My alma mater—and—*Phil's* alma mater—I can't do it!"
ANNOUNCER: "And as Wetherell Dexter, choking, turns away from Mavis Calhoon and staggers out the French windows, he hears the sound of whiplashes in the room he has just left . . ."

And we've got another classic instance of delayed-action conversation all ready. Amanda's little sister Cathy, who is stoically enduring a series of radium treatments for dry scalp, is going to have a b-a-b-y. Now it should be noted that the locale of a serial is the one place in the world where it can take a baby 16 to 20 months to be born. Here's how our plot thickens.

231

Little Cathy, bored with her dull life in Round Corners, has followed Amanda to Centerville. Eventually she meets up with Fenton Carruthers, who had paid marked attention to Amanda when *she* first arrived in Centerville:

AMANDA: "Fenton, this is my little sister."
FENTON (*Giving wolf whistle*): "Zowie!"
AMANDA: "Cathy, he's a cad. Remember that."
CATHY (*Gently*): "There's good in *every* man, Amanda."

Amanda is right, of course. Having been spurned by Amanda, Carruthers successfully turns his attention to Cathy, thereby establishing the justice of Amanda's judgment that beneath his polished exterior is a polished interior. And, tiring of this marriage born of revenge, before too long he packs his attaché case and leaves town. So we find Amanda in her little office in Mental Therapy sorting rattan into small, medium, and large lengths. Cathy, sitting on a patient, is twisting her handkerchief:

Sound: (*Twisting handkerchief.*)
CATHY: "Amanda—?"
AMANDA: "Yes?"
CATHY: "Amanda—"
AMANDA: "Yes, Cathy?"
CATHY: "Amanda, I—I have something to tell you."
Music: (*Neurotic theme ending with querulous note.*)

This plot development continues for a number of programs until, finally, a couple of weeks later, we approach the climax.

CATHY: "Amanda—"
AMANDA: "Finish your sentence, dear."
CATHY: "I'm—I'm—"
AMANDA: "Yes, dear?"
CATHY: "I'm—going—to—have—a . . ."
Music: (*Same neurotic theme but ending with petulant note.*)

Next day, we reach it:

CATHY (*Finishing yesterday's speech*): "—baby."

Amanda of Mental Therapy

AMANDA: "What did you say?"
CATHY: "I'm going to have a baby."
AMANDA: "Oh."

Music: (*Same neurotic theme with countermelody, Melancholy Baby.*)

In fairness to the script writers, the stall-and-stutter technique of handling dialogue has many advantages—other than guaranteeing that the writer's checking account will continue in good order. The busy housewife, plugging away at her many daily chores, can hardly miss even the slightest detail of the continuing story.

Why, we've handled the b-a-b-y sequence in such a way that the listener can hear Cathy getting into the taxi for the rush to the hospital on Monday, and four days later—when the house is finally shipshape for the week end—she can tune in and the cab will only have gone through the first stop light.

And to ensure further that the audience will not miss a single gripping detail, each day's program will begin with a recapitulation of everything that has gone before. "Amanda" always comes on the air with an opening announcement like this:

ANNOUNCER: "(Name of sponsor) presents another episode of . . . Amanda of Mental Therapy!"
Music: (*Tremulous yet hopeful chord.*)

ANNOUNCER: "You will remember that yesterday we left Amanda, the girl from Round Corners, a little mining town out West, who was married to Geoffrey Traverse, a ne'er-do-well who deserted her to return to England to become Lord Fanshawe after the death of his father, the haughty Earl of Cranthorne, who disliked Amanda and caused her to be discredited by circulating false rumors about her, which stirred up a hornet's nest in the little town of Centerville, where she is now working in the hospital as a mental therapist, a job through which she met and fell in love with young Dr. Thurston Forbush, a brilliant intern who has discovered a new method of weaving rattan, and who has observed that she is on the verge of complete emotional collapse because her sister Cathy has been seen in the Purple Lantern Tearoom with Fenton Carruthers,

233

a local cad who is planning to betray Cathy in order to revenge himself on Amanda because she has repulsed his advances. Now as we listen, we hear Amanda say . . ."

And when Amanda says whatever it is she has to say, we know exactly where we stand, where Amanda stands, where Fenton Carruthers stands, where Thurston stands, and where Cathy stands. (There's a shortage of chairs in Centerville.)

Finally, where would we be without suspense? So, naturally, we have a sign-off, or what-will-happen-tomorrow, announcement. As each daily installment comes to an end and the American housewife unashamedly mops up her tears with the corner of her apron, the announcer tells her in no uncertain terms that she ain't heard nothing yet; there's always tomorrow. We believe in making the hint sizable, so that she can hardly wait for the program the following day:

ANNOUNCER: "Well, things certainly do seem to be going badly for plucky little Amanda. What will happen tomorrow? Is Fenton Carruthers really a spy for a foreign power or were those plans for the A-bomb his own design, as he claims? Will Doctor Charley recover from his paralysis and complete the delicate brain operation on the mysterious stranger who looks so much like Geoffrey Traverse? And, don't forget the terrible probability that young Dr. Forbush may have to hand over his rattan-weaving secrets to the board of trustees at the hospital, instead of patenting them himself." *Sound: (Ambulance siren screaming.)*

ANNOUNCER: "Be sure to tune in tomorrow, same time, same station, when (name of sponsor) presents Episode 3,648 of . . . Amanda of Mental Therapy!"

It should live so long!

Arthur Kober

The author of *Bella, Bella Kissed A Fella* is also the author of several other equally knowledgeable volumes, with such appropriate titles as *Thunder Over the Bronx, Pardon Me for Pointing,* and *That Man Is Here Again.* Arthur Kober is also responsible for *Having Wonderful Time,* a play which ran a year on Broadway, was awarded a prize by his fellow dramatists for the best comedy of the season, was made into a film and, a dozen years later, appeared as a musical comedy with words and music by Harold Rome. Kober's career is a curious perversion of the Horatio Alger formula. He fled from school at the age of fifteen because he could not master the elements of mathematics, and went to work for a real estate broker. "My job," he confessed, "was to add the sums collected for rent each day. So great was the difference between the amount I had recorded and what they claimed was actually received, and so great were their insults, that I promptly withdrew from the firm. My next job was with the Treo Corset Company. Not only was I expected to keep an accurate inventory, but I had to record the sizes, styles, number of corsets shipped out, etc.—a job obviously meant for Albert Einstein, as I heatedly pointed out when I quit. It was about this time that I was attracted to the literary life. My interest in writing took the form of studying shorthand. I became indentured to Grenville Kleiser, the author of books on public speaking and writing, and the avid hunter of 'the felicitous phrase.' I broke into print on a part-time job, employing the most unfelicitous phrases in reviewing vaudeville shows for a magazine called *Theatre World.* . . . Eventually I became a press agent for the Schuberts, and got to Hollywood, where I wrote a number of films, the titles of which time has gratefully erased from memory.

"Mathematics no longer troubles me, for the reason that I delegate all such matters to my agent, a colorful character who has proved to be most rewarding. . . . In conclusion, I might add—*Add?* My God! Arithmetic!"

"I'm Not Gonna Cowtail to That Bubble-headed Bastid, if It's the Last Thing I Do!"*

After I arrived at the Racquet Club in Palm Springs, I changed into tennis clothes, left my room, and headed for the courts. I was threading my way among the tight little knots of guests on the lawn when a diminutive figure jumped from a chair and rushed up to me.

"Artie!" cried Benny Greenspan, vigorously shaking my hand. "Boy, am I gladda see you! Why, this here joint is so clustered up with moom-pitcha stars and high-sessiety rift-raft it's a real, genu-wine pleasure to look on a common peasant's puss; namely, yours. Hey, hoddeya like my outfit?"

Benny was wearing Hawaiian trunks, rope sandals, a light-blue terry-cloth jacket, a checkered beret, and a pair of enormous sun-glasses. "Pretty nifty, eh, kid?" he said, and then, suddenly, he became mournful. "But that's oney on my outside, Artie. Inside"— he tapped his chest—"inside, I'm bleedin' like a stuffed pig, and. that's fa sure!"

"Who is it this time, Benny?"

"Who, he wantsa know yet!" snorted Benny. "Don Bowers, the director, that's who! The minute I starts thinkin' about Don, that cracked-pot, that fugitive from a loony-bin, the blood starts curlin' in my stomick. Sit down, kid," he said, waving me to a chair, "and grab yesself an earful."

I sat down, and Benny brought his chair and placed it directly in front of me. Then, delicately depositing himself on the edge of the seat, so that his short legs could touch the ground, he leaned forward and began his story.

"Artie," he said, "I'll nutshell you the whole situation in a couple words. Here is a guy, Mr. Donald Bowers, fa nine straight years he's been workin' over there at Monarch Studios. Fa nine straight years that dough's been comin' in hand over foot, regella like clock-work. He never had it so good in his whole, entire life, believe me! But he hadda go ahead and shoot off his big trap a his! So what's the result? Namely, he alecks hisself the hell outa the studio—that's the result! Good-by job, and farewell my commissions! And all on account this so-called big brain, this Mr. Blow-Mouth, he din folly his own advice!"

"Wait. You've lost me," I said. "I don't—"

"I'm talkin' about the advice he was awways handin' out," Benny said petulantly. "Time again he useta say to me, 'Benny,' he says, 'the trouble with the averitch director, he's awways knockin' hisself out tryin' to make a pitcha which the public will lap up like a hot plate wheat cakes. Why? What for, fa cryin' out loud? To me,' he says, 'the public is like a mythical kingdom; namely, it don't exist. So far I'm concerned, Benny,' Don says to me, 'the one person my bread is buttered on is Sonny Grant, my boss. And so long I can please him, which I can with this system I got all worked out, I don't give a thinker's damn about the public.' His very own words."

"Did he ever explain this system?" I asked.

"Natchelly he explained me it. Take, finstance, each time Sonny handed him a scripp he should direck. First thing—irregardless if it's good, bad, indiffrint—first crack outa Don's box is 'What is with you, Sonny? You nuts, or what? Why, this here is the worse dribble I ever laid my own two eyes on!' Why?" inquired Benny, anticipating my question. "On account if it turned out a terrific bust, Don's awready on record as the guy who warned him it was lousy in the first place. But if it so happens it's a colossal money-maker, then Don goes round claimin' how *he* took this awful piece cheese and *he* made it a big box-awfice smash."

"Quite a system," I remarked.

"Listen, you oughta get a loada this character operatin' in a story confrince. There he is, see, slashin' away the story, poppin' out with a million-one idears, and before Sonny has a chance to even maul one thought over in his mind, Don's shootin' out suggestions galore. He's wavin' his cigar, poundin' the dest, flashin' him his choppers, and makin' with the personality, while Sonny sits there flappergasted, prolly thinkin', Oh, boy, is this a terrific guy, this Don—but a real human domino! Talk about dazzlin' a person, Don Bowers takes the prize hands up, believe me!"

"Doesn't sound possible," I said. "I can't believe a director with all his credits—"

"You can't believe, you can't believe!" mocked Benny. "What

237

the hell you want I should do, show you affidavids yet? Listen, I know this character intimately well, like the Warner Brothers know their own relatives."

"But nine years at the same studio—"

"And workin' just fa Sonny Grant alone!" Benny said, nodding. "Why, in them nine years over at Monarch, he made a lifetime study from Sonny. He knew him backwards and forwards, but thoroughly, like a liberrian knows a book. Finstance, he knew that if there's one thing Sonny was rabbit about, it's he just couldn't stand being topped by nobody. No matter what, Sonny simply hadda be the best, and that went fa cards, sports, jokes, and specially fa pitchas.

"Why, you take when Zanuck or Dore Schary got rave notices in the trade papers on some new pitcha or other, Sonny felt like it was a personal insult. He'd go round with his kisser so low it pradically scraped away his knees. Don knew this, see, so he'd come breezin' inna Sonny's awfice, very bright, very chippy, and he'd say, 'Oh, boy, did I catch a sneak preview last night, and did it smell high to heaven! Pee-yew!' he'd say, and he'd grab holt his own nose. Then he'd tell Sonny all about this here pitcha which the critics doted, oney accordin' Don's way, it loused up the joint, and the audience, they walked out in groves. Right away Sonny'd pert up, and he'd begin smilin' from one ear to the next, like if he just heard some movvellous news, which to him it was.

"Another thing," continued Benny animatedly. "You take the commissary, at the executives' table, when Sonny started in crackin' some joke or other. Before the words are hot outa his mouth even, there'd be Don, yockin' it up like crazy, bustin' his gut, he's so hysterical with loyalty laughter. Believe me, Artie, I defy you the best expert mechanic you could name, he never done a more perfeck greaze job than the one Don done on Sonny, and that's fa sure!"

"Then why did he lose his job?" I wanted to know.

Benny expelled his breath in a long and sad sigh. "Sometimes," he said, "a guy gets too big fa his own head, whereby he gets stubborn, see. He figures, by God, this time I'm gonna have it my way, come hell and hot water! Here, lemme give you a finstance."

He reached down and yanked at his chair, pulling it so close to mine that our knees were touching. "A couple months ago, Sonny hands Don a scripp he wants he should direck. Before he looks at it even, Don knows he's gonna say it's lousy, but still in all he goes ahead and he reads it and, Artie, the thing atchelly turns out to *be* lousy, but a real, first-class stinker, which is what Don tells Sonny it is.

" 'Don,' Sonny says to him, 'it seemsa me that ever since time immemorium you been gripin' about the scripps, and yet, somehow, they finey turn out O.K. in the end. I'm sure the same will be likewise here.' 'Oh, no, Sonny,' says Don. 'This here is strickly from Dixie, but a real cornball.' 'You tellin' me my judgment is so bad whereas I go round producin' stinkers?' says Sonny, givin' him the chill.

"Right away Don sees he is off on his wrong foot, so he figgers what the hell, he might as well take the assignment, but he'd better proteck hisself by gettin' a couple big-name stars with plenty box-awfice pull. 'You talk like your head ran outa grain matter!' Sonny yells on him. 'Why, with current conditions in the industry like they are today, who the hell can afford to pay the absorbent salaries like the big stars are demandin'? Besides,' says Sonny, 'I got you lined up a couple players we got under contrack,' and he mentions him some actors who are strickly from left field. Right away Don starts in beefin', and next thing you know, the two a them are at it hammer and tongues, Don screamin' hisself black-and-blue in the face, and Sonny screamin' him right back again. A real rhubarb!

"Folling day I'm over on the lot, over there at Monarch, and I meets Don, who comes up to me, and, brother, is he burnt up, but like a criss piece toast! 'Evvey time I open my yap fa this, that, the other, that damn Sonny thumbs me down. From now on,' he says, 'I'm not gonna cowtail to that bubble-headed bastid, if it's the last thing I do!' Natchelly I figger the guy is blowin' off steam, so I lets him blow. But he certainey meant it, aw right," declared Benny in portentous tones.

"Meant it in what way?"

"Well," replied Benny, "take, finstance, when Don goes to the commissary fa lunch. He sits down at the execatives' table, as per usual, and he waits fa Sonny to start in poppin' the corn. Sure enough, Sonny goes ahead and he tells one a his crummy stories, see, and then he looks over to Don. Lo and behold, no yocks from

Don! Not even one weasly little smile! In fack, Don tells him he got the joke all wrong, and then he goes ahead and he repeats him the exack same joke, oney he tells it the right way. Well, sir, evveybody at that table, they're screamin' with laughter galore. Evveybody exceptin' Sonny. He sits there with his mug at half-mass, like if he's just come from the dentist or some other extortionist.

"Oh, and that ain't all," Benny went on as I started to speak. "A couple days later, just when Sonny is yackin' about somethin' or other, in comes Don to the commissary, and this time he is carryin' a book. Right away he starts givin' out with a big pitch what a movvelous book he's got, it's all about makin' a movie, and how evveybody in the industry could learn somethin' from it, irregardless no matter who. And then he flashes the book in fronna Sonny's kisser, and there is the writer's name all over the front. Guess who? Dore Schary, no less! So while Sonny sits there with his face red like a beetle, not sayin' a word, Don pops off all about when the Academy bunch gets together to discuss the Oscars, they oughta give Dore the Irvin' Thalberg award just on the strenntha this here book alone! You hear?"

"No wonder he was fired," I said. "After all—"

"Uh-uh," said Benny shaking his head. "That ain't what done it, Artie. What done it was the remarks Don passed a couple weeks ago, when Sonny calls me up, I should come right over to his awfice. Well, sir, in two shades of a lamb's tail I'm over in his awfice, and he's got Don there. 'Benny,' Sonny says to me, 'the reason I sent you should come over is on account Mr. Bowers, here.' Minute he says 'Mr. Bowers'—uh-uh, I gets an inklin' in my bones somethin' is up, and I'm right! 'I don't think your client is very happy with his assignment, Benny,' he says to me. 'And, frankly speakin', I ain't very happy with his suggestive changes he keeps on makin'. In my opinion they are simply God-awful. Leasewise, that is my judgment.' 'But your judgment ain't awways right, is it, Sonny?' pipes up Don, very sarcastical. 'Oh, no?' says Sonny. 'Oh, no!' says Don. 'Hozz about that time you were gonna show Cecil deMille hodda really make a religious pitcha? So you went ahead and you produced that four-million-dollar epic "The Beloved Sinner," all about John the Babtiss and Salomey. Remember? You said it got sex, it got action, it got drama, it got religion. The one thing it din

240

have, though,' says Don, 'was customers at the box awfice, on account it laid one terrific bomb, and it set religion back about a hunnard years. You and your judgment!'

"Artie, it was so quiet in that awfice, you coulda picked up a pin. Yes, sir, that Don took the sails right outa Sonny, who just sits there, not sayin' a word, he's so agasp. Then, finey, he speaks up. And *how* he speaks up! 'Why, you dirty, no-good rat! You lousy ingrid!' he screams on Don. 'You get outa this here awfice before I part your skull with a pig-ax!' 'Sure, Sonny,' says Don. He goes to the door, he stops, then he turns around. 'You wanna know the one thing wrong with that religious pitcha?' he says. 'Insteada Salomey carryin' John's head on that tray, she shoulda carried yours! So long, Sonny,' he says, and out he blows.

"Before Sonny could open up his trap and take it out on me, I lets out a blast on what a jerk that Don is. 'Why, that double-headed cluck,' I says, 'where the hell does he get off to criticize you, a man who occupies a prominent notch in the industry, whereas what is he? A director!' 'An *ex*-director,' says Sonny. 'Mock my words, Benny,' he says, 'he'll never work on this here lot again.' 'And I don't blame you,' I says. 'Here you been carryin' this cloth-head on your payroll all these years outa friendship, not ability, then he turns around and insults your very face. Guys like that,' I says, 'should be tarred with feathers and run outa Hollywood, where they belong!' Believe me, Artie, by the time I left his awfice my head was dizzy from goin' up and down, yessin' the guy, but I finey done it," he proudly announced.

"Done what?"

"Sold him one a my clients to take over Don's job," replied Benny, surprised at my question. "Listen, in this here business, namely, the flesh-peddlin' game—a person's gotta be sharp and ack fast to take care of hisself, else he never will. Well, Artie," he said, rising briskly to his feet, "I better nosey around and find me a gin-rummy pigeon, so's my week end shouldn't be a total loss. So long, kid. Have yesself a nice game tennis." He waved his hand, and hurried away.

Robert M. Yoder

A humorist in the best tradition, Robert M. Yoder conducted the old Eugene Field column, "Sharps and Flats," in the Chicago *Daily News* for three years. A collection of these columns in book form appeared as *There's No Place Like Home*. Then the war broke out. Yoder was an employee of Secretary of the Navy Knox, who, at that time, was owner of the Chicago *Daily News*. Whereupon Yoder enlisted in the Navy and rose to the rank of lieutenant. Just before he went away to fight for his country, he was playing with one of his three children and broke his ankle, which meant that all his battles were fought in Washington. After the war, Yoder joined the staff of the *Saturday Evening Post*, from which he recently retired to free lance in a suburb of Philadelphia with the unpronounceable name of Cynwyd.

It Can Happen in Any Family*

THE MAN: Offer him six hundred and seventy thousand dollars just to sit at the table with us.

THE GIRL: He spurns your six hundred and seventy thousand dollars.

THE MAN: Do you think he knows what we're having?

THE GIRL: No. What are we having?

THE MAN: Roasted young rhinoceros.

THE GIRL: It sounds delicious.

THE MAN: Your mother shot it herself, over by the drugstore.

THE GIRL: No good.

THE MAN: All right, she strangled it, then.

THE GIRL: I wonder if we've got a platter for it.

THE MAN: Well, I'm tired of this. Tell him if he doesn't answer in two minutes, we'll kill his wife and three golden-haired children.

THE GIRL: It seems to be all right with him.

THE MAN: Then it's got to be torture. *Torture,* do you hear me?

THE GIRL: *I* do, but the victim doesn't.

THE MAN: We'll start by putting lighted matches under his fingernails.

* Reprinted by permission of *Woman's Day*.

242

THE GIRL: We might even clean them, with a nail file. That should get him, if he's conscious. Is he?

THE MAN: It's pretty hard to tell, in his case. I say, it's pretty hard to tell, in his case.

THE GIRL (*watching the motionless figure in the chair*): Insults won't do it. Does he know his bicycle was stolen?

THE MAN: It wasn't stolen. His grandfather sold it for drink. Well, then, his father sold it for opium.

THE WOMAN (*coming in from the dining room and wearing an apron*): Who sold what for opium?

THE MAN: Doctor Warner, the minister. Sold his grandmother's shawl.

THE WOMAN: What on earth are you talking about?

THE GIRL: Everything, just about. You can see how far we're getting. He hasn't said a word.

THE MAN: We started out by yelling that dinner was ready.

THE GIRL: We said the house was on fire.

THE WOMAN (*advancing menacingly*): I'll cut off his foot.

THE GIRL: Mother! Not with the bread knife.

THE WOMAN: We never use it, anyway.

THE MAN: It isn't the concentration that gets me, it's the position. The last time I saw a fellow with his feet that high above his head, it was in the accident ward of Jefferson Hospital, and it took six or eight pulleys and ropes to hold him. What do you suppose is holding this one?

THE GIRL (*It hasn't been many years since she made a habit of doing this herself*): He's gripping the chair arm with the back of his neck.

THE WOMAN: This is how I get footprints where most people have pictures.

THE MAN: Did I tell you the news? (*He speaks loudly, with his eyes on the figure in the chair.*) The John J. Balderwickle Public School burned to the ground at five o'clock. There won't be any school tomorrow.

THE GIRL (*clinically*): He didn't bat an eye. What else is new?

THE MAN: Plastic men from Mars are dropping by parachute into North Dakota.

THE GIRL: He's alive. He turned a page.

243

THE WOMAN: What's got him this time?

THE GIRL: A story about a jet pilot. He goes too fast, or something, and gets stuck in the fourth dimension.

THE WOMAN: You don't suppose there's anything wrong with his ears, do you?

THE MAN: No! He just turns them completely off, that's all. Nobody over twenty can possibly do it. It really must be wonderful.

THE WOMAN: You'd think he'd get himself a nice bed of nails. He couldn't possibly be more uncomfortable; not even upside down in a barrel.

THE GIRL: Dad asked him if he wanted boiled suitcase for dinner, and he said, "Ump."

THE MAN: Jane read him a sentence from her French book, and he said, "Right away." Watch this. *It's an outrage!*

THE GIRL: You scared *me*, but that's all.

THE MAN (*violently*): Running the new superhighway right through a boy's bedroom! It'll wreck the place.

THE WOMAN: You haven't seen his room lately.

THE MAN: Think of the traffic! Trucks, *zoom!* Buses, *zoom!* What else?

THE GIRL: Fire engines, *ray—ay—yow!*

THE MAN (*defeated*): Followed by Robert Fulton in the *Robert E. Lee.*

THE WOMAN: Try food. Meat loaf, hamburger, hot dogs, steak. Mashed potatoes.

THE GIRL (*wistfully*): You've got *my* attention.

THE MAN (*speaking very clearly*): I've got a piece of news, but keep it a secret. J. Edgar Hoover is coming to see us at nine o'clock tonight. And his visit isn't a social one.

THE GIRL (*reporting on the reaction*): He sneers at J. Edgar Hoover, or maybe it's somebody who got stuck in the fourth dimension.

THE MAN: Hoover is coming in a helicopter.

THE GIRL: He'll be wasting his time.

THE MAN: In a helicopter run by a trained gorilla. That's my last offer. I give up.

THE WOMAN: Well, we can't wait any longer. If you two can't manage to do it, I can.

It Can Happen in Any Family

(*She turns off the table lamp by which the boy has been reading. He puts the book on his knees, turns his head, and discovers he is surrounded by his father, his mother, and his older sister. He makes this discovery in total—but mild—surprise.*)

THE BOY (*just interested, that's all*): What's the matter?

HIS MOTHER: It's time for dinner, dear.

HIS FATHER: Yes, dinnertime. You know, food.

HIS SISTER: We all get around a table and pass things.

HIS MOTHER: Everybody in the family has yelled at you at least six or seven times.

HIS SISTER: Once in very good French.

HIS FATHER: We figured on using massed trombones, next.

(*The Boy, upended in a position that would exhaust a professional trapeze artist and would win a dervish a great reputation for stoicism, lowers his legs from the back of the chair to one arm, and flops nimbly out. He stands there, as thoroughly alert as he was totally oblivious twenty seconds before. He looks at his three relatives tolerantly, but in slight puzzlement, clearly wondering what dopiness keeps them standing in the living room instead of advancing purposefully to the dinner table. It seems up to him to make a suggestion, one you'd think they'd think of themselves. He does it kindly.*)

THE BOY: Come on, let's eat, shall we? I'm hungry. Why didn't somebody call me before?

Dillon Anderson

A Houston lawyer, civic leader, director of a half-dozen eminent associations and member of a dozen more, Dillon Anderson is the last man who might be suspected of sponsoring the irresponsible and wholly reprehensible activities of Clint Hightower and Claudie Hughes. Yet the Texan attorney and author spoke up for his ne'er-do-wells after *The Atlantic Monthly* and *Collier's* presented the pair of rascals who talk their way in and out of trouble, tangle with the law, and live more or less dangerously by their wits—Clint's wits, to be exact. When the picaresque couple appeared in book form (*I and Claudie*) the hard-working and socially overoccupied Mr. Anderson wrote: "The experiences of *I and Claudie* are in no sense autobiographical, but sometimes I am sorry they are not. Clint and Claudie are not go-getters, boosters, or pillars in anybody's community. They don't entertain people they don't like. They are free from amenities, protocol, and taxes. The only rules they have to worry about are the laws that parallel the Ten Commandments, and the speed limits imposed on highways. However, they do not have a car that can exceed the speed limit."

The Weather Prophet *

"Listen, Claudie," I said, "I'd about as soon be plumb out of money as to have only five dollars."

"I druther have this here five dollars, Clint," he answered.

"But what I'm trying to tell you is this," I went on—"we've got to get our car fixed, and that five dollars won't do it. You know what the man at the garage said; he won't touch the burnt-out bearing for less than twenty dollars."

Claudie just stood there on the docks looking at a battered-up old shrimper nudging its way into the pier. It was late in the afternoon, the hot Texas sun was beginning to ease up on us a little, and the mosquitoes were moving in. We'd been watching the fishing boats for an hour or so as they came in from the Gulf of Mexico to unload their catch at the Rockport wharf.

"Remember, Claudie," I said, "we've been here on the waterfront for three days now, and nobody has offered us any kind of a job at all. You know that. The only thing we've been asked to since we broke down here is the crap game on that big yacht to-night. Who worked up that invitation? Me or you?"

"You did," Claudie admitted, "but you didn't have to tell the man on the yacht that you was a friend of the Governor of Texas. He'd have asked you anyhow."

"Well," I said, "I can't figure how I'm going to get even one roll with the dice if I haven't got any money."

"You shoulda thought of that last night before you tried to break all them pin-ball machines," he answered.

"Listen, Claudie," I went on, "do you know what happened to the man in the Bible with five talents?"

"No. What?"

"I'll tell you," I said. "He put the talents to work, that's what; and in the long run he turned out better than the fellow that just sat on what he had."

Claudie's stubborn look was softening up around the edges.

"Another thing, Claudie," I went on, "you might have no-ticed how I've been watching the birds in the sky all day."

"What have they got to do with it?" Claudie wanted to know as he kicked against a rotten pile on the docks and watched the splinters fall among some jellyfish that were squooching around there in the water.

"Plenty," I told him. "It's in the sky that changes in a man's luck first begin to show up. You can tell it first in the flight of the birds—the gulls mainly, but now I can feel it in my bones too. This is my lucky day with the dice."

"Trouble is," Claudie fussed, "you've felt it before and been wrong."

"Tell you what I'll do, Claudie," I said. "You keep four dollars and let me have one. If I'm wrong, the whole five wouldn't last long; but if I'm right, that'll be enough to get me started. I'll give you exactly half of what I win, and your dollar back to boot."

That got him; he fished out an old dollar bill and turned it over to me, and I said: "Thank you, Claudie. Now I want you to come along to the crap game with me. You might bring me even more luck."

247

When we got down to the private docks about dusk we found the yacht we were looking for. The name was printed in gold letters on the rear end: *The Pride of Texas, III.* It was the biggest of eight nice long shiny boats tied up there. The lights were already burning inside, and we could see how fine it was fixed up in there; big comfortable chairs and sofas, a radio, and pretty rugs on the floor.

The man that had asked me to the crap game stuck his head through a window and said, "Come aboard, men," and we climbed on the boat's rear end, where it was like a porch with a big awning over it.

I said to the man, "I didn't get your name this morning, Captain."

"Hinder," he said, "but they call me Squatty," and I could see why. He wasn't much over five feet tall, and he was nearly square. His jaw set out a little like a bulldog's, but he had nice, friendly little eyes. He was wearing a blue cap with some gold palms on the front.

"Clint Hightower is the name," I told him, "and this big guy here is my associate, Claudie Hughes. He came to bring me luck." Claudie grinned, and we went inside.

While we waited for the other crap shooters to come along, Squatty told us the *Pride of Texas, III,* belonged to a rich oil man named Easley who lived in Fort Worth. Squatty said he was pretty sure that Mr. Easley was still in Canada on a vacation, and that, he explained, was why the crap game was going on in the owner's cabin that night.

Squatty told us he lived on the boat and kept it shipshape all the time. He was real proud of the way it looked, too, and he should have been. All the brass was shining, the windows were clean, and you couldn't see a speck of dust anywhere.

It wasn't long before the other crap shooters came along. I remember one was a San Antonio plumber with one eye; there was a fat shrimp boat captain that they called Fishmouth; there was a Mexican, too, and a Bible salesman with a peculiar motto tattooed on his arm. It said, "Oh hell, what's the use?" There was another one, too; a very grubby-looking character that came late, lost his money, and left early. His name was "Bird Dog" something. I noticed they all called Squatty "Captain Squatty."

That owner's cabin was something! There were two big bunks, wide almost as beds, a dresser with real drawers and a mirror above it, and bright lights all around. A nice, smooth rug covered the floor—perfect for dice—and there was plenty of room to move around on it.

We all got right down on the rug and went to work with the dice. The first time I rolled I shot a half and ran it up to five dollars before I fell off. It looked like my lucky day, but Claudie just sat there on one of the bunks with a droopy look on his face. Then I faded some of the others, as the dice went around, and when it came my turn again, I was down to about where I had started. But I put down a dollar and made four passes before I fell off again. I almost didn't drag in time, but I came out with three dollars.

It went along like this for three or four hours; several times I was up, but not much; other times I got down to nearly even. Along about midnight people started to gape and stretch, and it began to look like the game was about over. The luck had been pretty even all around, except I could tell from the ugly looks they were giving Fishmouth that he had been stashing some money away.

I figured it was time for me to hit a big lick if I had one in my system, so when I got the dice I counted out and put down all I had—eight dollars and a half. They covered it, and I rolled two big, ugly sixes—boxcars. They gathered up my money and yelled, "Go ahead, Clint; you've still got the dice."

I looked at Claudie, and he was sound asleep there on the bunk. "Wake up, Claudie," I said. "I need another dollar." Claudie woke up, but he did not give me another dollar. I whispered to him that I still had the dice and told him it was the unluckiest thing in the world for a man to pass a roll he had coming to him, but Claudie just sat there blinking. Everybody was looking at me, and I had to do something right away. It is at such times as this that a man may have his best ideas. The best one I had was to say, "Gents, my associate here, Claudie, will shoot for

249

me. I've got a little cramp in my right arm." Nobody said no, so I said, "Go ahead, Claudie, and shoot a dollar."

He was still too drowsy to argue, so he put a dollar down. Somebody covered it, and Claudie rolled the dice out on the rug. He made a neat seven.

"Fade it, men," I said. "We shoot the two dollars." The two got to be four, the four got to be eight, and when it was sixteen, Claudie said he wanted to drag it and quit.

"Are you crazy?" I asked him. "I knew I'd seen luck for somebody in the sky today. It wasn't me. It was you. Let it all ride!"

Claudie let it ride and passed again. Next he made two hard points: a nine and then a ten. We had sixty-four dollars won, and they had to dig deep to cover it, but they did. Claudie came out with eight for a point, and on the very next roll he made it the hard way—two fours. His luck was in the light of the moon.

"Eighter," I yelled, "from Decatur, the county seat of Wise," and all I got was some black looks. Then I said, "We let it all ride. A hundred and twenty-eight dollars is begging."

Captain Squatty went through a little door in the front of the owner's cabin and came back with a roll of bills you could have wadded a cannon with. He counted them out, and with what Fishmouth dug out of his jeans they finally got our pile of money covered. There on the cabin floor was two hundred and fifty-six dollars—half ours and half theirs—and one more pass was all we needed to break up the game. I looked at Claudie, and I could see he was ready. He was lightning ready to strike, and he did! He rolled a great big sparkling eleven, and it got so quiet we could hear the oysters clapping their shells together on the bottom of Rockport Bay.

Captain Squatty spoke up first; he said he was out of cash, but he had a government bond in the bank at Port Lavaca; he wondered if he could put in his I.O.U. to cover the two hundred and fifty-six dollars.

"Sure. Let's have it," I told him, so he wrote it out on the back of an envelope and put it on top of the pile of bills there on the cabin floor. By this time Claudie had a wild, rich look in his eyes, like a trapeze artist taking a bow. He was blowing on the dice and whispering soft words to them. Captain Squatty was pale as a ghost, and little beads of sweat were cropping out all over his face, but he said, "Go ahead, Claudie, and shoot; but you'd better roll them hard against the bulkhead."

"Against the what?" Claudie asked.

"The door to the head, right there in front of you," the Captain told him. He was almost fussy with Claudie, I thought.

Claudie snorted like a mule colt as he came out with the dice. "Come seven," he said in a hoarse voice. The bones bounced against the door and settled back on the soft rug—a six and an ace.

"Seven it is," I said as I picked up the pile of bills and Captain Squatty's I.O.U. "You can't beat a shooter that is in tune with the sky."

After all the others left, I and Claudie stayed on the boat a little while to speak with Captain Squatty alone about the I.O.U.; but before we could, he went to the icebox and got out three bottles of cold beer. A little color came back to Captain Squatty's face as he swigged the beer, and he licked his lips where they'd been drying up after Claudie's last roll; then he said, "Gents, I am worried about that I.O.U. you've got there."

"We're not, Captain Squatty," I told him. "You can get your I.O.U. back in the morning when you cash the bond."

He swallowed, and his face got the color of the underside of a raw oyster. "Trouble is," he said, "the bond ain't enough to do it. It's only a twenty-five-dollar bond."

Claudie began to count on his fingers, and I said, "Captain, I wouldn't worry a minute about the difference. It ain't but two hundred and thirty-one dollars."

He lit a cigarette and took a drag that burnt it about halfway down before he said, "That's what I figure it, but I haven't got the money."

"Think nothing of it, Captain," I said. "I and Claudie can take it out in board and room on this yacht. We'll use this room right here and credit you with ten dollars every day we stay. Before long it'll be paid out."

Captain Squatty said, "But this is the owner's cabin—"

Then I cut in, "And now I wonder if you could pass us another couple of bottles of that nice cold beer. We're going to like it here fine."

II

The next morning it was cloudy and a little cooler, so I and Claudie slept late. As I was waking up, I thought what a shame and a waste it was for those lovely mattresses not to be used every night of the world. When Captain Squatty came from the little room in the front of the boat where he had his bunk, I told him that I and Claudie had one weakness we hoped he could get used to.

"What's that?" he asked.

"We like our breakfast in bed. The other meals we get up and dress for."

Without a word, Captain Squatty went into the kitchen and started pumping away on the alcohol stove.

"Claudie," I said, "would you like a little coffee first, or with your breakfast?"

"I like coffee first thing, Clint," Claudie answered.

"Hear that, Captain Squatty?" I yelled. "I and Claudie like coffee first; one lump for me and two for him. No cream please; we like it hot and black."

After breakfast we got dressed, and I sent Claudie up to the garage to get the burnt-out bearing on our car fixed. "See about a new battery too, Claudie," I told him as he left. "I like for a battery to turn the starter over fast, and you might want a coon or fox tail for the radiator cap. Get it if you like."

While Captain Squatty cleaned up the kitchen and washed the dishes, I went out on the rear end of the boat and stood under the awning to study the sky. Higher up it was solid gray, and dark clouds were rolling in low from the gulf. The gusty air had the feel of worse weather coming, and I called Captain Squatty out to speak with him about it.

"Tell me, Captain," I said, "what do you make of this weather?"

"The glass is low, Clint," he answered.

"The what?" I asked.

"The barometer," he said. "It's below twenty-nine. There's a hurricane somewhere out there in the gulf."

"Don't tell Claudie," I said. "He's always been afraid of storms."

But when Claudie came back to the yacht around noon, he had already heard about it. In fact, he said, the town was pretty full of hurricane talk. The storm was still way down in the Gulf of Mexico, close to Yucatán, they were saying, but it could blow in anywhere along the gulf coast.

The next day the sky looked a lot better, and there was almost no wind at all. The talk along the waterfront was that the hurricane was about to peter out down around Mexico somewhere. Captain Squatty said the glass was higher, and told me he liked the feel of the weather. I said, "Couldn't we fire up this here yacht, Captain, and go out there in the bay and catch ourselves a nice mess of fish?"

"I can't do it," he answered.

"I don't know why," I said. "We'll credit you ten dollars on the I.O.U. for every fishing trip we make."

"Mr. Easley's orders are not to move the *Pride of Texas* from this dock except for a hurricane."

"What?" I asked him. "You mean you would go right out in a hurricane?"

"Sure," he said. "In case of a big blow, the *Pride of Texas* would be bashed all to hell against this dock here if I left it tied up. Out in the bay you can anchor a boat and ride it out. That's part of my job; to pull out in the bay if there's a hurricane coming."

The next morning our car was ready to run again, so we left Claudie to watch the boat and the weather while I drove Captain Squatty over to Port Lavaca to get our bond. We cashed it for twenty-five dollars, and I marked up the Captain's payment on the I.O.U. I gave him credit for another twenty dollars to cover the two days we had lived on the boat and another five dollars on account of the Captain's fine cooking. That cut it down to two hundred and six dollars.

On the way back from Port Lavaca, the sun broke through

253

the clouds, and Captain Squatty said he believed that old hurricane must have blown itself out somewhere.

"Don't be too sure," I answered; "the sky don't look too good, and the air don't feel right to me yet."

The Captain grunted and said, "I just think you want to go fishing, Clint, but you wouldn't get me in any more trouble with Mr. Easley then I'm already in, would you?"

"The last thing I'd want to do," I told him, "would be to get you in trouble with Mr. Easley."

The next morning there wasn't a cloud in the sky, the water was clear and blue, and the air felt fresh and clean. A lot of fishing boats shoved off early. I and Claudie got up, and dressed for breakfast. Captain Squatty served it to us on the rear end of the boat under the awning. While he was bringing us toothpicks, I credited him with ten more dollars for another day; then, while I was at it, I credited him with another ten dollars for the next day and said, "Captain, from here on we're going to pay in advance every day. See here, this I.O.U. is down now to a hundred and eighty-six dollars."

Captain Squatty only nodded his head and chewed a while on one of his thumbnails.

After breakfast Claudie went to get us some cards and cigars and bring Captain Squatty's mail back from the post office. We smoked and played pitch all morning on the deck while the Captain freshened up the boat. He wiped all the windows with a chamois skin; he swept the boat out from one end to the other and waxed the floors and the wood inside; then he hosed and mopped the outside of the boat and polished all the brass on it. By noon there wasn't anything about the boat that wasn't shining, except our cigarette trays, and Captain Squatty emptied them and wiped the ashes out inside. Then he went to the store where Mr. Easley had a charge account and bought provisions for the day.

When Captain Squatty came back with a big basket full of groceries and things, I asked him how the glass was, and he said, "Rising; the hurricane must be gone."

"That's what I want to speak to you about, Captain," I told him. "I have a feeling about the weather"

254

"The glass is good enough for me," he answered as he went down to the kitchen with the food. I followed him down there and left Claudie at the card table.

"Captain Hinder," I spoke very serious and firm, "suppose you got warned that a hurricane was coming and you didn't take the *Pride of Texas, III,* out in the bay to ride it out. Then if a hurricane did come, you'd really be in trouble with Mr. Easley, wouldn't you?"

"I'll say I would," he answered.

"Well," I said, "I'm warning you, Captain; there may be a hurricane. Don't tell Claudie; he's afraid of storms, but I figure we'd better get this yacht out in the bay."

The Captain's jaw tightened up, and his eyes seemed to get smaller, but he didn't say a word.

"Of course," I went on, "we can fish until it comes up. We'll give you an extra sixteen dollars' credit for the trip. That'll cut the I.O.U. down to a hundred and seventy dollars. I'll bet you never thought you'd work it off so fast!"

"I'll do it if you credit me with twenty-six dollars for the trip," he answered, and I took him up in a hurry.

I pulled out the I.O.U., wrote the credit on the back, and showed it to him. "See?" I said. "Paid in advance."

Captain Squatty fired up the motors while Claudie untied us from the docks, and we took off. As we hummed along through the water with the motors singing together, I and Claudie sat back in the deck chairs on the rear end smoking cigars and feeding bread crumbs to the gulls.

"Claudie," I said, "this is the way a man should live every day of his life. A lot of people get themselves so tangled up in work that they never take time to pleasure themselves; they get old before they learn to enjoy the finer things in this great big world. Take Mr. Easley; I'll bet he's up there in Canada bothering himself about taxes and expenses the way the government is spending money all the time."

"I shore feel sorry for Mr. Easley," Claudie said.

When we got out in the middle of Copano Bay, we saw a big bunch of gulls working above the water, close to a little green island, and the Captain said that was a very good sign, the gulls were eating mullet that had been driven to the top of the water by a school of bigger fish. We circled the island and found that the gulls were working above a long narrow reef where the water was light green and so shallow that the waves broke and splashed in a line along the surface. Captain Hinder said it was an oyster reef where the fishing was sometimes good. He eased the boat across the blue channel that lay betwixt the island and the reef and backed us up to the edge of the green water. He showed Claudie how to throw the anchor over, and we settled down to fish from the rear end of the boat.

Mr. Easley had the fanciest hooks and lines and winding reels I ever saw anywhere. Captain Squatty rigged our tackle and baited our hooks with shrimp, and from the first the fishing was fine. We caught speckled trout, gaff-top catfish, croakers, whiting, and a few little sharks that we threw back. Claudie caught a sting ray about the size of a catcher's mitt, and that long stinger whipping around scared Claudie aplenty. I stepped inside the boat and watched Claudie dodge and dance away from the sting ray until Captain Squatty got it back in the water.

The sun was slipping behind a big blue cloud bank in the west, and we had the fish box half full when Captain Squatty pointed out that the other fishing boats were leaving.

"We better get back to Rockport, Clint," he said. "It'll take us an hour or more."

"You must be forgetting my warning, Captain Hinder," I said, looking him straight in the eye. He looked down.

"What warning?" Claudie wanted to know.

"Never mind, Claudie," I said. "We'll be on the reef at daylight, and that's when fishing is always best."

The Captain moved the boat away from the edge of the reef into the deeper water, and Claudie threw the anchor in the water. He was getting very handy with it. Captain Squatty fried us a mess of fresh fish in corn meal, and we had a big supper on the yacht. We washed it down with cold beer. The slap, slap of the water against the sides and the easy sway of the boat back and forth made us sleepy on top of all that food and beer, so we turned in early.

III

When a man has got himself used to the finer things in life, it jolts him to be roused in the middle of a deep sleep. This thought bruised my mind way in the middle of the night when I felt the boat take a big sway that batted my face up against the magazine rack next to my bunk. I wondered why they couldn't put shock absorbers around the owner's cabin to save him from such rough movements of the boat. Then Claudie said, "What the hell was that we hit?"

Captain Squatty came in and turned on the lights. He said that a big wave had hit the boat.

"It ain't gonna sink, is it?" Claudie wanted to know as he got up and started buttoning his shirt.

"No, Claudie," I told him, "it ain't gonna sink," but I wasn't too sure, since by this time the yacht was rolling and swaying around more than ever. Then another wave hit us, and a lot of water flew in the porthole by my bunk and sprinkled me all over. It tasted salty.

"Captain Hinder," I said, "take a look at the glass." He did and said it was low and falling.

"Here's your hurricane," I told him. "I'm glad your dad-gummed glass has found out about it."

Then another wave hit and slammed us all down on one side of the owner's cabin. It broke loose the pots and pans below, and you couldn't have matched the racket they made if you'd beaten a tow sack full of tin cans against the bottom of a wash-tub.

We went out on the rear end and, sure enough, it was blowing hard, and the rain was coming down in sheets. The awning was flapping around back there, popping in the wind like a buggy whip, until Captain Squatty finally got it down and brought it inside. Then the hurricane really got into high gear.

I've seen the wind blow the wash right off a clothesline, and I've seen it blow knotholes out of pine fences, but that was on dry land. It's worse on the water. The wind was coming in gusts; hard, howling gusts, each one stronger and longer and louder, un-

257

til I had a feeling deep in my insides that something had to give somewhere; then it would ease up a little before it came again, harder each time than the time before, until the *Pride of Texas, III,* was bobbing around like a dead fly in a churn.

I told Claudie how the yacht was better off where we were, and he tried to believe me, but all he could say was, "I've allus been scared of storms." He began to gulp and swallow like an old tomcat with a fish bone in his throat, and a light skim came over his eyes. He turned green around his mouth and chin like the sticky, gummy green of scums that form on stagnant water. He said he might be a little sick if the wind didn't die down pretty soon. It didn't, but as it went on and on, howling and screaming and whining out there, we got down on the floor of the boat and tried to get used to it—as used to it, that is, as a man can get to that much wind. For a long time nothing happened except a whole lot more of the same thing, and Captain Squatty told us that was about all there'd be to riding out the hurricane. Claudie said he figured that was enough.

When daylight came it made us feel better to see that we were still where we'd been the night before and not away off somewhere in the middle of a stormy ocean. The little island was right where it had been, and on the other side the waves were still piling up and breaking over the reef, but the water wasn't green any more; it was muddy gray. The gusts were getting easier by the time it was broad-open day, and the rain was pouring almost straight down in between them. In an hour it was dead calm, and Claudie was looking more like himself. He said his liver was still bothering him some, though, and he believed he'd go back to bed.

"I wouldn't," Captain Squatty told him. "It's only half over. The center is passing us now. In a little while we'll have the other half."

He was a man who knew his hurricanes all right, and pretty soon the wind started to blow again—but from the other direction. The yacht swung around on the anchor rope so that the rear end was pointed toward the reef, and the island was up ahead. We drank some coffee while we could, and by the time we were through, the hurricane was up to full steam again—and then

258

some. It was raining harder again, and it was raining plumb side-ways—that's how hard the wind was blowing.

"Two halves of a hurricane is all they is, ain't they?" Claudie asked once between gusts.

"Certainly, Claudie," I told him. "You got that far in arithmetic, I know."

I don't know what made me glance out in front of the boat as it swung back and forth against the anchor and rolled in the wind, but when I did I saw that something awful had happened to the island. It was a long way off. First I thought it had moved, and then I knew it must have been the yacht moving. Captain Squatty saw it at almost the same time that I did; then we looked back of us, and there were the waves piling up on the reef not fifty feet away. The Captain's little eyes got big, and he said, "Good God, we're dragging anchor!"

"How's that?" Claudie asked.

"We're dragging anchor," he said. "If we pile up on that oyster reef, there won't be a piece of this here yacht big enough to pick your teeth with. Get up on the bow and get ready to raise the anchor. I'll start the motors."

I said, "Who? Me?" as Squatty ran to start the motors and yelled, "Both of you, or it'll be too late."

I looked at Claudie, and Claudie looked ready. We went through Captain Squatty's cubbyhole to the lid that opened on the front of the boat where the anchor rope was tied.

"Go on, Claudie," I said. "I'm coming behind you." He opened the lid, and when he did a gust of wet wind swept through it and slapped us down on the floor.

"Go ahead," I urged him, "we haven't got much time," and somehow Claudie got his six and a half foot bulk through the hatch. Then I got out, and we both held onto the little stob on the front of the boat where the anchor rope was tied. We were in a long, high gust that got harder and stronger until I felt like it would buckle in my eardrums if it got any worse.

Finally we both got a good hold on the anchor rope. It was tight, and I could feel a quiver in it as the anchor would give and drag a little. I knew that anchor was plowing a furrow there on the bot-

259

tom of the bay. I looked back once and saw that on one of our long swings against the anchor the rear end of the yacht was nearly even with the breakers on the reef. I figured we might clear it once more, but I figured if we did, it would be the last time. When the wind slacked between gusts, I knew it was our last time to get her away before all hell broke loose on the rear end. By this time the motors were whining and groaning, and we could feel the whole boat throb as they fought against the wind. We eased forward a little, and I and Claudie pulled the rope in and kept it tight, coiling up the slack behind us. Finally, we were right over the anchor, and the rope went straight down from the front of the boat.

"It's now or never, Claudie," I yelled, and we heisted hard on it, but the anchor wouldn't budge.

Claudie reached down and got another hold on the rope; I got one just behind him, and we pulled with everything we had. I could see the big veins standing out on his neck like chicken guts, and it seemed that new muscles rose up around his eyes and ears as he strained to lift it. But the anchor was stuck solid in the bottom of Copano Bay. Captain Squatty was yelling something at us, but it wasn't any use. You couldn't hear anything above the roar of another gust that was building up, and by that time we were pulling as hard as we knew how, just to hold our own. Then we weren't holding our own; we had to pay out some rope or go over with it, and I yelled, "Latch it onto the stob, Claudie, or we'll be back where we started."

Claudie wrapped the anchor rope several times around the stob there, as the gust blew out, and then the boat was pitching and rolling hard against the tight rope. That was what broke the anchor out, and as soon as it gave way, we pulled the rope in until the anchor was out of the water. I could see we were moving forward, away from the reef, with both motors screaming and straining down in the heart of the *Pride of Texas, III*.

In a few minutes we were clear out in the deep water, a hundred yards or more away from the reef, and Captain Squatty was yelling and motioning for us to drop the anchor again. We did, and this time it held. We got back down into the boat and closed the lid as another gust came and grew into full flow. Then

Claudie was sick—very sick—but Captain Squatty said it was all right, since he'd cleaned up after seasick people before.

The hurricane petered out almost as fast as it had come. In an hour or so the yacht settled down to an easy roll, and the rain slacked up, but none of this cured Claudie. He was stretched out on the floor of the owner's cabin, blinking his eyes and swallowing.

Around noon we pulled up the anchor and started back. As we left Copano Bay and headed south for Rockport, the water was plumb smooth again. I got out Captain Squatty's I.O.U., and gave him credit for another day's room and board, and showed him how this cut it down to a hundred and fifty dollars.

Then I went down to the owner's cabin to check up on Claudie. He was still on the floor, and he had laid beside him some things out of his pockets—wet matches, cigars, a deck of cards, and a letter. When I saw the letter was addressed to Captain Earl Hinder and postmarked Fort Worth, I said, "Where the hell did you get that, Claudie?"

"At the post office, whenever it was I went to get the mail," he answered and rolled over on his stomach. "I must have forgot to give it to Captain Squatty."

I took it up to the Captain, and as he read it, the muscles started working and quivering around his jawbones. He said, "It's from Mr. Easley. He will be here Tuesday night with two guests."

"Tuesday night was last night," I reminded him.

"Oh, my God!" he yelled. "I'm ruined."

"Ruined?" I said. "What do you mean ruined? Suppose you hadn't taken the *Pride of Texas, III,* out on Tuesday?"

By this time we were getting close to Rockport, and we could see what an awful mess the hurricane had made there. Tree limbs and chunks of wood were floating all around in the water. Four of the other yachts were partly sunk, and the back end of another one was battered and busted plumb out. There wasn't a one of them that wasn't bashed in one way or the other. One yacht, a blue one nearly as big as ours, was turned over and half sunk. There was a hole in the bottom a horse could have walked through.

A crowd of people stood there on the docks looking at all the damage, and as we eased up to the place where the *Pride of Texas, III,* belonged, they all came over toward us. They grabbed our ropes and helped us tie up, and we climbed back onto dry land.

Mr. Easley was there to meet us. He was a nice little gray-haired man, all macked out in sport clothes. He shook hands with Captain Squatty and shook hands with us.

"Any damage to the *Pride of Texas, III?*" he asked.

"None, sir," Captain Squatty said, standing straight and looking Mr. Easley in the eye.

"Hinder," he said, "you are a real skipper. I knew you could smell out a blow if anybody could."

Squatty said, "Mr. Easley, I couldn't have done it without the help of these two fine seamen here, Clint and Claudie."

Mr. Easley beamed on us and took out a big green roll. He peeled off a hundred-dollar bill and handed it to me. He gave Claudie one, too, and said he wondered if it was a big enough tip at that.

"Mr. Easley," I stated, "this is your change," and I gave him fifty dollars out of the roll we'd won in the crap game.

"I don't get it, fellows," he said.

"I and my associate, Claudie, are professional men," I said. "We do not work for tips. A hundred and fifty is all we are due, and that is all we will take. If you feel like it, you might want to give that extra fifty to Captain Squatty, though. He's a fine skipper."

Robert Thomas Allen

One of Canada's outstanding writers, Robert Thomas Allen's casual but keen humor has crossed the International Boundary, has penetrated south of the border as far as Ohio, Kansas, and Kentucky, and is read even as far to the east as New York City. A native of Toronto, Allen was born June 5, 1911, and, he admits, very little of interest happened to him for quite a while. While still in his teens, Allen worked in the advertising department of a department store, became a copywriter, and emboldened himself to launch out as a free-lance writer. Today he is a celebrated journalist, and one of the mainstays of *MacLean's Magazine*. He is something of a specialist in man's inhumanity to woman, and vice versa; his contribution to the preceding *Best Humor Annual* details the difficulties of teaching your wife to drive and solving the mystery of a woman's hair-do. As for recent data, Allen replied: "Nothing much has happened to me since last year that could be printed in a book, except that I became 40. But most of the things I have to say about that couldn't be printed in a book either. Also I've moved to a farm in Eastern Ontario, have become very interested in astronomy, my eldest daughter came fifth in a spelling contest, I've got to like cochina soup, I read *The Horse's Mouth,* I nearly broke my back on my other daughter's eighth birthday trying to jump and touch the ceiling, I've had four teeth filled, learned to do the crawl, gave up drinking, and can now identify Scotch Pine."

Allen adds that he received more violent letters about the woman's-sense-of-humor piece which follows than any other article he had ever written. One woman said that the only funny thing about him was the fact that he had got someone to marry him.

Women Have No Sense of Humor *

When I was six I said to a little girl who lived next door, "I bet I can stand two inches away from you and you can't touch me."

"How?" she asked.

"By standing behind a door." I laughed so hard that marbles and chestnuts rolled out of my pants pockets.

The little girl looked at me as if I were a frog. "What's so funny

* Reprinted from *Maclean's* Magazine, Toronto.

263

about that? *Nobody* could touch you if you were silly enough to stand behind a door."

I gave up fooling around with women then until I was seventeen. Then one night when I called on a girl named Lorna Gulch to take her to a movie I rolled up my pant legs, creased my hat into a shape like a canoe, pulled my coat down off my shoulders, brought my front teeth out over my bottom lip, and rang the bell.

When Lorna opened the door Mr. and Mrs. Gulch were standing beside her. The old man took one look at me, let out a great wheezing roar, bent over and whacked his knee, went into a coughing fit and finally said through his tears, "By golly, son, that's the funniest thing I ever seen. Come in. Come in. You old enough to take a nip of dandelion wine?"

Lorna, in the meantime, looked at my rolled-up pants, then at my hat, then right past me at the autumn night and said, "Do you think I'll need a topcoat?"

Her mother looked at me: "Something has dented your hat, Mr. Allen?"

Later on I got married. I found out a lot of things about women, but one thing always threw me, and still does: I haven't yet been able to figure out a woman's sense of humor.

Women either laugh at the wrong time or at the wrong joke or they don't laugh at all while I'm slapping my forehead and howling. I know one quaint little elderly woman who says: "Hmmmm —then what?" after the joke is over; and another who laughs all the way through the joke until the punch line, then sobers up and asks me where I'm living now.

I've found that women either don't laugh at any dirty joke or they laugh at all dirty jokes, whether they're funny or not. I've seen my best jokes go as flat as if I'd read the instructions from a box of cereal; yet more than once I've sneaked in the back way during a bridal shower or afternoon bridge and sat on the cellar steps listening to hysterical feminine laughter from upstairs, burning with curiosity about what they were laughing at, and concluding that the women were all making faces at one another or reading out their husbands' old love letters.

The whole thing, of course, is that the humor in a joke doesn't come from the joke itself, but from a lot of mental pictures, ideas, feelings, and associations that the joke suggests. A person whose interior atmosphere is made up of mental pictures of new living-room drapes, wall paints, cute little spring suits, permanents, Gregory Peck, and half-inch bias tape is sure to see things differently from a person whose psyche evolves around main bearings, lake trout, eager-eyed little stenographers, prize fights, and the income-tax department.

One thing, for instance, that makes a woman an entirely different audience is the fact that she is essentially more practical. She carries around with her a solid ballast of down-to-earth realism that won't let her bounce very high. This is one reason for the dismal way they react to shaggy-dog stories, which derive their humor from being directly contrary to all normal channels of reasoning.

The first week after our honeymoon I came home fresh from a couple of quick ones with the boys at the office, and as soon as I got in the door I said: "You want to hear a really funny joke, honey? Well, there was a guy, see, and every day he sat in a restaurant with a piece of celery behind his ear. Then one day he put an onion behind his ear, and another guy who had been watching him every day couldn't stand it any longer so he went over and said, 'Say, Mac, why you got an onion behind your ear?' and the guy says, 'They didn't have any celery.' " The last words I just got out before I collapsed on our only easy chair, wheezing and gasping in helpless mirth.

My wife said, "Why didn't they have any celery?"

I broke off in the middle of a guffaw. "Well, I mean, the thing is, see this guy always put a piece of celery behind his ear—"

"That reminds me," my wife said absently. "We're having Bill and Grace over tonight. We need some cheese."

For the rest of the evening until our company arrived I didn't try anything funnier than asking whether my blue suit needed pressing. That night I told the joke to Bill and Grace.

Bill put his head back and let out a great belly laugh. Grace smiled amiably and said, "Celery is so expensive, too," then turned to my wife and said, "I said to myself just today that if food prices keep going up I'll have to get a husband that makes more money."

At this my wife let out a shriek and the two girls went into gales

265

of laughter while Bill and I sat there solemnly sucking olives.

From that time on I tried to figure out a woman's sense of humor. I tried different kinds of jokes. I kept it up after our two daughters had arrived. It got worse.

A woman doesn't give herself over to pure play as readily as a man, which is the reason most women can take a drink or leave it alone, whereas most men just take it. A man will hold up a business conference, sales talk, speech, or introduction to tell a joke. A woman will listen to one when the dishes are done and the kids are safe with a sitter and she's out for the evening. In between she gives only a fraction of her mind to it, which isn't enough.

I remember one time I told my wife the one about the Englishman whose wife had died. "You want to hear a really funny joke, dear?" I said. "Well, there were two old guys sitting in an English club, see, and one says: 'Sorry to hear you buried your wife this morning, old boy,' and the other"—here I added a toothy effect that I thought was a pretty good imitation of a Colonel Blimp—"the other Englishman said, 'Yes. Had to. Dead, you know.'"

My wife looked at me with the same expression she'd started with. We both looked at one another. My smile felt as if it were falling off my face in chunks.

"What did she die of?" my wife asked.

"Look," I said, flushing. "One guy says, 'Sorry to hear you buried your wife—'"

"I got that part," my wife said. "And don't start shouting. How can I understand a joke when you won't explain it to me?"

"Well, for—look—the *OTHER* guy says—"

"Just a minute." My wife reached across the table and fed Mary a couple of spoonfuls of spinach. "Now, what were you saying? Is this the same story?"

I gritted my teeth. "There was a guy—"

"Can I have some more milk?" Jane asked.

"You're old enough to get it for yourself," my wife said. Then, turning to me, "That reminds me, you forgot to put the milk bottles out last night."

"I'M TELLING A JOKE," I hollered, pounding the table. "THERE WERE TWO GUYS—"

266

"If you're going to act that way," my wife said, "I don't want to hear it."

On the occasions when a woman does give herself over completely to a joke she does it the way she drives a car—all enthusiasm for the objective but little interest in how she gets there. Sometimes my wife laughs as hard as I do at the end, then says something that makes me wonder just what she's been laughing at.

I remember one time I told her a joke about a connoisseur of rare foods who had tasted every kind of food but *poi,* and who had taken four months to reach a remote Pacific island by ship, launch, dug-out canoe, and pack mule, just to taste a very special kind that was prepared by one of the islanders. When he finally reached the tiny eating place, the proprietor beamed and said: "Sure a-mister. We gotta apple a-poi, a-strawberry poi, a-cherry poi, a-peacha-poi."

My wife laughed as hard as I did. When she'd stopped she wiped the tears from her eyes and said, "What did the other man do with it?"

"What did the other man do with what?"

"What did the man do with the mule?"

There's another reason why things often go flat when a man tries to make a woman laugh. It's not the joke that's wrong, but the fact that a man is telling it. A woman thinks a man is funny most of the time, although she rarely lets him know. I've seen women go into hysterics telling one another how their husbands shop, or the way they pamper their cars, or behave with blondes. But to have a *man* start thinking he's funny spoils the joke. It's like children being shown how to act cute, or dogs dressed up like professors. One thing cancels out the other.

After seeing some of my best jokes torn to shreds I made the mistake of thinking that something of a more visual, slapstick nature might go over better. I had a party-act at the time that used to have the boys hollering encores. It was an imitation of a certain type of girl playing the piano. It was very funny. At least, it had been while I was single.

The first time I tried it at a party after I was married my wife just sat there looking at me as if she wished there had been marriage schools in her day. She didn't say anything about it but, from then on, whenever she referred back to the party she always said, "You know, that night you made such an ass of yourself."

Practical jokes once got me into an awful mess. I lived next door to a chap who told me of a trick he'd pulled on his wife. One night he'd gone to bed a few minutes ahead of her, left the light out, and crawled under the sheets with his head at the foot of the bed and his feet on the pillow. The idea fascinated me. I tried it the night after he'd told me about it, and lay there waiting for a startled shriek followed by a burst of appreciative laughter.

My wife didn't notice that my head wasn't on the pillow for about five minutes. Then she said: "WHAT on EARTH! . . ."

I sat up at the foot of the bed, grinning from ear to ear, waiting for the full humor of the situation to strike my wife.

She looked at me with a puzzled expression. "Why are you sleeping that way?"

"It was just for fun." I was beginning to feel silly already.

She looked at me with a worried little frown. The next night she told my mother about it. My mother said that even when I was a boy I hadn't liked a hard pillow. The following day my wife told her girl friend who was visiting her from Waterloo about it, as an illustration of how *different* writers are; and she was still telling people about it a week later when Grace and Bill were over for the evening. Grace looked at me with a quizzical yet friendly smile.

"With his feet on the *pillow?*" she said. "I could never sleep that way. My head always has to be higher than my feet."

I found that it wasn't just *my* wife's sense of humor I couldn't figure out. I ran into the same trouble with other guys' wives. Occasionally at a party when things got rolling and one or two of the girls would tell a couple of jokes of a biological type, I'd dig up a juicy one of my own. The girls, including my wife, would all stop laughing. They'd look at their shoes, then turn to one another and say brightly, "Your hair looks lovely since you let the ends grow." The whole thing would leave me feeling the way I do in one of those dreams where I suddenly find myself Christmas shopping in my pyjama tops.

268

Women Have No Sense of Humor

I've gradually learned to tread lightly when it comes to mixing humor with women. Now I save my jokes till the boys are out in the kitchen watching me measure the drinks, and let the women go on talking about the little summer dress they picked up for next to nothing. Then dropping their voice to a whisper and bursting out into gales of laughter.

Someday, somehow, I'll find out what's so funny.

Ken Englund

Ken Englund's credits fill half a dozen crowded pages. He has written (and ghost-written) sketches, vaudeville routines, radio shows, screen plays, mysteries, farces, romances, musicals, and philosophical comedies, including a joint adaptation of Shaw's "Androcles and the Lion" from a play into a screenplay. Born in Chicago, Illinois, Englund studied engineering at Lane Tech and, before he entered his teens, started cartooning. At twelve he sold his first effort to *The American Boy;* between twelve and eighteen he saw his cartoons and gags published in the old *Life* and *Judge.* He began to "make" O. O. McIntyre's and Walter Winchell's columns, after which he wrote a weekly column for a local butcher's window. "The butcher wanted to be known as a neighborhood wit," writes Englund, "so I ghosted the column for him and titled it 'Gabriel Over the Butchershop.' Later in life I wrote for peanuts, but this time it was for liver sausage—which was what I got paid off in." At fifteen he won a story contest run by RKO. It was the fifth prize and it netted him $50.00. "At my mother's urging, I placed it carefully in the bank—and the bank crash came next day."

Englund's first steady job was with Phil Baker. He was hired, says Englund "on the strength of my loud ties and one joke submitted for Baker's radio show: 'Things are so bad in Hollywood that King Kong is working for an organ-grinder.' " Ever since then (1929) Englund's career has been a series of successes; he has been connected with stage, screen, and radio not only as play doctor and adviser but as playwright. At present he is writing the story and screenplay for the first Sid Caesar-Imogene Coca film. Both his children are prominent in the entertainment world. His son, George, is an actor-director; his daughter, Patricia, is a charming actress who played "Oklahoma's" Ado Annie in America and England.

The Day Hollywood Stood Still*

AFTER PRESENTATION CREDIT:
HYPERTHYROID PICTURES PRESENT—and the trade-mark
—a midget with a sucker hitting a mothball—TITLE appears:
 'THE DAY HOLLYWOOD STOOD STILL'

* Reprinted from *Variety.*

270

OVERSHOTS OF: Worlds colliding, shooting stars shooting, the Aurora Borealis; and generally milking the Milky Way for whatever it's worth pictorially.

FADE IN:

INT. BOARD ROOM OF THE CHEMICAL BANK—N. Y. C.—DAY—MEDIUM FULL SHOT—THE MEMBERS OF THE BOARD AND PRESIDENT ZORAB.

(*The latter presiding. Zorab, Salmon P. Zorab to be exact, wears an iron-gray, crew cut, is Princeton '08, and the scion of a fine old Wall Streetfaring family.*)

ZORAB: Then it is generally agreed, gentlemen, that we finance the Doctor's mission knowing full well the risks?

(*There are grave, white-haired nods of agreement.*)

ZORAB: (*into intercom speaker*) Send in the Doctor——

(*Zorab presses a concealed button and the thick doors open to permit DOCTOR SIGISMUND SPACE to enter. He wears a Rocket Suit, smog helmet, ray and Flit guns in his belt, an electric blanket strapped to his back. He slides open the glass panel in his smog helmet permitting him to speak. He has the slightest trace of a Brooklyn accent, but it is charming.*)

DR. SPACE: Gentlemen, everything is in readiness. I only hope that you have all agreed——

ZORAB: We have, Doctor (*the Doctor beams*). And we feel that the Space Ship you have built could reach its destination. BUT, once there, can you exist long enough to complete your mission?

DR. SPACE: I've taken that all into account. We know there is some life there different from ours. We also have reason to believe that somehow the inhabitants exist in an atmosphere dense with a substance called smog. This will not, as you see, catch us unprepared. (*Taps his helmet proudly. It echoes hollowly.*)

ZORAB: That answers that question. Who are you taking with you beside The Thing? You'll only have room for two more and, in all fairness, of the thousands of scientists who have begged to go, I hope you have chosen the two that'll be the most use to you.

DR. SPACE: I have. (*Speaking into radar phone mouthpiece attached to helmet.*)

271

Send in Doctor O'Day.

(*The doors open, admitting a beautiful lady scientist, measuring 38-23-36. She wears the regulation lady scientist's rocket attire, tight satin blouse, short skirt, 4-inch heels, and an ankle bracelet inscribed with scientific calculations. The board sits up and collectively straightens its tie. One or two arteries are heard softly snapping.*)

ZORAB: (*frowning at Dr. Space*) This lady is a scientist?

DR. SPACE: One of the greatest, Doctor Dawn O'Day. The most notable living authority on oxygen——

DR. O'DAY: (*deadpan—automatically*) Oxygen O.K.

DR. SPACE: (*sotto voce*) Not yet, dear. (*To Zorab*) Her experiments with lung expansion are enormous——

ZORAB: And your other teammate?

DR. SPACE: (*into radar phone*) Send in Dr. Latour.

(*The doors open and the second beautiful lady scientist enters—36-25-38—attired in the same costume as her sister scientist. The board gapes.*)

DR. SPACE: Doctor Taffy Latour, gentlemen, greatest living authority on elevation and guided missiles.

DR. LATOUR: (*solemnly, efficiently*) Raise the elevators!

DR. SPACE: Doctor Latour is also the daughter of Professor Latour at Columbia, helping to finance her aged father's experiments in the effects of hot air by dancing at the Copa along with Doctor O'Day.

ZORAB: Well, you seem to have chosen wisely. After all, it is your rocket and it is a long tedious trip——

DR. LATOUR: Raise the elevators.

DR. SPACE: (*redfaced*) Not yet, Doctor. (*To Zorab*) And now, sir, any last-minute instructions? I've already read my sealed orders. I thought you wouldn't mind. I had to know which way to point the rocket—they can be balky things——

ZORAB: Yes—well then you know that you are to try to reach the West Coast with The Thing intact.

DR. O'DAY: Huh?

DR. SPACE: Never mind, Doctor——

ZORAB: The last two men we sent on this vital mission never reached there by rail. We have reports, unconfirmed, that they got

272

off at Phoenix by mistake and are now selling Indian blankets.

DR. SPACE: Poor devils!

ZORAB: And, remember, DeMille couldn't even find the place at first, and has never returned or been heard of since!

DR. SPACE: Don't worry, chief—we'll be back.

ZORAB: One more thing.

(*He goes to a wall graph charting the rise and fall of the various motion picture stocks.*)

ZORAB: Whether these go up or whether these go down depends on your successful carrying out of secret plan RW.

DR. SPACE: We won't fail the Chemical Bank, sir. And now I believe we'll take off——

DR. O'DAY: Oxygen O.K.

DR. SPACE: (*gently*) Not yet—not till we get in the rocket.

DR. O'DAY: Oh, I haven't even seen your old rocket anyway! I'll bet you don't even have one— (*The board laughs good-naturedly.*)

ZORAB: Have the girls—I mean Doctors—everything they need? Are those flying suits going to be—er—adequate?

DR. SPACE: Oh, these are just their launching skirts. Their flight attire is more practical for fooling around the controls.

(*Doctors O'Day and Latour, demonstrating, step out of their launching skirts to stand revealed in black lace rocket flight pants. The bank's President Emeritus faints dead away.*)

ZORAB: (*to Dr. Space enviously*) Godspeed!

DISSOLVE

EXT. ROCKET LAUNCHING GROUNDS—NIGHT—FULL SHOT—THE SPACE SHIP—THE BOARD IN F. G.

(*Zorab and the Board wave good-by as the three Doctors enter the ship, Dr. Space stopping at the fuselage door to wave back.*)

DR. SPACE: And away we go!

(*Zorab breaks a roll of quarters over the nose of the rocket, the explosive gas bursts into flame at the tail, and the ship takes off. SOUND EFFECT: SWISH!*)

DISSOLVE

EXT. STRATOSPHERE—LONG SHOT—NEAR SATURN (*The space ship is skyrocketing through the heavens.*) INT. SPACE SHIP—MEDIUM SHOT—THE THREE DOCTORS

273

(*It is two light years and some three days later. The three Doctors lie at the controls exhausted. A giant packing crate takes up the bulk of the interior stenciled: "THE THING—this end up." Doors lead off to three restrooms, their signs reading "LADY SCIENTISTS"—"GENTLEMEN SCIENTISTS"—"THINGS."*)

DR. O'DAY: Where the hell do you think we are now?

DR. SPACE: (*peering out irritably*) I told that engineer to wipe the windshield!

DR. LATOUR: I don't get it. Isn't this going around Hogan's Alley just to get to the West Coast?

DR. SPACE: (*studying radar compass*) I wanted to approach from the Pacific Ocean side by an indirect route, hoping that the ocean breezes would blow away the smog allowing us to find some landmark, and if my calculations are correct——

DR. O'DAY: They're not—we're lost, bud!

DR. LATOUR: Hey! What's that big fat thing? It's coming right at us.

DR. SPACE: (*leaping to controls*) Right rudder!

DR. LATOUR: (*leaping, too*) Right rudder.

DR. O'DAY: Oxygen O.K. (*They miss Saturn by an inch.*)

DR. SPACE: Whew! That was a close one. (*Pleased with himself.*) You have to be pretty nimble where a nimbus is concerned!
(*But his joke is lost on both his colleagues.*)

DR. O'DAY: I'm getting sick of this! You said I'd have a future in Hollywood and we can't even find it!

DR. LATOUR: Me, too. Let's turn back. This is strictly for the birds!

DR. SPACE: Let's take a vote on it. I say keep on. And you, Doctor Dawn?

DR. O'DAY: Go back!

DR. SPACE: And you, Doctor Taffy?

DR. LATOUR: Go back but def!

DR. SPACE: There you are; that makes three in all—we go ahead.
(*The lady scientists frown and start counting on their fingers.*)

DR. SPACE: Wait! Look in the Terra Detector! That black smoky mass—that's smog. Hollywood should be directly south or north of us! Down rudders!

DR. LATOUR: (*taking her station*) Down rudders.

DR. SPACE: Oxygen O.K.? (*no answer*) I said Oxygen O.K.?

274

DR. O'DAY: Oh—yeah—Oxygen O.K.

DR. SPACE: Stabilize neutralizers.

DR. LATOUR: Stabilize neutralizers.

DR. SPACE: Neutralize stabilizers.

DR. LATOUR: Neutralize stabilizers.

DR. SPACE: Wait! There's something on the Visibility Screen— lettering on a water tower—L—A—S—V—E—G—A—S. Fasten money belts!

DR. LATOUR: Fasten money belts!

DR. O'DAY: Oxygen O.K.

DR. SPACE: Full speed—North North East.

DR. LATOUR: Full speed—North North East.

(A few moments of silence as they straighten out and zoom over the California countryside.)

DR. SPACE: *(looking out, jubilantly)* We're passing over Burbank. What does that sign read? W—A—R—N—E—R— B—R—O—S. Punch time clocks!

DR. LATOUR: Punch time clocks.

DR. SPACE: I see a clearing in the fog! Here goes—Don crash helmets!

DR. O'DAY. Oxygen O.K.

(They brace themselves as the ship descends.)

EXT. A HOLLYWOOD CLEARING—FULL SHOT.

(As the rocket ship taxis onto the greensward a waiting group of press agents and newspaper photographers run to it excitedly.)

GROUP *(ad lib)* It's King Gable! No, it's Coop! He said he was gonna buy a helicopter to shoot ducks from! Maybe it's MacMurray bringing back some more Black Angus for his ranch— or Bing and his boys!

(The fuselage door swings open and the three Doctors alight, and start blinking and coughing.)

DR. SPACE: Don smog helmets! *(to group)* Where's everybody?

PRESS AGENTS AND PHOTOGRAPHERS: *(disgustedly)* Aw—they're not anybody.

(They start to turn away.)

DR. SPACE: But wait—we're from another world.

A PRESS AGENT: Good for you.

275

DR. SPACE: (*getting sore*) Now, listen, I want to talk to all the executive heads of the studios—the fate of the industry hangs on it!

(*The Group laughs but their spokesman, a more serious type, steps forward!*)

SPOKESMAN: None of them are here, anyway. Most of them are out of town receiving plaques. Hartman is in New York baking out a virus he got in Palm Springs, and Zanuck is tied up on the Riviera putting out the place cards for Elsa Maxwell.

2D SPOKESMAN: He did however leave Jessel as his deputy but he had to fly to Erie, Pa., and bury the mayor, a former stanch worker for the Democratic party and a pretty good soft-shoe dancer.

DR. SPACE: I'm afraid you do not comprehend the gravity of my mission. If I cannot convince you with words, well I have terrible power——

(*The newshawks jeer, hurling taunts: "You have terrible power, ha, ha, that's rich!" "The Kid's from another world all right. A fugitive from Menninger's!"*)

DR. SPACE: (*with a grave sigh*) I don't want to do it but I'm afraid I'll have to. It will happen at the stroke of four!

QUICK DISSOLVE:

MONTAGE OF SHOTS SHOWING IN SEQUENCE

(*Interiors of studio steam rooms—and seminude executives disgusted when the steam is turned off, then panicked . . .*

The lights going out over the pastry table at Romanoff's—six exhibitors' wives from Dubuque trampling eclairs underfoot as they run out screaming "I can't see! I've got rich food poisoning—I'm going blind" . . .

The studio generators stopping and every sound stage going dark. "Another jurisdictional union dispute," sigh the actors, huddling against the actresses for simple animal comfort.)

THEN INTO: CLOSE SHOT OF NEWS COMMENTATOR AT MICROPHONE.

NEWS COMMENTATOR: —and everything is at a standstill. The electric horse Mario Lanza was riding has stopped, the refrigerating unit at Grauman's Chinese has ceased to function, and a steady stream of chocolate-coated ice cream is flowing down the center aisle. The antique and student lamp factories are idle, and many an executive croquet playing field will be empty this week end for the production of wickets has been completely halted. What dreadful power do these strangers possess?

DISSOLVE

EXT. THE CLEARING—NIGHT-FULL SHOT OUTSIDE THE SPACE SHIP. (*The heads of all the studios stand in solemn assembly as Doctor Space addresses them.*)

DR. SPACE: Executives, producers, gentlemen—I am an emissary from the Chemical Bank in the faraway world of New York—and our bank is a heavy investor in motion picture stocks . . . (*the executives are restless and frightened*) Now recently a mechanical monster has threatened to smash our world to bits —a monster named TV! And what steps have you taken to combat it?

ONE EXECUTIVE: We've trimmed our sails.

DR. SPACE: I'm not talking about sailing but about budgets. You can't do much about overhead, or actors' salaries; some are still worth $400,000 a picture. But the waste lies, as we see it, in the Writing Costs! In the early days the D. W. Griffiths depended very little on the writer. Then came the talking picture and suddenly, God only knows why, the screenwriter became a necessary thorn in *your* side—and the bank's side, too! He organized the Screen Writers Guild—he got himself agents— he wanted Saturdays off—came in all hours—but that was the least of it! He wanted pictures based on adult themes—— (*There are low mumblings, "Dirty intellectual trouble-makers!"*)

DR. SPACE: Instead of good old-fashioned showmanship, insisting that there isn't just one public with the taste of a teen-ager, but many publics, some with an appetite and appreciation for intelligent entertainment. (*Low murmurs and curses.*) The result—overpaid, underworked, rebellious writers. Now are you going to keep on taking that from them?

EXECUTIVES (*gasp*): (*in chorus*) No!

A LEVEL-HEADED PRODUCER: But what are we going to do? We're too busy or we'd write the scripts ourselves.

277

DR. SPACE: (*smugly*) I believe we have the answer. (*he turns and calls toward the ship*) Hack! Platitude, Cliché, Showmanship, Knowhow——

(*There is the SOUND of The Thing's crate splintering, then a second, and a Huge Steel Robot appears and clanks with measured mighty tread down the ramp to the side of Doctor Space.*)

DR. SPACE: Gentlemen, you see before you the first Mechanical Screenwriter, Robert Robot, or as the board of the bank calls him—"The Thinking Machine." (*There is an awed silence.*)

2D LEVEL-HEADED PRODUCER: But—does it really work, Doctor?

(*With a confident smile Dr. Space signals Doctors O'Day and Latour who slip a large checkered sport coat on the robot and Dr. Space takes a pointer and indicates a row of lighted buttons on the robot's chest.*)

DR. SPACE: Robert is a man of millions of words based on your favorite seven plots, everything classified and cross-classified. If you want a story with heart you just press the button marked HEART (*presses button over Robot's heart*). And every classification is subdivided. For example—under Heart, there is B. HEART WITH AFFLICTIONS. Then the *kinds* of afflictions. You'll find "Of Human Bondage" under Clubfoot In Love With Tart—the button reading simply HEART AND TART.

3D LEVEL-HEADED PRODUCER: (*excitedly examining buttons*) You've got all the neuroses and complexes indexed?

DR. SPACE: They're all here. Under N, for instance, you'll find NOSE.

(*presses Robot's nose*)

ROBERT ROBOT: (*speaking in mechanical tones*) Theme—Boy is born without nose. Girl has faith in him and teaches him how to smell.

DR. SPACE: For the TITLE (*presses another button*)

ROBERT ROBOT: "Night without Nostrils."

DR. SPACE: They're all here. Foolproof. Adventure yarns—Westerns (*indicates another row of buttons*), Meaty dramas like "King Solomon's Delicatessen," psychological stuff like "Nancy Goes to Pieces"—You want a Big City Triangle? Just press it. (*Presses triangular shaped button on Robot's groin.*)

You can listen to the big finish without having to wade through the whole script.

ROBERT ROBOT: (*a mechanical throb in his voice*) FADE-IN: INTERIOR PENTHOUSE LIVING ROOM NIGHT—TWOSHOT—JOHN AND BETTY. *Betty:* "John I'm fed up with this tinsel existence —the jewels, the theater, these thick carpets, where has it all gotten us? What do we add up to? Mr. and Mrs. Zero. Is it any wonder I turned to Leland? I'm going away with him, John. He's so much more fun than you in every way——"

(*A bell inside the Robot's brain rings interrupting.*)

DR. SPACE: This is the Breen Office warning bell. It rings automatically—(*to Robot*) Rewind, Robert.

(*The studio brass crowd forward, their interest mounting.*)

ROBERT ROBOT: (*after a pause*) "I *was* going off with him, John but I realize what a fool I've been and I want you to take me back—" *John:* "Take you back! A girl no better than those I could find on the streets! What have you done to pay for your sins?" *Betty:* "Look, John." *John:* "My God, two broken legs!" *Betty:* "He pushed me off the ladder as I tried to get on that plane that's taking him to South America." *John:* "And you crawled to me from the airport *like that?*" *Betty:* "Yes, you know how hard it is to get a cab at this hour." *John:* "You have suffered!" *Betty:* "Oh, John, be careful, my arms are fractured too." *John:* "I'm afraid my heart is the same." *Betty:* "Let's grow well together, shall we, John?" Music Up. Fade Out.

DR. SPACE: There—and we're working on "Melody Max," a musical robot to replace composers.

(*The astounded executives and producers press forward with eager cries.*)

1ST EXECUTIVE: I'll take a dozen!

2D EXECUTIVE: Me too! (*There is a chorus of "Me toos."*)

DR. SPACE: Don't crowd! I'll take your orders—we're gearing for production——

1ST LEVEL-HEADED PRODUCER: Can I order a woman writer—I need someone who understands the feminine angle?

DR. SPACE: I'm afraid Fanny Robot is still in the experimental stage. We haven't found an iron figleaf that will stand the gaff.

279

POINTED-HEADED PRODUCER: Will they come in on time?

DR. SPACE: Six A.M. on the dot. No lunch, or sick leave or holidays
—Nothing to go wrong except for oil, new screws—

(*Several producers clap their hands in glee*)

(*Breen Office bell rings in the Robot.*)

DR. SPACE: It's all right, Robert.

(*The assemblage, in Seventh Heaven, crowd up giving their orders to Doctor Space. Suddenly they freeze and stare as a Huge Bald-Headed Robot lumbers into scene, wearing iron suede shoes, his wires covered with chopped chicken liver.*)

2D LEVEL-HEADED PRODUCER: Who are you?

SAM ROBOT: (*in raspy voice*) Sam Clinchmetal, Bob's agent. My boy is loaded with talent but remember he's a member of the Screen Robot Writers Guild so we gotta have iron-clad contracts! Get the picture?

(*The earth starts to tremble. Then suddenly from over the horizon come clanking thousands of mechanical agents. The producers shriek, collide, and run amuk. The three Doctors defending themselves with their Flit guns gain the safety of the ship and take off once again, this time in search of a finish.* MUSIC UP.)

FADE OUT.

John Lardner

John Lardner's latest book, published toward the end of 1951, was called *Strong Cigars and Lovely Women and Forty-Nine Other Misleading Titles by John Lardner with Walt Kelly at the Drawing Board.* "This," wrote Red Smith, "established a record for book nomenclature . . . Inasmuch as he disqualified himself by implicating an accomplice, the laconic Mr. Lardner's exercise in syncope doesn't quite manage to unseat the old champion, but it does serve to make the book a double delight. You can pass one joyous evening curled up in front of the fire reading the dust jacket and still have a second evening of pleasure spelling out the words between the covers. Or you can do it backwards, which—the author would confess if pinned down—is how the pieces were written in the first place."

Lardner, born in Chicago, was graduated from Phillips Academy and, after attending Harvard University, decided that two years of Cambridge was enough. He became a reporter, columnist, war correspondent, weekly commentator for *Newsweek,* and an invaluable contributor to *The New Yorker.* He also became one of the freshest and funniest sportswriters in the country. His ironic prophecy "How They Played a World Series of 1955" was one of the features of the previous *Best Humor Annual.* As already stated in that publication, Lardner's feeling for farce proceeds from a real grasp of satire.

One World and the Kipper*

Did you ever try to change a man's breakfast habits? The British have successfully sold Scotch whisky to Americans, if you call that selling—it is more like rolling coal down a chute. But Scotch, except among certain independent voters with heliotrope eyeballs, is not a breakfast dish.

The kipper is a breakfast dish. There is a kipper in my icebox now, wearing a cellophane kimono and the look of wild dignity which is peculiar to alumni of the North Sea. It is the last survivor of a party of six that was adopted by my family on the recommendation of Sir Frederick Bell, a herring-hustler from Scotland.

* From *Strong Cigars and Lovely Women,* by John Lardner. Copyright, 1951, by Funk & Wagnalls Company.

281

Like all patriotic businessmen of the British Isles, Sir Frederick is looking for ways to convert British rituals into dollars. If Americans are willing to drink whisky as fast as Scotland can make it, why should they not (Sir Frederick wants to know) eat Scotch herring as fast as they are kippered? Why not, indeed? I ask myself the same question each morning when I open the icebox door and study the clean, graceful lines, the high, intellectual forehead, the winy bouquet of the last of our house guests.

On closing the door again, firmly, I recall to myself that my wife and children (I never did understand any of them) have eaten the other five kippers. I remember the bright confidence of Sir Frederick when he told me he would sell 'em by the millions here. But after that, impressions of another sort well up in me from the experience of a hard, though wholesome, life. Such as:

The breakfast tastes of the poet Henry Grantland Rice, who is partial to sliced oranges covered with ketchup.

The morning workouts of the Yale coach, Herman Hickman, an archetypal specimen of American eater, who favors a "setting" of eggs (10 or 12) with his ham and red gravy.

The recent war in Italy, when the late H. R. Knickerbocker and I, as war correspondents, tried to sell a British officers' mess on the idea of hominy grits for breakfast. I found out at that time that international breakfast propaganda is an exceedingly tough business, coming and going.

Italy, at the moment, was crawling with grits. That is, there was about an acre and a half of them standing in buttes and hummocks in a United States rations dump in Naples. The British mess, which we were then members of, was hungry. Knickerbocker and I went to the U.S. Army and asked if they had any fresh butter or beefsteak to spare for our allies.

"Nope," said the officer in charge, "but we have something better. Hominy grits."

We went away from there with our jeep loaded with grits to the height of a low Himalaya mountain. We served them, fried, at breakfast next morning. The memory of the British reaction to this pioneer move is seared on my brain.

After ten minutes of brooding silence, a major, an adventurous chap, touched one of the grits with his fork. It moved, and he jerked his hand back. Two minutes later a captain gingerly put a small consignment of the stuff into his mouth. All eyes were on him (as on Casey at the bat) as he rolled it delicately on his tongue. He swallowed with a convulsive movement, exactly the kind of thing that won the Battle of Agincourt, and rose from the table.

"Have work to do," he said quietly as he left.

The rest of the mess had work to do also. They thanked us politely, as they went out, for a rich experience in American folkways. I heard one of them murmur softly that he would trade his soul at current exchange rates for a bloater.

That reminds me that a glossary is called for. A kipper is split down the middle, like the 81st Congress, and then salted and smoke-dried. A bloater is the whole herring, cured but unsplit. Salmon swim upstream, whales yield ambergris, and piranhas will cut you to ribbons if you're not very careful about them. I think I will go to the deep-freeze and have another look at my kipper. It may well be that Sir Frederick Bell is right and I am wrong.

Death of a Simian and Scholar *

As fine an ape as I knew was Gargantua, the circus star, who passed from this footstool not long ago. He is gone but not forgotten. I have postponed my private obituary of this congenial gorilla until I was absolutely sure he was dead. An airplane transporting his remains lost 1,000 feet of altitude when the pilot heard a thumping noise amidships. It turned out to be a loose crate, or a gremlin, or something, not Gargy come to life.

While we were acquainted socially, it was my business relationship with the noted entertainer that I valued most highly. In association with Mr. Gene Tunney, a gifted performer in his own right, in a lower weight division, I once tried to promote a match of skill and strength between Gargantua and Tony Galento, the

* From *Strong Cigars and Lovely Women,* by John Lardner. Copyright, 1951, by Funk & Wagnalls Company.

spheroid barkeep of Orange, N. J. Had Galento not declined the test, we would all have cleaned up.

As it was, the thing fell through and the four of us went our separate ways. Tunney became a uranium miner. Gargantua has gone to his reward. Galento is a wrestler, and your correspondent changes ribbons on typewriters. It is useless to sit around and speculate on what might have been.

Gargantua was an up-and-coming young ape of about five years, beginning to make his presence felt in show business, when he caught the eye of Mr. Tunney. Tunney was then sports editor of a paper called *The Connecticut Nutmeg*. As an editor he thought he had to take a stand. So he took a stand against Gargantua. "Gorillas are overrated" was the editorial policy of Mr. Tunney.

That, of course, was directly opposed to the policy of another editor, the late Arthur Brisbane, who thought a gorilla could lick any five human beings. Reaching for his *Encyclopaedia Britannica*, Mr. Tunney made some rapid notes and announced that any third-rate heavyweight fighter could lick Gargantua. When your correspondent proposed Galento, a third-rate heavyweight second to none, as a worthy contender, Mr. Tunney leaped at the idea. So I went around to contact the rival camps.

Now it happened that Mr. Tunney had misread his *Britannica* or got hold of an early edition with incomplete returns. He thought it said that a gorilla has thirteen ribs, as against twenty-four for a human being, or an Orange, N. J., barkeeper. What a gorilla really has is thirteen pairs of ribs, making twenty-six in all.

"Tunney is being ridiculous," said Gargantua's manager, a Mr. Dick Kroener, whom I found moodily biting his fingernails while Gargantua did roadwork around the inside of his cage. "It never pays to knock gorillas. My principal, here, can make shredded wheat out of the likes of Galento."

Galento's manager, Mr. Joe (Yussel the Muscle) Jacobs, seemed to share that suspicion, though he put it in another way.

"Let Tunney fight the ape. I will carry the bucket for him," said Mr. Jacobs coldly. "My tiger fights nobody but humans and such. Besides, our engagement book is full up. Ain't it, Anthony?"

"Right to the ears," agreed Mr. Galento. "I would like to belt over this circus bum, but I got no time."

Soon afterward a rumor began to circulate in the prize-fight business that Mr. Tunney had deliberately misrepresented the number of Gargantua's ribs in order to lure Galento into the ring with the crowd-pleasing African. Now, since I know that Mr. Tunney was prepared to bet handsomely on Galento, that he is the soul of honor, and that he still thinks gorillas are overrated, I am certain that no such stratagem was in his thoughts. If ever a chap believed in the cause of man over monkey, it is this same Mr. Tunney.

However, I am forced to disagree with him. I saw a good deal of Gargantua between that time and the time of his death. We had little to say to each other, being both of a reserved, introspective turn of mind, but whenever I watched him tear an automobile tire in two, I mused on the folly of man and his vaulting ambitions. So, no doubt, did Gargantua. May he walk in green pastures.

How Video Artists Are Born*

Last year people began to be worried by the appearance on their television screens of a curious, sporadic disturbance, namely, me. They sometimes asked me in private how it happened. Today, more often, they ask me when it is going to stop. I prefer to ignore the second question, which is a churlish one at best, but I will try to answer the first, because the facts throw a rather lurid light on the video dodge and prove that television is still in its infancy.

To put it bluntly, I am in the medium through a misunderstanding. One day a radio-video critic named Crosby, who has a wide public, referred to me in his column as "John Lardner, a man who has never forgotten anything." Only two people in the world, the critic and I, knew what that meant. I immediately went around to this Crosby and gave him $5.

* From *Strong Cigars and Lovely Women*, by John Lardner. Copyright, 1951, by Funk & Wagnalls Company.

"I remember now," I said. "You loaned me a fin in September."

"August," corrected the journalist coldly. "I thought it would come to you."

That column was misinterpreted in certain quarters. I said that Crosby has a wide public. Some of its widest members are television executives. One of these read the piece and rang for a vice-president. Their conversation, I have since been told, went as follows:

"This Larkin, or Lardner," said the head man. "Is he telegenic?"

"There's a picture of him on the post-office wall in the town wnere I spend the summer," said the vice-president. "He looks kind of unusual. Wanted in St. Joseph, Mo."

"If they want him," snapped the chief, "we want him too. Grab him and put him on one of our quiz shows."

They put me on a show called Think Quickly and Carry a Big Stick. Confusion ensued, but it was not till some weeks later that the master of ceremonies spotted the trouble. They asked me the question: "What popular band uses the theme song 'Sugar Blues'?" I replied, "The Red Fox of Kinderhook."

"Just a moment," remarked the M.C. "That is the answer to a question, all right, but the wrong question. The right question for that answer is 'What was President Van Buren's nickname?' Haven't you heard that the questions and answers should match?"

"Nope," I admitted humbly.

"That explains a great deal," said the M.C. "Go to the dressing room and remove your make-up. Tell them to strip off your epaulets too, while you're at it."

But television people, like the police of St. Joseph, Mo., hate to let go of a property once they have their hands on it. Someone decided that I might be a Milton Berle-type comedian. On the first few shows I used a stolen line which I have always thought was pretty funny: "Run for the roundhouse, Nellie, the brakeman can't corner you there." The producers watched the studio audience closely; there were no yaks or hearty laughs.

"Maybe that line would be better in dialect," they said. "Try it again, making all the j's sound like y's, as in 'yumping yimminy.'"

"All right," I said. " 'Run for the roundhouse, Nellie, the brakeman can't corner you there.' "

That being a cul de sac, I was next assigned to televised wrestling. I threw Primo Carnera one week, he threw me the next. In the fourth week Primo threw me into the northeast part of British Columbia, several miles from the nearest railway station. It took me seventeen days and $225 in fares to get back to the studio. By that time they had a new partner for Carnera and I went into a crime show.

A California citizens' group complained to the FCC in December, 1949, that there were ninety-one murders in one week on local video stations. Obviously television's answer must be fewer, but longer-lasting, murders. At the moment a gang of cattle rustlers is engaged in killing me by having a single drop of pure orange juice fall on my head every week. The gang leader, an educated fiend, estimates that this will do for me in three years and eight months and clear him with the FCC. I will then be given away with two box tops. I apologize for the delay.

The Incident at Fort Boggess *

One day not long ago a small war party of Brooklyn Dodgers rode up to the breastworks of Dusty Boggess, a fortified National League umpire, and tossed a few words. Boggess replied in kind from behind his portcullis. At a certain point in the skirmish someone forgot to say "Oh, pshaw!" which would have been the logical remark, and said something else instead. The repercussions were immense.

It was not the first time in the age of television that ball players and arbitrators had failed to take note of sonic conditions, but it may have been one of the last. It seems that neutral ears burned over a radius of fifty miles and outrage spread like a scarlet tide. In press and pulpit the brawlers were denounced for using lan-

* From *Strong Cigars and Lovely Women,* by John Lardner. Copyright, 1951, by Funk & Wagnalls Company.

guage unbecoming to gentlemen and definitely unsuitable to a sound track.

Womanhood, it is said, was appalled, and childhood was frozen in its tracks by the Incident at Fort Boggess (as it will be known in future to historians of border warfare). A few spiritual leaders, including Mr. Red Barber, the Brooklyn broadcaster, implied very strongly that the guilty mouths should be washed out with soap. I forget which brand.

We do not propose to deal here with the impact of the crisis on women and children. Experience tells us that women and children, even in a state of shock, are generally able to reform their lines and strike back. In the last resort they have access to that grand and final weapon in society's struggle with radio and television—setting the knob a little to the left of the click.

But the ball players may need help. It is our purpose to supply them with a glossary of sanitary words and phrases for use in forced actions under the microphone. These words will be proof even against lip-readers, of whom the age of television has produced a vast and sinister number.

It should be pointed out that ball players, in their confusion over being televised, have caught up with the video side of the problem before mastering the audio side. Ham is rampant in the ball park today. Take a look at the pregame conferences at home plate, when the managers or captains meet the umpires to discuss, with gestures, the ground rules they all know so well. You get the impression that they are auditioning for David Belasco, or —to mention a quick director rather than a dead one—Jed Harris.

Audio is something else again. The boys are well aware of what they want to say, of what they have always said in given circumstances, but it becomes increasingly plain that they cannot say it any more. Your correspondent has made a wide study of clean language in various forms. I figured I might never know when I needed it, and it looks now as though the hour had struck. Paul Revere, move over.

The following glossary is compact but covers the principal points:

Oh, fudge—$%&%$.

288

For goodness' sake—%&!&!&?.

Oh, sugar—$%&!*&&$.

Oh, dear—&&&!!!&.

A murrain on you—$$$!!!!.

I object—$$$!!!!!

Drat it—**$&%!$.

Tsk, tsk—%&**%&*.

Tch, Tch—French for tsk, tsk.

Low bridge—!**$&%*.

Are you doing anything for your myopia?—**$$**$$!.

Remember, we're working with a live mike—**$$**$$!!.

Have the goodness to take your spikes out of my mouth—=*) (*&%/.

In the case of suspected dusting or bean-balling, the following dialogue is offered for televised ball games:

Batter—"Are you throwing at my head, old fellow?"

Pitcher—"Dear boy, it's the farthest thing from my thoughts."

Batter—"Well, the way you're throwing the ball, it ain't—beg pardon, is not—the farthest thing from *my* thoughts. In fact, it came within half an inch of them."

At a signal from the studio director the audience laughs appreciatively at this jest. The pitcher joins in. He then resumes dusting as though nothing has happened. And the beauty of it is, nothing has.

James Reid Parker

James Reid Parker is a lucky author. He worked his way up several ladders, served a long term as teacher and a shorter one (two years) in the U. S. Army, published several volumes of keenly perceptive short stories, and achieved what most of his fellow authors would write their thumbs off to accomplish: a home in Nantucket, Massachusetts, and a winter haven in Bermuda. Before this devoutly-to-be-wished consummation Parker covered a lot of territory. Born (June 2, 1909) in Jersey City, New Jersey, he got himself educated all over the map; he received his B. A. degree from Lafayette College, did special work in Canada at McGill University, and attained his M. A. degree at Columbia. He was instructor at Brooklyn Polytechnic Institute and, later, professor until the Army took him and advanced him from first lieutenant to major. In between and subsequently, some half-dozen volumes of Parker's prose made their appearance in the bookstores as well as (enthusiastically) in the reviews. It is not without significance that the first book was entitled *Academic Procession* and the latest *Open House*.

The Parker piece which follows is a particularly suave study of marital hostility veiled by an ordinary domestic situation, an episode which will bring brute chuckles from any husband and sympathetic looks of protest from any wife.

Westchester Igloo *

Dinner had been sketchy, because Mrs. Talbot had experimented, and by no means successfully, with an eggplant dish as a meat substitute. Mr. Talbot, very much aggrieved, had denounced the creation and had added sharply that if he was to go on having light lunches in New York, as he had been doing lately at Dr. Brodie's suggestion, it didn't seem to be asking too much to expect a few ounces of meat at the end of a hard day. He said that after driving to White Plains, taking a train to Grand Central, packing himself into the I.R.T. and going all the way down to Pine Street, working like the devil for eight or nine hours, and then coming all the way back again, he considered himself entitled to a halfway decent dinner.

After the eggplant fiasco, they had consumed a few spoonfuls

* By permission. Copyright, 1952, *The New Yorker* Magazine, Inc.

of a dreary pudding that a newspaper column had vivaciously advised Mrs. Talbot to "throw together, quick like a fox, and steam in your pressure cooker for one of those meals when it's later than you thought and you're all in a tizzy." Mr. Talbot's comments on the pudding had been much less playfully worded.

Now the Talbots were carrying their coffee cups into the living room. Mrs. Talbot was especially sorry that Mr. Talbot was in such a vile mood, because she had a small surprise for him and he sometimes reacted unfavorably to small surprises even after prime ribs of beef and apple pie à la mode.

She had propped the surprise against Mr. Talbot's humidor, so he discovered it almost at once. "This must be something of yours," he said, picking up a book entitled "Inuk" and handing it to her. "Damn silly name to give a book, if you ask me. Where's my 'Murder in Black and White'?"

"Why, I took it back to the Browse-Awhile this afternoon and exchanged it for you," she said. "I thought you'd finished that one."

"Well, I hadn't!" he snapped. "Please go to the shop first thing tomorrow and see if it's still there. And if it is, take it out again. Didn't you get me *anything* to read tonight?"

"Of course I did," she said placatingly, and handed "Inuk" back to him.

Glowering, he inspected the jacket blurb and learned that "Inuk" was an anthropological work, a French priest's study of the primitive civilization of the Eskimos who inhabit the forlorn wastelands in the shadow of the North Pole. "Eskimos, for God's sake!" Mr. Talbot snorted. "What gave you the idea I'd feel like spending an evening reading abut Eskimos? Why didn't you get me a detective story?"

Mrs. Talbot, regretting the eggplant more than ever, said soothingly that she had honestly thought he might enjoy something different, just for a change. "Something worth while," she explained in self-defense. "It was the new reviewer we have this winter for the monthly meetings of our book department at the club who gave me the idea, really. She's perfectly wonderful, Charlie. About ten times better than the one we had last year, we all think. The one we had last year just summarized plots, but Adelaide Darlington Foss tells lots of anecdotes about well-known people, like about John Marquand wearing somebody else's overcoat all the way home by mistake after a party. Things like that. And every time she lectures, she has a special feature at the end that's her own idea. She calls her last five minutes 'Something for the Husbands,' and she always recommends three good books that men will like. What gave me the idea about 'Inuk' was the way she praised it to the skies the other day in her last five minutes."

Mrs. Talbot waited hopefully, but soon realized that she had not improved the situation. So great had been her treachery that Mr. Talbot said nothing at all but lighted a cigar and smoked it in silence and with an air of injured majesty.

They drank their coffee, and it occurred to Mrs. Talbot that two cups clicking against two saucers made quite an astonishing lot of noise if people weren't chatting at the same time. There would be no point, she knew, in bothering to offer Mr. Talbot the Frances Parkinson Keyes novel she had selected that afternoon for her own enjoyment. The principal character was a woman in her late forties whose emotional life teemed with incident. It being beyond question that Mr. Talbot would react even more violently to such fare than he had reacted to the eggplant dish, Mrs. Talbot opened her book, and soon was altogether engrossed. Looking up at the end of the first chapter, she noted with heartfelt relief that Mr. Talbot was reading "Inuk" and that if he wasn't doing so in a spirit of domestic coöperativeness, at least he wasn't uttering the grunts and snorts of disapproval that might have been expected in the circumstances.

Half an hour later, when Mrs. Keyes' heroine was saying no very charmingly to a handsome diplomat, Mrs. Talbot was recalled to reality by her husband's voice remarking, "This book you got for me turns out to be darned interesting, you know it? I never had a very clear idea before of what life is like up there in the arctic. This fellow tells you. He's a pretty good writer, too."

"Is he, dear?" said Mrs. Talbot, thankful that all was turning out well. "Isn't that nice! I'll start it myself tomorrow while you're in New York." She had a hazy but pleasant mental picture of Mr. Talbot and herself reading the same books in the future.

Really good books, and not detective stories. "Oh, didn't you like 'Thus-and-Such'?" she would be able to say to people. "My husband and I did. We enjoyed it immensely." And perhaps even "No, I haven't read the new Boswell yet, but just as soon as my husband finishes it, I'm going to start right in." She decided to proceed cautiously at first, however, and to prop no more than one good book a month against his humidor.

"Listen to this," Mr. Talbot said. " 'The Eskimos are a race of men. Their opinion of women is not high. Only a few women are permitted to live, and these few carry no weight whatever in Eskimo society.' This writer says that an Eskimo woman is essentially an igloo-keeper, and nothing more. There's a lot in here about what this man calls 'the prescribed Eskimo life pattern.' It seems they all live exactly the same way. For example, 'He, the man, will build the igloo; she, the woman, will tend it. He will kill the seal; she will cut out the blubber and keep the lamp filled with oil. He will kill the caribou; she will tan the skin and fashion their clothes. To him the rifle, the knife, the dogs, the whip, and the right to give orders. To her the lamp, the cooking, the sewing. . . . For an Eskimo woman to think of assuming even the most trifling male prerogative would be unthinkable.' "

Mrs. Talbot sighed. "I guess they *are* awfully primitive, probably," she said.

"Well, it seems to work out pretty well," Mr. Talbot said casually, and again became lost in literature. Presently, Mrs. Talbot was able to get back into the swing of Mrs. Keyes' narrative, and for a while she and her husband enjoyed their disparate pleasures in silence.

"Nobody can say the Eskimos go in for sentiment," Mr. Talbot remarked suddenly.

"Don't they, dear?" Mrs. Talbot asked with vague forebodings.

"Life's kind of rugged for the girls up there," he said with an anthropologist's detachment. " 'The birth of a girl to an Eskimo family is a keenly felt deception, a cruel joke nature has played on them. . . . Here, among the Eskimos, it is almost an insult, and all too often the tiny girl baby is scarcely born, has hardly taken her first breath and uttered her first plaintive, helpless cry, before she is exterminated.' "

293

"Well, really!" Mrs. Talbot gasped. "I never heard of anything so dreadful in my whole life!"

"Oh, they let *some* of the girls live, of course," said Mr. Talbot, still the calm scholar. "Apparently, it all depends on the community's requirements. Sometimes more girls are needed, and sometimes they aren't. Or, as this man says, it may hinge on something else. He says, 'Perhaps the family happened to have struck it rich just before her birth and be living in abundance. Perhaps the father just feels good that day.' For one reason or another, it may be decided to let her live, and so she starts to grow up. 'At seven, and eight,' he says, 'she is already a servant, helping with the chores, and she understands the kind of life that is in store for her. It is a grim future.'"

Mrs. Talbot closed the Keyes book and placed it on the table beside her chair. "I don't feel like sitting up and reading till all hours, do you?" she asked. "In fact, I feel sleepy right now. Do *you* feel sleepy?"

"Not a bit," Mr. Talbot said pleasantly. "You go ahead and go to bed if you want to."

Mrs. Talbot hesitated. "Well, maybe not just yet," she said. "Would you like me to fix you a drink or something?"

"No, thanks," he said. "I'll just read. Later on, I may make myself a sandwich. I'm still kind of hungry."

Mrs. Talbot nervously began to wonder what there might be in the refrigerator that would help him to forget that disastrous dinner. He was fond of bacon-and-tomato sandwiches, and fortunately she had the ingredients on hand.

"Listen to this," Mr. Talbot said again. "'Soon . . . the little girl is put to work, mending the old clothes, scraping the fresh skins, feeding the dogs, and helping to harness them. She is called out, at any hour of the night, to quiet the fighting, snarling dogs. Her real servitude has started, and it will end only with the grave.'"

"How about a nice bacon-and-tomato sandwich, or maybe a club sandwich if I can find a can of chicken?" Mrs. Talbot suggested brightly. "*I'd* like one." She now was firmly resolved never again to trust the recommendations of Adelaide Darlington Foss,

294

who certainly had some very strange ideas as to what constituted worth-while reading for men.

"O.K.," Mr. Talbot said. "Sounds fine. A dill pickle would taste good, too. This man says that Rasmussen, the Danish explorer, cites a typical community situation. Rasmussen speaks of a settlement on King William Island where from eighteen marriages a total of ninety-six children was produced. Thirty-eight of the infants, being girls, were killed at birth. This book says the average Eskimo woman apparently accepts this practice as she accepts her whole life—a monotonous sojourn of work and subjugation. Say, could we have some coffee along with those sandwiches?"

"Why, of course we could!" Mrs. Talbot cried, adding sycophantically, "What a good idea!" In a playful manner she whisked "Inuk" out of his hands and said, "Come out to the kitchen with me, and we'll fix our snack together."

Mr. Talbot retrieved the book at once. "No," he said with considerable determination. "You fix it. I'd rather read." He searched for his place and, finding it, went back to the Eskimos.

"Well, I must say it isn't much fun for me when you just keep sitting there like an old stick," she said in an aggrieved tone. "You used to *like* to help fix late snacks."

"This fellow tells about a night he spent in an igloo with an Eskimo named Ayallik and his wife, Ongirlak, and their family," Mr. Talbot said, resuming his report to her of high life in a cold climate. " 'I slipped into my fur bag,' this writer says. 'The kids squeezed themselves under the skins, and the wrinkled granny, grumbling and complaining like any old lady, squatted on her heels and stripped off all her clothes. She got into bed, muttering to herself and grunting, tossing about for a while before she fell asleep. Ayallik, meanwhile, had stripped to the nude. With a cheerful "Alapa!" . . . "Cold!" he vanished under his covers. Ongirlak was the last to bed. She plugged the door hole with a snow block and fixed her lamps for the night, beating out all the flame except for a tiny glow in the corner, a night light. Then she distributed small empty tins, improvised chamber pots, placing one at each of our heads. At last Ongirlak was finished with her long day's work. She peeled off her fur clothes, displaying her

295

huge breasts for an instant, and then disappeared under the skins. Like most Eskimos, she was asleep the moment she was in bed. They seldom are troubled with insomnia. For one thing, they are too tired, and for another their lives are too simple to build up worry.' He certainly gives you a good idea of how those people handle their day-to-day problems. You've got to hand it to him."

Mrs. Talbot sniffed but said nothing. She felt extremely sorry for herself, although she couldn't have said exactly why. When Mr. Talbot repeated, "Yes, sir, you've got to hand it to him, all right," she tossed her head.

"Say, what about those sandwiches, honey?" Mr. Talbot said.

Mrs. Talbot's first impulse was to reply that she couldn't possibly have gone out to fix the sandwiches for the simple reason that he had been detaining her by reading aloud, but instead of putting this thought into words, she said, quite meekly, "I was just going out to make them." When Mr. Talbot went on to say "You know something else about Eskimos?," she quailed privately. But, concealing her distress, she merely said, "No, what?"

"Eskimo men often exchange wives for a night, and without consulting the wives, either," Mr. Talbot said, chuckling. "What do you know about that? Kind of as if I were to phone Ed McGarvey and say, 'Send Ida over. I'm sending you Grace.'"

"May I ask why it should just so happen that Ida McGarvey's name suddenly popped into your mind—?" Mrs. Talbot began.

"Cut it out," Mr. Talbot commanded fondly. But he was still chuckling to himself. "Go fix the sandwiches."

Mrs. Talbot went out to the kitchen and methodically assembled bread, lettuce, mayonnaise, and other items. She arranged several strips of bacon in a skillet and began to slice tomatoes. Allowing herself an extreme flight of fancy, she visualized Ida McGarvey peeling off her fur clothes, displaying her huge breasts for an instant, and then disappearing under the skins—with Mr. Talbot. Employing a corner of her apron, Mrs. Talbot wiped away a tear or two.

Suddenly the blubber in the skillet began to sizzle, and Mrs. Talbot regarded it with horror for a moment, until she realized that it wasn't blubber at all but bacon and that she was under no compulsion whatever to use the fat that was oozing out of it as a filling for lamps.

"That *damn* woman!" Mrs. Talbot muttered to herself vindictively. She wasn't thinking of Mrs. McGarvey—a fundamentally harmless creature—but of Adelaide Darlington Foss.

Ralf Kircher

Ralf Kircher is at least two men. One of them is the staid factual president of a large advertising firm; the other is the fantasy-loving author
of many examples of what he calls "essay-type nonsense." Born May
22, 1907, in Pittsburgh, Pennsylvania, Kircher attended Ohio University and settled in Dayton, where he is now head of Kircher, Helton &
Collett, Inc. Two of his books have been published—*There's a Fly in
This Room* and *Wrap It as a Gift*—and he is at work on an untitled
third. Somehow Kircher also manages to write a weekly column, "Fid-
dlesticks," and take care of a wife, a son, a daughter, and a ménage
which is a small menagerie including a cocker, a beagle, two nonde-
script cats, and a horse appropriately named "Rusty."

"It's a __Big__ World!" *

Each spring I brood a good deal about what I'll say when people
begin to inquire whether it is warm enough for me, and each
year I resolve to think up some crushing answer for this foolish
question but, what with one thing and another, I don't get
around to it and so I just stay grouchy all summer, which I don't
think is very good for me.

There is a similar problem, however, that I have recently
solved, thanks to a world atlas and a lively imagination. When
people now ask whether I don't think it is a small world I am
ready for them. Already, I have settled the hash of several.

"Isn't it a small world, after all?" is the way the question is
generally put.

"After all what?" is one peevish answer that gives them a good
deal of pause, though that is not the only way to make folks
wish they had asked me something else.

For example, I had lunch with a friend last Monday and then
encountered him on Tuesday in the Union Terminal at Cincinnati. Nothing odd about that. We both happened to be in Cincinnati and we both turned up at the station. But my friend was
completely thunderstruck by this poor coincidence and pumped
my hand and slapped my back as though we had not seen each

* Reprinted from *Collier's* Magazine.

other since the Panic of 1907. He then made the inevitable inquiry: Did I not agree that it's a mighty small world, after all?

"Isn't it though?" I replied. "Only 8,000 miles thick."

This quick thrust missed him.

"What do you mean? What's 8,000 miles thick?"

"This small world," I replied, warming to the topic. "If you were to start digging right here, or out there on the esplanade where the digging would be easier, and you shoveled down, you would have to dig a mere 8,000 miles before you emerged on the other side. Surely one could ask for nothing smaller than that. And incidentally, you might be interested to learn that such an excavation would fetch you out in a rice paddy near Mingkiang, a rather backward little village in the Honan Province of China."

My friend regarded me uncertainly, mumbled something about catching a train, and backed away. I expect no more small world trouble from that direction.

Have you noticed that it takes very little to excite this comment from the most rational of people? The recent discovery that a neighbor and I have uncles named Horace produced it. He stood in silent awe for a moment and then, shaking his head over so monumental a coincidence, said that this beat anything he ever heard—it did indeed!—and that surely no other proof was needed of the smallness of the world.

I told him he was right; no further testimony need apply. I then observed that the world weighed a scant 854 trillion long tons (I invented that figure, but regard it as close enough), and also that a recent survey made by the American Uncle Institute revealed that if all the Uncle Horaces in the nation were placed end to end they would reach from Allagash, Maine, to Shungopavy, Arizona, a mere walk-around-the-block of 3,186 miles. I also said that I had been reading a scientific article proving that the earth, in its headlong whirl through space, was losing weight at the rate of 200 pounds per minute and that, with the earth getting smaller and smaller, we might confidently anticipate the day when it becomes so small that *all* uncles will be named Horace.

I waited to see whether he wished to continue the conversation

299

but he elected not to do so. I doubt that he will ever broach the subject again.

Let it be learned that you and a friend have a mutual acquaintance in Chicago, that you both have insomnia, dislike chives on your cottage cheese, have driven to Florida on Route 21—any such simple discovery will provoke an excited comment about the smallness of the world. I cite as a final example the pretty young thing I recently encountered at a cocktail party. She observed that we both had twists of lemon instead of olives in our Martinis. She needed no further encouragement. Wasn't it a small world?

"You said it, blondie," I replied. "Only 14,921 miles from Panama Roads to Bombay."

"I beg your pardon?"

"I said, beautiful, that the Pacific Ocean is a scant eight miles deep east of the Philippines."

"But—"

"Not but, dear. It is pronounced Butte and it's in Montana which, oddly enough, is a mere stone's throw of 17,894 kilometers from Farafangana, the so-called Riviera of Madagascar."

She began to back away, so I stalked her.

"And speaking of this small world, baby, you must surely be taking into account the molehill known as Mt. Everest which is a piffling 29,141 feet high. Gives one pause, doesn't it?"

She was beginning to panic. "I only said—"

"I heard you, darling. You said it's a small world and not every girl would be so observing. On top of that you are cute as a button. Tell you what. We must discuss this matter further, you and I. Tomorrow at one-thirty you run into me—just accidental like—at Forty-eighth and Madison, and you'll say to me 'My! It certainly is a small world, isn't it?' and I'll say to you 'Toots, you took the words right out of my mouth' and then we'll—"

But she fled and, pleading a migraine, slipped into her marten stole and left. My martini having evaporated I got another one. With lemon. It looked so good that I proposed a toast to no one in particular. "Here's to a big world, folks!" I said loudly.

Peter DeVries

Poet, essayist, short story writer, and one of the mainstays of *The New Yorker,* Peter DeVries was born in 1910 in Chicago, Illinois, where he helped edit *Poetry: A Magazine of Verse* and, to keep himself from starving, engaged in an incongruous variety of odd trades. He operated a candy-dispensing machine, acted bit parts on the radio, composed random rhymes for an advertising digest. In his early thirties he joined the staff of *The New Yorker* and, like many New Yorkers, commuted between Manhattan and Connecticut. In 1951 he followed Greeley's advice and went West—from Southport to Westport. His new book, *No, But I Saw the Movie,* is appearing simultaneously with this volume.

From There to Infinity *

(After reading *From Here to Eternity,* by James Jones)
> *We all have a guilt-edged security.*
> —*Moses.*

"Stark romanticism" was the phrase that kept pounding through his head as he knocked on the door of Mama Paloma's, saw the slot opened and the single sloe plum that was Mama Paloma's eye scrutinizing him through the peephole. "Oh, you again," the eye grinned at him, sliding back the bolt of the door. "The girls are all pretty busy tonight but go on up." A dress of sequins that made her look like a fat mermaid with scales three quarters instead of halfway up tightly encased the mounds of old snow that was her flesh. She glanced down at the must-be-heavy-as-lead suitcase in his hand as she closed the door. "I don't dare ast how many pages you're carting around in that by now," she grinned.

He mounted the steps with that suffocating expectation of men who are about to read their stuff, the nerves in his loins tightening like drying rawhide, the familiar knot hard in his belly. Shifting the suitcase from one hand to the other, his head swam into the densening surf of upstairs conversation, above which the

* By permission. Copyright, 1951, *The New Yorker* Magazine, Inc.

tinkle of the player piano was like spray breaking all-the-time on rocks. Standing in the upper doorway, he reflected how, just as there can be damned senseless pointless want in the midst of plenty, so there can be the acutest loneliness in the midst of crowds. Fortunately, the thought passed swiftly. The whores moved, blatant as flamingos in their colored gowns, among the drinking-grinning men, and his eye ran tremulously swiftly in search of Dorine, gulpingly taking in the room for her figure moving erectly womanly through it all.

"No Princess to listen tonight," Peggy grinned toward him. "The Princess went away."

He could have slapped her. It puzzled him to find that beneath that hard, crusty exterior beat a heart of stone. What was she doing in a place like this? He turned and hurried back down the stairs.

"Come back soon, there's listeners as good as the Princess," Mama Paloma laughed jellily jollily as she let him out into the street.

With Dorine not there he couldn't bear Mama Paloma's, and he didn't know another place. Yet he had to have a woman tonight. Another woman would have to do, any woman.

Colonel Stilton's wife, he thought. Why not? She was from Boston, but there was no mistaking the look of hard insolent invitation she gave him each time she came to the Regimental Headquarters to ask if he knew where the Colonel had been since night before last. He hated Stilton's guts, or would if he, Stilton, had any. Hated that smirk and that single eyebrow always jerking sardonically skeptically up, like an anchovy that's learned to stand on end. Why not transfer out, why be a noncom under that bastard? he asked himself. I'm a noncompoop, he thought. He tried to make a joke of it but it was no good.

He knew where the Colonel lived from the time he'd taken him home stewed. He got out of the cab a block from the house. As he approached it walking, he could see Mrs. Stilton under a burning bulb on the screened terrace with her feet on a hassock, smoking a cigarette. She had on shorts and a sweater. Her slim brown legs like a pair of scissors made a clean incision in his mind. He went up the flagstone walk and rapped on the door.

"What do you want?" she said with the same insolent invitation, not stirring. He was aware of the neat, apple-hard breasts under the sweater, and of the terse, apple-hard invitation in her manner.

"I want to read this to you," he said, trying not to let his voice sound too husky.

"How much have you got in there," her voice knew all about him.

"A quarter of a million words," he said.

She came over and opened the screen door and flipped her cigarette out among the glows of the fireflies in the yard. When she turned back he caught the screen door and followed her inside. She sat down on the hassock and looked away for what seemed an eternity.

"It's a lot to ask of a woman," she said. "More than I've ever given."

He stood there shifting the suitcase to the other hand, the arm-about-to-come-out-of-its-socket ache added to that in his throat, wishing he wouldn't wish he hadn't come. She crossed her arms around her and, with that deft motion only women with their animal confidence can execute, pulled her sweater off over her head and threw it on the floor. "That's what you want, isn't it?" she said.

"You with your pair of scissors," he said. "When you can have a man who's willing to bare his soul." He gritted his teeth with impatience. "Don't you see how much we could have?"

"Come on in." She rose, and led the way inside. Nothing melts easier than ice, he thought, sad. He watched her draw the drapes across the window nook and settle herself back among the cushions. "I'm all yours," she said. "Read."

The female is a yawning chasm, he thought, glancing up from his reading at the lying listening woman. He found and read the passage explaining that, how she was the inert earth, passive potent, that waits to be beaten soft by April's fecundating rains. Rain is the male principle and there are times for it to be interminable: prosedrops into rivulets of sentences and those into streams of paragraphs, these merging into chapters flowing in turn into sectional torrents strong and hard enough to wear

303

gullies down the flanks of mountains. After what seemed an
eternity, he paused and she stirred.

"What time is it?" she sat up.

"A quarter to three."

"I never knew it could be like this," she said.

Each knew the other was thinking of Colonel Stilton.

"He never reads anything but *Quick*," she said, rolling her
head away from him.

"The sonofabitch," he said, his fist involuntarily clenching as
tears scalded his eyes. "Oh, the rotten sonofabitch!"

"It's no matter. Tell me about you. How did you get like this?"

Bending his head over the manuscript again he readingly told
her about that part: how when he was a kid in downstate Illinois his uncle, who had wanted to be a lawyer but had never
been able to finish law school because he would get roaring
drunk and burn up all his textbooks, used to tell him about his
dream, and about his hero, the late Justice Oliver Wendell
Holmes, who in those great early days of this country was working on a manuscript which he would never let out of his sight,
carrying it with him in a sack even when he went out courting
or to somebody's house to dinner, setting it on the floor beside
his chair. How his uncle passed this dream on to him, and how
he took it with him to the big cities, where you began to feel how
you had to get it all down, had to get down everything that got
you down: the singing women in the cheap bars with their
mouths like shrimp cocktails, the daughters-into-wives of chicken-
eating digest-reading middle-class hypocrisy that you saw riding
in the purring cars on Park Avenue, and nobody anywhere
loving anybody they were married to. You saw that and you
saw why. You had it all figured out that we in this country
marry for idealistic love, and after the honeymoon there is bound
to be disillusionment. That after a week or maybe a month of
honest passion you woke up to find yourself trapped with the sow
Respectability, which was the chicken-eating digest-reading middle-class assurance and where it lived: the house with the, oh
sure, refrigerator, oil furnace and all the other automatic contrap-
tions that snicker when they go on—the well-lighted air-con-
ditioned mausoleum of love. She was a better listener than Fil-

low, a middle-aged swell who had eight hundred jazz records and who would sit in Lincoln Park in Chicago eating marshmallow out of a can with a spoon with gloves on. Every time he tried to read Fillow a passage, Fillow would say "Cut it out." Fillow was a negative product of bourgeois society just as Stilton with his chicken-eating digest-reading complacence was a positive one, whom his wife had and knew she had cuckolded the minute she had let the suitcase cross the threshold.

"It'll never be the same again, will it?" she said fondly softly, seeing he had paused again.

He read her some more and it was the same. Except that the thing went on so long the style would change, seeming to shift gears of itself like something living a hydramatic life of its own, so that side by side with the well-spent Hemingway patrimony and the continental cry of Wolfe would be the seachanged long tireless free-form sentences reminiscent of some but not all or maybe even much of Faulkner.

The door flew open and Stilton stood inside the room. His eyes were like two wet watermelon pips spaced close together on an otherwise almost blank plate (under the anchovies one of which had learned to stand on end).

"So," he said. The word sailed at them like a yoyo flung out horizontally by someone who can spin it that way. It sailed for what seemed an infinity and came back at him.

"So yourself," she said. "Is this how long officers' stags last?" she said.

"So he *forced his way in here*," the Colonel cued her, at the same time talking for the benefit of a six-foot MP who hove into view behind him.

Realization went like a ball bouncing among the pegs of a pinball machine till it dropped into the proper slot in his mind and a bell rang and a little red flag went up reading "Leavenworth." He remembered what he'd heard. That an officer's wife is always safe because all she had to do was call out the single word rape and you were on your way to twenty years.

Why did he just stand there, almost detached? Why wasn't his anger rising from his guts into his head and setting his tongue into action? But what could you say to a chicken-eating digest-

305

reading impediment like this anyhow, who with all the others of his kind had gelded contemporary literature and gelded it so good that an honest book that didn't mince words didn't stand a chance of getting even a smell of the best-seller list?

"This is my affair," he heard her say coolly, after what seemed a particularly long eternity.

The Colonel lighted a cigarette. "I suspected you were having one," they saw him smokingly smirk, "and since Klopstromer was seeing me home from the club I thought he might as well—" He stopped and looked down at the suitcase. "How long does he expect to *stay?*"

"I have something to say," he said, stepping forward.

"*Sir.*"

"I have something to say, sir," he said, picking up the suitcase to heft it for their benefit. "When Justice—"

"You'll get justice," the Colonel snapped as Klopstromer sprang alertly forward and bore down on him and wrested the suitcase from his grasp. "If you won't testify," the Colonel went on to his wife, "then Klopstromer at least will. That he assaulted a superior officer. It won't get him Leavenworth, but by God six months in the stockade will do him good."

"But why?" his wife protested. "You don't understand. He's a writer."

"Maybe," they saw the Colonel smirkingly smoke. The anchovy twitched and stood upright. "Maybe," he said, motioning to Klopstromer to march him out through the door to the waiting jeep, "but he needs discipline."

Frances Gray Patton

A writer most of her life, Frances Gray Patton did not become a professional author until she was in her late thirties. Her first work was composed at the age of three. It was a nature poem and it consisted of two memorable lines:

> The wind is blowing sof'ly
> The birds are singing awf'ly.

Born in 1906 in Raleigh, North Carolina, of a long line of North Carolinians, Mrs. Patton was educated at Trinity College (now Duke University), at the University of North Carolina, and lives in Durham, North Carolina. Hers is a family of literary Carolinians. Her mother, the first coed to register at the university, wrote for *St. Nicholas* and *The Youth's Companion;* her father, trained to be a lawyer, was on the staff of *Munsey's Magazine;* her two brothers are newspapermen. At one time, when she was in college, Mrs. Patton considered becoming a professional actress; she worked two summers with the Stuart Walker Company in Cincinnati, when Ilka Chase was with the company. Nothing much came of it, and it was not until 1944 that, at her husband's suggestion, she decided to try writing seriously. Her stories began appearing in *Harper's, Collier's, McCall's,* and particularly in *The New Yorker.* Her book, *The Finer Things of Life,* is light but unusually perceptive. Adding sensitivity to social satire, Mrs. Patton creates a tender humor in which the ridiculous is faintly touched with pathos—and vice versa.

A Spring Motif *

Like many very masculine men, Henry Cameron found the society of ladies refreshing. Their chatter had a tangential quality that loosed his mind from the tethers of grim reality; there was something debonair about the gravity with which they approached the prettier problems of life—planning of a party, for example, or the frosting of a cake, or the selection of a frivolous, unnecessary hat—that made him feel protective and strong and determined to keep them contented. So, when court adjourned early on Thursday afternoon, he declined an invitation to play golf with the presiding judge

* Reprinted from *Collier's* Magazine.

307

and hurried home with the notion of working in the garden with his wife. The weather was just right for gardening and he expected to find her already outdoors, but the yard was deserted and when he entered the house he guessed immediately that it was deserted, too. He went from one serene, airy room to another, calling his wife's name: "Julia! Oh, Julia!" But he didn't find her. There was only a faint odor of cologne in the air. Finally he said: "Isn't anybody home?" in a loud, somewhat injured tone, and went into his den.

The den was the sort of "man's room" that only a woman profoundly impressed with the difference between the sexes would have arranged for her husband. (Even the name by which it was designated—not library or study, but den—denoted feminine awe, Henry had often thought; for, by implication, the occupant of a den was a creature in whom the beast was not entirely tamed, a creature to be cajoled and fed raw meat and permitted to growl in peace.) An engraving of a lordly stag hung over the fireplace; a tobacco jar in the shape of a human skull stood on the mantel. The books that lined the walls were bound in somber colors. The red leather armchairs, the sofa, and the large kneehole desk all sacrificed elegance of line to a ponderous solidity that seemed calculated to withstand a kind of wanton mistreatment that Henry, who was fastidious to a degree, would never subject them to. There were times when he felt the room to be a fitting tribute to the preeminence of the male, but today it made him feel caged and lonesome. He went to the window, drew apart the monk's-cloth curtains, and gazed out.

The scene outside was charming. Near the window a big cherry tree was "hung with snow," just as Housman had said. (Henry was fond of the poets and always pleased to see proof of their accuracy.) On the lawn a host of daffodils danced, for all the world as if they'd been reading Wordsworth, and, beyond them, across the road, a patch of woodland was gauzy with the foliage of early May. Up the road, homeward-bound from school, came three half-grown neighborhood children.

Those children—the Camerons' own daughter, Mary Anne; her bosom friend, Miss Bitsy Blackburn; and a boy named Everett Jones, who looked like the bookish son of a professor, which, indeed, he was—were all at that age, fourteen, which is traditionally accepted as representing, in the human lifespan, the carefree, budding season of the year, but they gave little evidence of juice and joy. They neither danced like the daffodils nor assumed, like the delicately brooding trees, an air of contemplative bliss. They climbed the hill with textbooks held sloppily in the crooks of their arms (current fashion scorned such tidy devices as briefcases or buckled straps) and appeared to be intent upon personal problems which no fine weather could dissipate.

Everett Jones, a gangly boy who wore horn-rimmed spectacles and whose frame hadn't yet filled out enough to prevent his enormous feet and noble Roman nose from looking comical, was considerably in the lead. He walked with long, stiff strides, as if he were being pushed from behind by a steady wind. He lifted his jaw at a defiant angle that suggested studied contempt for the opinion of society, his own rapid growth, and everything else that mortified him.

Observing Everett, Henry Cameron winced as if some old vulnerable spot of his own, still tender beneath the callus of years, had been pressed. " 'The troubles of our proud and angry dust.' " he quoted under his breath. Far in Everett's wake, and, in comparison with the boy's speed, at a snail's pace, came the two girls. Bitsy Blackburn moved with the dogged slowness of one who must face a new morning with the irons of a discouraging dream dragging at her ankles; her magnificent shoulders sagged, and at intervals she stopped stock-still in the road, a statue of apathy, while Mary Anne —a girl half her size—talked to her, spreading out her hands in the pantomime of exhortation. Mary Anne had an air of being in command of any given situation, which her father often found vaguely disconcerting. At the moment, however, he was curious to know what she was saying—and to know what ailed Bitsy, and what had stung Everett. He was in a mood for diversion.

Everett, glancing neither to left nor right, stalked by and disappeared over the brow of the hill. The two girls paused at the entrance to the Camerons' yard. Bitsy stared up the empty road. Her muscles went slack. She stood there with her mouth half open and her free arm dangling so that her hand had the effect of hanging down below her knee. A pencil, stuck loosely among her load of books, slid to the ground. Mary Anne stooped and retrieved the pencil. She stooped correctly, as she'd been taught in dancing school to stoop for a handkerchief—not bending from the waist, but dropping gracefully to one knee—for seldom, even in the most remote and unlikely places, did she forget the possibility of a public. Rising, she tapped Bitsy's shoulder and jerked her head toward the house. Her manner was brisk and bluff, like that of a man urging a friend who is down on his luck to come in and have a quick one and drown his troubles. Bitsy raised her limp hand slowly, as if through water, and made an indecisive gesture in the direction of her own house, whose white cupola was visible above the cedars in the Camerons' side yard. Mary Anne grasped her firmly by the elbow and steered her up the flagstone walk.

Henry Cameron watched them, fascinated. He had the sense of mixed empathy and detachment that he had experienced once, camping in the mountains, when he had waked to see a pair of heifer does, their flanks rosy with dawn, each lifting a forefoot and sniffing the air outside his pup tent. And, oddly enough, it was Bitsy, more than his own daughter, who compelled his imagination. For Mary Anne, young as she was, was a finished product. Like a daffodil responding to the first overtures of spring, she had already blossomed, with no perceptive effort, into her predestined pattern, and it was only at rare moments—when she wanted extra pocket money or was stumped by a Latin construction—that her father presumed to consider her in need of his aid. Bitsy's essential shape, on the other hand, was still as uncertain as the course of the season itself. Her tentative shoots of beauty were sporadic and almost painful, like flowers on a naked, thorny bough.

On her birth certificate, Bitsy's name appeared as Louise, but, before the inky footprint upon that document had dried, her parents had given her the name she was never to lose. The elder Blackburns, built on the grand scale that results from a long line of well-fed ancestry, had been enchanted by the sheer littleness of the infant they had produced. Yearning over the miniature perfection of her ears, her nose, her toes, and her fingers, they had delved in their minds for a word to express all the exquisite tenderness that these miracles excited in them. Being not especially endowed with vocabulary, they had come up with "Itsy Bit," which, with proud coos

310

of delight, they had contracted into "Bitsy." For a short time this *nom d'amour* hadn't seemed entirely inappropriate; Bitsy had started life as small and pink as most babies, and, dandled in her mother's arms, she had suggested nothing bigger than a cabbage rose on the bosom of a large and beautiful woman. But the Blackburns had ignored the probable consequences of heredity and a high-protein diet. Before her first birthday, Bitsy had been muscled like the infant Hercules, who strangled a serpent in his cradle. At eight, she had been a giant of a child; clad in outsized smocks she had towered above Lucetta, the dainty Negro maid who had walked her to and from school. At ten, by popular acclaim, she had been elected captain of the neighborhood baseball team. Now, at fourteen, she stood five ten in her bobby socks and hung her head to minimize her height.

In silence the two girls passed beneath the cherry tree. A few petals, snowing down, lighted on Bitsy's dark, thick hair. As they reached the porch, Mary Anne spoke in a clear, encouraging voice. "Take it easy, Bits," she said. "Other women have lived through this. Just play it cool."

Henry Cameron chuckled—Mary Anne's airy sententiousness was always leaven to his spirits—but he burned to know what universal cross of womanhood Bitsy Blackburn bore. When he heard the girls thrump their books down on a table in the hall, he opened the door of his den. "Hello," he said, trying to keep his tone disarmingly casual, "I *thought* I heard human footsteps."

"Hi, Daddy," said Mary Anne.

"Hello, Mr. Cameron," said Bitsy in a dull, uninflected voice. She added, from routine civility, "Nice day."

"Too nice to waste indoors," Henry said. "You girls worn out?"

"We're exhausted," Mary Anne replied promptly. She was evidently anxious to scotch the chance of being invited to embark upon some chore like pulling wild onions out of the grass. "Utterly exhausted."

"So am I," her father said amiably. "Come in and relax with me."

The girls looked uneasy. Their presence had been tolerated, but never courted, in Mr. Cameron's retreat.

"Why—thank you, sir," said Bitsy.

"Okay," said Mary Anne. She gave her father the sort of quick, bright-eyed glance that the fly in the nursery rhyme probably gave the cordial spider. As she allowed Bitsy to precede her across the threshold, she let an opaque expression, like a visor of moral resistance, drop over her face.

"I just want company," Henry said. "I don't intend to improve your minds."

"Don't read 'em, either," Mary Anne said. She dimpled demurely to take the edge off her impudence, but she continued to look suspicious. She plumped down upon the sofa and began to examine her varnished fingernails.

Bitsy sat beside her. She lowered her body by degrees, as if she'd learned from a succession of broken couch springs the value of physical caution.

Henry perched on the corner of his desk and lit a cigarette. "How was school?" he inquired. As an opening gambit, the question had, at least, the virtue of familiarity.

"About as usual," Mary Anne said. "Miss Whitty's making us memorize the last part of MacArthur's speech, and Everett Jones put on this act in the cold-lunch line that got us all in stitches and made Junior Bailey suck chocolate milk up his nose. Everett said: 'Old teachers never die—and oh, Iago, the pity of it!' "

"Everett knows millions of literary quotations," Bitsy said. Her voice was sad and tender.

"I think Miss Whitty heard about it," Mary Anne continued. "In Activity Period she told Everett he had an unfortunate attitude toward life."

"Miss Whitty has something there," said Henry. "I saw him, not long ago, streaking up the road like a bat out of hell." He had chosen, deliberately, this somewhat rakish description of young Jones' progress. He waited to see what reaction it would produce in the girls.

"Ha, ha! You're a card, Daddy," said Mary Anne. "Hellbat Jones. That's a good name for him!" She glanced significantly at Bitsy.

"I was using a trite figure of speech," her father said quickly. "I trust you won't repeat it. It might hurt the boy's feelings."

"He has no more feelings than a slice of boiled ham," Mary Anne said. "But I won't repeat it because, as you say, profanity is trite."

312

Bitsy looked directly at her host. She had very fine eyes, he noticed—clear hazel in color like autumn water in a beech grove. But the expression in them now was so bleak that it wrung the heart. "Everett was getting away from me, Mr. Cameron," she said. "He called me his social—his social— *What* was it, Mary Anne?"

"Nemesis," Mary Anne said. "Whatever that may be!"

"That's a singularly ungallant name to call a lady," Henry Cameron said. "And, in this case, unfair."

"Well, Everett *reads*," Bitsy said. "I guess he learns so many new words he has to use 'em on somebody."

"I commend your charity," Cameron said dryly.

"Thank you," Bitsy said. She sounded grateful for the least crumb of approval.

"Speaking of Junior's misadventure in the lunch line, aren't you kids hungry?"

Bitsy shook her head. "I can't eat. I'm depressed."

"Bitsy depresses easy," said Mary Anne.

"I've lost my breakfast three mornings straight," said Bitsy.

Henry looked sharply at her. Observing the real misery in her face and the greenish pallor, as of sickness or fear, in the skin around her mouth, he was clutched by a bourgeois, old-wives' panic. Surely what leapt to his mind couldn't have happened to Bitsy. She was too nice and naïve and big! And yet, biologically, she was no longer a child, and in the courtroom he had encountered many sordid instances of precocious misbehavior among adolescents. (*"Other women have lived through this,"* Mary Anne had said.)

"Mother thinks I'll feel better when the dance is over," Bitsy said. "But I *may* feel worse."

"The dance?" Henry said weakly.

"That's what's giving me nervous indigestion," Bitsy explained. "I have to give a dance tomorrow night for seventy-five people. The whole ninth grade."

"Bits doesn't know when she's lucky," said Mary Anne. "A snazzy dance. With a real orchestra and a spring motif!"

"I wish I was dead," said Bitsy.

"Oh," Henry Cameron said. "I believe I heard your father say something about a dance." He wanted to laugh aloud from pure relief, until he reflected soberly that entertaining the whole ninth grade was no laughing matter.

Mrs. Cameron appeared in the doorway. She wore slacks—a garment that, her husband thought, made her figure look more feminine than ever in an absurd, agreeable way—and a bandanna tied around her short yellow curls. "Hank!" she cried. "What a grand surprise!" She came and kissed him. "Hi, girls. How was school?"

"About as usual," said Mary Anne.

"I've just come from your house, Bitsy," Julia Cameron said. "I've been helping your mother. I bet you can't wait for tomorrow night!" Her voice sounded false and chirpy.

"I wish I was dead," said Bitsy.

"Everybody worries before a party," Julia told her. "You'll have a wonderful time."

"It's different with me," Bitsy said stubbornly. "I've *been* to dances, and sometimes, beforehand, I thought they might be fun. But when I was at them I always wished I was dead." She stood up. "Mother wants to wash my hair."

Mary Anne walked to the porch with her friend. Julia sank down on the sofa. "I wish Bitsy'd show a little spunk and quit saying she wants to die," she said. "It's discouraging to her mother."

"The child's in a state of terror," her husband told her. "Why should she give a dance if she doesn't want to?"

"Bitsy needs a push," his wife said. "When you consider other girls her age—Mary Anne and the girls at the junior high school—you'll realize how little poise the child has."

"I *am* considering them," Henry said, thinking of the smooth, smug-mannered damsels who often came to his house and of how easily Mary Anne took color from them. "And I think it's throwing Bitsy to the lions!"

"I have my qualms, too," Julia confessed. "But Bitsy has to hold up her social end. And the way Al Blackburn's making money—did you know he gave Belle diamond earrings for her anniversary, and he's ordered her a new convertible for Mother's Day?—Bitsy can have unlimited fun if she'll only cooperate. If Mary Anne were like Bitsy—"

"I wouldn't care a rap," said Henry.

314

"You wouldn't?" Mary Anne exclaimed, coming into the room. "You wouldn't care a rap if I were a lummox like Bitsy and never even had a date to go to the movies or play Wee-Tee golf? I think that's darn mean of you."

"I'd like you any way you were," her father explained. "I like Bitsy."

"I love her like a sister," Mary Anne protested. "But I'm glad I'm normal."

"The norm isn't constant, my dear," said Henry in his blandest jury-box manner. "And it's my contention that no girl should be required to endure these social functions and this business of what you call 'dating'" (he pronounced the word as if it were slightly vulgar) "—this artificial pairing off of the sexes—until those things seem normal to *her.*"

"Oh, Bitsy believes in pairing off the sexes," Mary Anne said. "She's been in love for three years. With Everett Jones."

"Of all the arrant nonsense!" her father scoffed.

"The torch was lit in the sixth grade," Mary Anne informed him. "She was wrestling with Everett and he got his knee in her stomach so she had to bite him. When she tasted his blood, something happened to her."

Henry laughed in a helpless way that resembled weeping.

Mary Anne, with a rueful show of reluctance, joined in the mirth. "I know it has its funny side," she said. "But then love often does. And Bitsy couldn't help herself. It was lit."

"Lit, eh?" Henry said, wiping his eyes.

"The Torch," Mary Anne said. "At first she just picked on him. She followed him around and tripped him up and stuff like that, and he didn't mind too much. But then Everett's mother complained to Mrs. Blackburn and Mr. Blackburn told Bitsy a girl was supposed to be sweet and build up a boy's ego. So Bits started being real humble and telling Everett how gorgeous he was, and he began to prosecute her."

"Persecute," said Henry.

"I always get those words confused," Mary Anne said with a blithe unconcern that made her father wonder if she didn't use malapropisms on purpose, because she thought them winsome. "He gives her these hateful nicknames—Nemesis, you know, and The

315

Girl from Mars. And he made a poem about her, a take-off on that dumb Lucy Gray thing we had to read in Literature. Everett said: 'She dwelt among untrodden ways, among her pappy's loot, A dame whom no one cared to praise, and no one dared to shoot.' Bitsy cried when he passed it to her in Algebra."

"I can hardly blame her," Julia said.

"She saved it, though. It's sacred to her because Everett touched it," Mary Anne continued. "And Everett's furious because his mother's making him go to the dance. He has to be Bitsy's partner and wear his brother's tux."

Henry frowned. "A tux? At fourteen?"

"I warned Belle Blackburn to make the occasion as formal as possible," Julia said. "I've never recovered from the time Mary Anne had a Hallowe'en gathering and I made a fatal error of calling it *in*formal!"

"I was only thirteen," Mary Anne said, "but that party *made* me. People did things that wouldn't have been allowed in any other house in town!"

"They certainly did," her mother agreed. "The boys climbed on the roof and hurled vile epithets at passing cars. And, fool that I was, I put bunches of grapes around the jack o' lantern, and they picked them off, one by one, and threw them on the floor and slid on them."

"I remember," her husband said.

"I'm surprised you do," Julia retorted with a touch of old rancor. "If my memory serves, you claimed to be catching cold and went to bed in the spare room with the door locked."

"And the first dancing-school party!" Mary Anne cried with a nostalgic catch in her voice. "Miss Battle told the boys that no gentleman ever kicked a lady while they were dancing the conga. So they kicked us every time there was a waltz. That was Everett's idea." She sighed, as if for a vanished morning of life. "How juvenile those parties were! The one tomorrow will be an adult affair."

"Try to make it a success," Julia pleaded. "Keep the boys dancing."

"You know how boys are," said Mary Anne. "They won't listen to reason. They don't have human feelings." She clasped

316

her hands. "Oh, I suffer for Teentsie. If she'll only play it cool!"

"What do you mean—cool?" asked Henry.

"Oh, you know . . ." Mary Anne's voice trailed off vaguely. "Just cool."

"I see. Cool," her father said. But he didn't really hope to see. He was sufficiently acquainted with the jargon of the young to know that even when it made sense it never made the kind of sense it seemed to make.

"Belle is as scared as Bitsy," Julia said. "She and Al want us over to hold their hands and give them courage. They have some new D'Oyly Carte records we can play in the upstairs sitting room."

"Will the Joneses be there?" asked Henry.

"No. Everett won't appear in public with his parents," Mary Anne said. "They embarrass him."

"Will we embarrass you?" her father asked.

"Not me," Mary Anne said, shrugging. "My French teacher says I have *sang-froid*."

For a moment, Henry toyed with the idea of inquiring into the circumstances that had led to the teacher's remark. But, feeling that it was high time to re-establish a prudent distance between himself and his daughter, he rose. "I've enjoyed talking with you, my pet," he said. "And now, I daresay, you wish to practice your piano lesson. I intend to cut the grass."

The Camerons and the Blackburns had been friends a long time. Their houses—Henry's a modest, half-timbered structure and Al's a Victorian eminence which his grandfather had built, fifty years before its surrounding fields had been chopped into half-acre residential lots—stood within the proverbial stone's throw of each other, but the single stone, real or verbal, ever cast in either direction, had been one shied by Bitsy at the age of seven.

On that occasion (subsequently referred to in the neighborhood as "the night Bitsy shot a lawyer"), the child had slipped out after hours with the intention of summoning Mary Anne to join her in exploring the woods across the road. The little girls had plotted their clandestine adventure for some weeks, and the signal of Bitsy's presence was to be a pebble tossed lightly against Mary Anne's window. But, rattled by darkness, Bitsy had underestimated both the

317

size of her missile and the power behind her heave. And, dazzled, as she looked upward, by the luminaries of Heaven, she had forgotten which Cameron window was which. She had sent a rock as big as a pullet's egg into the bathroom where Henry Cameron had been shaving before a dinner meeting of the county bar association. The stone had come through the pane with a sound like the report of a pistol (and, in fact, as was noted later, it had made a hole as smooth as—if somewhat larger than—one drilled by a bullet), had whizzed within a quarter inch of Henry's ear, and had crashed into the mirror above the washbasin. All Henry's nerves, as if gathered into one gigantic knot, had given a mighty lurch; his razor had slipped, and, staring aghast at his reflection, distorted by splintered glass and a foam of blood and lather, he had cried shrilly: "Julia! I'm a dead man!"

At the sound of his voice, so unlike its usual calm and measured self, and at the horrid import of his words, Bitsy had collapsed upon the hard winter ground. "I've killed him!" she had moaned in the deep, desolate tone of a hound baying at the moon. "I've killed Mary Anne's daddy!" Then, being a child with a sense of sin and justice, she had begged: "Policeman, take me away! I'm a gangster!" At length, limp from weeping, she had been put to bed with a hot-water bottle and a pint of ice cream hastily fetched from the corner drugstore, but it had required a visit from her imagined victim, who looked normal and intact except for the band-aid on his left cheek, to console her. Then, leaping from her bed, she had half strangled him in her embrace and had kissed the seat of his injury with a violence that had dislodged its bandage.

While Henry Cameron mowed the lawn, he recalled that little comedy of errors. In it, he reflected, as within the frame of a skillful one-act play, Bitsy's salient qualities had been revealed. And the girl hadn't changed much since then. Oh, she had learned not to crush your furniture when she sat on it or your hand when she clasped it, but—as witness her attachment to the ridiculous Jones boy—she hadn't learned to gauge or disguise the strength of her passions. And her clumsy candor which, like crude health, aroused the admiration of an attorney on the verge of middle age, aroused only scorn in the breasts of her contemporaries.

The girl needed time, Henry thought. Unbadgered, allowed to

open her petals slowly, one by one, Bitsy would someday blossom into the majesty nature reserved for her. To force her prematurely into an alien pattern—and not even because the pattern was essentially good—was a stupid refinement of cruelty. He wondered that such softhearted women as Al's wife and his own Julia would have countenanced the scheme.

The next morning Henry went to his office early. He had a brief to prepare before court was called, a full day of examining witnesses and challenging jurors, and a dinner conference with a rich, greedy client who wished to break an uncle's will. He returned home just in time to change into the tuxedo, faintly redolent of camphor, that his wife had laid out for him.

As he came downstairs, Mary Anne said, "Hi, Daddykins, you look like a man of distinction. See what Junior Bailey sent me!" She was wearing a blue dress made of some stiff but filmy stuff, and she looked sure of herself as she indicated the gardenia in her blonde hair. "He's my partner, but I'm going with you and Mother. I promised Bitsy to come early."

"How is she?" Henry asked.

"In a daze," Mary Anne said. "Her dress is a dream number. Yards and yards of tulle sprinkled with rhinestones. Strapless. Her father's sending her a white orchid corsage."

"Good," said Henry.

"And the house!" Mary Anne went on. "They have this spring motif, you know. Even the ice cream is in the shape of flowers. And they've fixed these trellises in all the corners—kind of bowers where couples can sit out dances. They're covered with paper leaves all stuck with real roses from the florist."

"I hope Bitsy appreciates it," Mrs. Cameron said. "Let's start."

"Mr. Blackburn wanted to have canaries twittering round among the flowers," Mary Anne continued. "But Bits said birds had messy habits."

"I'm glad someone has remained sane," Henry grumbled.

The Camerons walked to the party. The night was warm and still. The moon was nearly full and the fruit trees, blooming all over the neighborhood, were like luminous clouds on the lawns.

The Blackburns' big, cut-glass paneled door was opened by

319

Lucetta, who wore a black taffeta uniform and a lacy cap and apron. Her smile was forced. "Good evening," she said. "My! Mary Anne, you look like you come straight from New York! Mrs. Blackburn said would the ladies step upstairs." She touched Mary Anne's arm. "Put some starch in Bitsy. The poor lamb's in misery." She took Henry's coat. "Mr. Blackburn's on the phone. He'll be here directly, sir."

Henry let his gaze rove the length of the big central hall and into the twin parlors with their folding doors flung open. The carpets had been removed, the furniture, except for scattered love seats and sofas, carted off, and the bare, waxed floors had a luster that hurt the eyes. The shade of the silly bowers that Mary Anne had spoken of looked sinister rather than cozy, and at the end of the hall, under a stained-glass window that had been the pride of the eighties, a five-man orchestra was ambushed among potted palms and oleanders.

"How does this strike you, Lucetta?" he asked.

Lucetta's eyes gleamed with the liquid fire that is a special beauty of her race. "Frankly, sir, I'm nervous," she said.

Al Blackburn hurried out from the library. "Greetings, Hank!" he said. "It's a comfort to see you." He clapped Henry on the shoulder. "I have a favor to beg. Belle doesn't know yet—I just got the call—but we're in a jam." He explained that the president of the local Building and Loan Association, an elderly gentleman by the name of Edgerton, had suffered a thrombosis and that both he and his wife were wanted at the hospital. If the Camerons would hold the fort . . .

"Sure, Al," Henry said bravely. "And stay as long as you're needed."

"I appreciate that," Al said. "Off the record, I'm in line for Mr. Edgerton's position, and it wouldn't look decent if I didn't show the concern I honestly feel. And Mrs. E. is inclined to be hysterical. She'll need Belle." He paused, scanning the spacious rooms. "I'm almost thankful to miss part of this shindig. I feel hollow—the way I did while Bitsy was being born."

"It's bound to turn out well," Henry assured him.

"It ought to," Al said morosely. "It's costing as much as a wedding."

320

Mr. and Mrs. Blackburn left as the guests began to arrive. The three Camerons and Bitsy stood together near the door to do the honors. In her full tulle dress Bitsy looked even larger than life. Mary Anne kept poking her in the small of the back to remind her to stand up straight.

"I wish I was dead," Bitsy muttered.

"Be cool," Mary Anne said.

All the girls were dressed much alike in the same sort of fluffy dresses that Mary Anne and Bitsy wore. They acted alike, too. They all said: "Isn't this a perfect night for a dance?" and "This house is like a fairyland" and "Bitsy, your dress is out of this world." And they all said those things in accents that sounded not only false but as if they were *meant* to sound false—as if a fashionable insincerity were the impression they strove to convey. The boys, practically indistinguishable from one another in their dark clothes, had their own patter. "How's life been treating you?" they inquired of Henry Cameron in a man-to-man tone. "Feels like summer out," they observed to Julia. "You're mighty dressed up," they told Bitsy. Only Everett Jones, doubtless against his will, seemed to retain his identity. His face, though he tried to make it blank, wore its usual expression of cynical hauteur. His dinner jacket was a trifle short in the sleeves. He thrust out his hand in a grudging way. (His palm was clammy to Henry's touch.)

"You look divine, Everett," said Bitsy. "Like a senator or something."

"Don't kid me, big girl," Everett said. He walked away.

The orchestra began to play the "Tennessee Waltz," slowly and sadly.

"Can't we have a livelier tune to break the ice?" Henry asked.

"No," his daughter said. "Well"—she looked significantly at her mother—"I guess Bits and I ought to circulate."

"We must disappear now," Julia told her husband. "The modern chaperone is invisible."

In the upstairs sitting room, with the heavy door closed against the dance music, Henry put "Iolanthe" on the record player. After half an hour, he said to his wife: "Hadn't you better take a gander at the kids?"

"Yes," Julia said, "but I dread to." She went out. In a few minutes she returned. "Hardly anybody's dancing," she reported. "Just Mary Anne and the Bailey boy and a few couples who're—"

She hesitated. "I hate the inelegant expression but I can't think of a better one—a few couples who're going steady."

"Low language suits a low practice," Henry said. "How's Bitsy doing?"

"She's sitting bolt upright on a sofa in the hall, with a tragic smile on her face. Most of the boys are huddled in one parlor, laughing coarsely. The girls are in the other, on the verge of tears. Everett Jones is leaning against the wall, trying to look like Lord Byron."

"I wish the Blackburns would come back," Henry said. "It's *their* funeral!"

"I rather hope they won't until the party picks up," his wife said. "It may yet. The evening's young."

Before long there was a rap on the door and Lucetta came in, carrying a tray that held two glasses, soda, and ice. "There's Bourbon and Scotch in the liquor cabinet, Mr. Cameron," she said.

"Thanks, Lucetta. I need a drink."

"I could do with a dram myself," said Lucetta.

"Have one then," said Julia.

"No thank you, ma'am," said Lucetta. "I promised the Lord three years ago that if He'd let me keep my teeth I'd never touch another drop of spirits."

"A rash vow," Henry murmured.

"I kept my teeth," Lucetta said. "I indulge in a can of beer now and then." She twisted her apron. "Oh, Mrs. Cameron, little Bitsy's heart is busting in two!"

"What went wrong?" Henry asked.

"It's like a mean dog smells fear and hounds a person," Lucetta told him. "Them boys know Bitsy's scared and they've set out to spoil her party." She narrowed her eyes. "I'd like to stomp 'em!"

"Send Mary Anne up," Julia said. "Maybe she can help."

Promptly, after the maid's departure, Mary Anne arrived. "The party's a flop!" she cried. "Bitsy's ruined forever! The Blackburns will have to move far, far away! To Alaska or Wisconsin."

"Now, now," said her father.

322

"Everett did it!" Mary Anne said angrily. "He told all the boys that dancing was a primitive form of amusement!"

"Has Bitsy danced at all?" Henry asked.

"Junior Bailey danced with her once. He always does the correct thing."

"Suppose I go down and suggest a Paul Jones," Julia said.

"A thousand times No!" Mary Anne exclaimed. "Stay where you are. This isn't a Grade-Mothers' Social. This is an *adult* affair!"

"Don't shout," Julia said. "I merely wished to help."

Mary Anne raised her eyes toward the ceiling. "Nobody can help but God," she said in a stage whisper. On that pious and not very hopeful note, she left.

Henry Cameron switched off the phonograph in the middle of the fairies' "tripping hither, tripping thither" chorus. He found a broached bottle of Bourbon in the liquor closet. "Would you like one?" he asked his wife, as he poured himself a stiff drink.

"No, thanks," she said. "I want to keep my breath pure in case I have to mingle with the guests. But it's stuffy in here. I could use some air."

Henry raised a window. As he did, a blast of wind, scented with new-cut grass and syringa and impending rain, rushed into the room. He lowered the sash with a bang. "A storm's coming fast," he said. "The sky's overcast and there's hairpin lightning on the horizon. We'd better see about the windows downstairs."

When they reached the landing, the Camerons saw that Lucetta, also, had remarked the change of weather. Assisted by the house-boy and two colored janitors borrowed from Al Blackburn's office building, she was closing the windows. The orchestra was still play-ing, but in a discouraged way. No one was dancing. One parlor was still crowded with boys and its twin with girls in various attitudes of dejection or transparent nonchalance. Everett was still sneering into space. Bitsy was still on the sofa, but she was no longer smil-ing. Her face wore a look of purpose, of gathering resolution.

The storm broke. Such thunder as might have heralded the de-scent of Jove from Olympus clapped its mighty hands above the roof. The music ceased abruptly; one melancholy trombone note wailed and gave up its plaintive ghost. An eerie tinkling trembled in

323

the air—the sigh of a house in which there are many crystal chandeliers. The guests screamed in mock terror. Everett Jones threw back his head and walled his eyes like a frightened horse.

As if at a signal, Bitsy arose. She swept into the center of the hall. In her full, besparkled dress she appeared to ride upon a starry, wind-borne cloud. She stuck two fingers between her teeth and emitted a blood-freezing whistle. "Aw right, kids!" she yelled in her old sand-lot voice. "Line up! Boys on that side! Girls on this!"

Startled, the children obeyed her.

Bitsy took her place in the exact middle of the rainbow row of maidens. Sternly, she surveyed the dark row of boys. "Get opposite me, Everett Jones!" she ordered in a clarion tone. "And take your glasses off!"

As if he had lost all power of volition, Everett did as he was told. He stuck his glasses in his pants pocket. A girl giggled.

"Shut up!" Bitsy roared. "Silence in the ranks! Everybody in his battle station?" She lifted her right arm in a commanding gesture. (Given a helmet, Henry Cameron thought, she'd have doubled for the Goddess Bellona.) "One. Two. Three. *Fight!* Men against women!"

There was an instant of shocked surprise. Then, to the accompaniment of coy squeals, the sexes exchanged playful swats. But Bitsy and Everett were in earnest. Silent, crouching, they advanced into the no-man's land between the lines.

Henry rallied to his duty. "Here! Here!" he cried, starting down the stairs.

A second peal of thunder, louder and closer than the first, rent the air. The house was plunged into darkness.

Julia Cameron touched her husband's arm. "You can't save him now," she said. Her tone was complacent.

Lucetta's voice said: "It's a fuse. The box is in the pantry." And for a minute after that everything was so still that Henry could hear the heavy breathing and the scuffling feet, as the boy and girl struggled for supremacy. A flash of lightning illuminated the hall. The guests stood in a wide ring around the protagonists. Everett, his face hideous with rage, had Bitsy by the hair. Bitsy held her fist clenched, like the fist of a gentleman who remembers, come what may, the Queensberry rules.

Bitsy's voice rang out. "Hellbat!" she screeched.

Thunder crashed. Its final reverberation was followed by a less ethereal noise that Henry, from a cursory acquaintance with crime literature, identified as the thud of a falling body.

"She felled him with a left hook," he said.

The lights came on.

Everett, limp as a propped-up rag doll, sat against the wall with his spindly legs stuck out before him. Bitsy, composed except for heightened color, stood over him. When the Camerons and Lucetta reached her side, she said: "I didn't give him all I had."

Bitsy was taken upstairs by Mrs. Cameron, Mary Anne, and the maid. Henry, waving aside half a dozen boys, helped Everett to the downstairs lavatory.

"If you'd like to lie down a while—" Henry began.

Everett, holding a cold, wet towel to his jaw, appeared astonished. "No, sir," he said. "It's not broken." His eyes darkened. "I *could* have killed her."

"You did right to use restraint," Henry told him kindly.

Everett curled his lip. "It wasn't a question of right and wrong," he said. "But there are things a gentleman can't do."

"Precisely," Henry said. "You have the matter of conduct in a nutshell."

Everett put on his glasses, tied his tie, and ran a pocket comb through his hair. Gazing in the mirror, he cocked one eyebrow. "She called me a hellbat," he said musingly. He didn't sound offended.

Returning to the hall with Everett, Henry Cameron noticed that the tempo of the party had changed. With verve and vigor the musicians were playing "There'll Be a Hot Time in the Old Town Tonight." The guests were in motion. They were dancing or chasing one another or pulling roses off the artificial vines and flinging them through the air. They all displayed that gaiety, that abandon, that spiritual elevation that is said to come to those who have been miraculously delivered from peril.

Bitsy descended the stairs. Her hair was sleek and shining. She

325

held her head high and walked with the dignity of a queen who condescends to share the simple pleasures of her subjects. Everett, with Henry close on his heels, ready to prevent a renewal of hostilities, approached her. The two children stood face to face. Unsmiling. Taking each other's measure.

"Shall we dance?" said Everett.

Henry saw his wife sitting on the landing. He joined her.

"The storm passed as quickly as it came," she said. "Moon's out."

"The air's cleared in here, too," said Henry.

It was just on midnight—supper had been served, couples had retreated into the deflowered nooks to be hauled out with shrieks of innocent ribaldry by their friends, general happiness had prevailed, and the orchestra was signing off with "Goodnight, Sweetheart"—when Mr. and Mrs. Blackburn returned. They joined the Camerons on the steps.

"We were sorry to miss the fun," Belle Blackburn said, "but it was touch-and-go with Mr. Edgerton." With a radiant face she looked down upon the cavorting couples, the rose-strewn floor, and the listing trellises. "It's perfect. Like a madhouse!"

" 'There was a sound of revelry by night,' eh, Hank?" Al said. He looked boyish and taken with himself. He wasn't a man who read much poetry. "Shakespeare?"

"You're warm, Al," said Henry.

When the last guests had gone, the Cameron family walked home, in companionable silence through the fresh, lovely night. The storm had left a charming kind of wreckage on the lawns. Snapped-off heads of daffodils, budding twigs, and a drift of fruit blossoms were littered about like the debris of a successful party.

"Bitsy's on the map," Mary Anne said, as they went into their own house. "Nobody'll ever forget that dance!"

Her mother laughed softly. "What was it she called the Jones boy? A *hellbat?*"

"She was quoting Daddy, sort of," said Mary Anne.

Julia stroked her husband's cheek. "Everybody quotes him. He's smart," she said. She smiled at him. "But you look tired. I'm going to sit you down in your den and fix you a nice nightcap. You never did finish your drink at the Blackburns'."

Ensconced in his favorite chair, with his shoes off and his feet comfortable in the loose slippers that Mary Anne had brought him, Henry Cameron thought himself the most fortunate of men. His wife came in from the kitchen. On a silver tray she brought a high-ball for him and two cups of warm milk for herself and Mary Anne.

"What are you looking so salubrious about?" she asked.

"I *feel* salubrious," Henry said. "I was thinking of Bitsy's triumph and of Woman with a capital W—of her infinite variety!"

Mary Anne sat down on the floor. She rubbed her nose against her father's knee; it was a trick she'd had in her early childhood to denote ecstasy. "That Bitsy Blackburn!" she murmured. "I won't ever have to worry about her again!" She closed her eyes and yawned. "Oh, brother—did she play her hand cool!"

Will Cuppy

Will (christened William Jacobs) Cuppy was an oddity in his life as well as his work. Born August 23, 1884, in Auburn, Illinois, Cuppy blamed his amazing collection of historical flotsam and jetsam on the fact that he was considered bright enough to skip the eighth grade, "where I seem to have missed all the main facts of English grammar, punctuation, history, and that sort of thing." To atone for this, Cuppy became the passionately interested collector of curiosa. He was surrounded by countless files, card indexes, and boxes bursting at the seams with thousands of notes on everything from fossils to philosophers, from snakes to saints, from little-known details of the Roman conquests to secrets of the French courtesans. He kept all these about him in his Greenwich Village flat and a shack on Jones' Island which he aptly called "Tottering-on-the-Brink." Before his death in September, 1949, he had written innumerable reviews of murder mysteries and was the author of half a dozen volumes with such characteristic titles as *How to Attract the Wombat, How to Be a Hermit, How to Tell Your Friends from the Apes,* and *How to Become Extinct.*

Fred Feldkamp, Cuppy's best friend, inherited Cuppy's accumulation of encyclopedic notes; he set about editing and publishing them. Two posthumous books appeared in 1950 and 1951: *The Decline and Fall of Practically Everybody* and *How to Get from January to December.* Both were enormously successful, which was something of an irony, for Cuppy never once made the best-seller list during his lifetime. While he lived Cuppy's audience was select and enthusiastic but never large. It was not until after he died that more than 75,000 readers discovered the man who had elevated the footnote into an art—and, at the same time, burlesqued it to death.

*How to Get from January to December**

January 24

If an animal does something they call it instinct. If we do exactly the same thing for the same reason they call it intelligence.

Entomologists say that ants, for example, are guided entirely by instinct and not by intelligence. They say the ants do not know what they are doing. And do the entomologists know what *they* are doing? Besides watching ants, I mean. I'm only asking.

I guess what they mean is that we all make mistakes, but intelligence enables us to do it on purpose.

That's all very well, but *I* believe the toad is thinking as he sits there, perfectly still. He *must* be.

February 15

"Dear Sir: I see where the Big Dipper is breaking up and will be an entirely different shape in about 50,000 years. Is there nothing we can depend on?

Disgusted"

No, there isn't, *Disgusted,* if you come right down to it. You must try to realize that nothing stays put forever and act accordingly. It is true that the five central stars of the Big Dipper are rushing toward the sun at eight or ten miles a second and that eventually the Big Dipper will look like something else. This will be tough on people whose only interest in life is something the shape of a dipper, but there is a brighter side to the picture.

The real name of the Big Dipper is Ursa Major, or the Greater Bear, and my hope is that in 50,000 years it will look a lot more like what it's supposed to be. Whatever happens, it couldn't look *less* like a bear than it does at present. Long, long ago, when Ursa Major was named, bears probably looked more like dippers than they do today. You can't depend on bears, either.

March 5

There are people who make rules on how to converse. They tell you to be a good listener. (Go ahead and listen and see what it gets you.)

Listening may do as an ideal. In actual practice I find that you have to keep going if you want to get a word in edgeways. The best talker I know says she regards conversation as a hand-to-hand struggle to say the most words possible in the least possible amount of elapsed time and the devil take the hindmost. She gets away with it, too.

Doctor Samuel Johnson wasn't bad at that, either. After talking a blue streak for four or five hours, he was wont to remark: "Well, sir, this has been a good evening. We have had good talk. The communication of mind is always of use. Thought flowed freely this evening." He was right, at that.

As for those little things I stick in my ears, it isn't that I'm not interested. I may have some form of auditory hyperesthesia, the doctor says.

April 8

Lorenzo De' Medici, alias Lorenzo the Magnificent, the great Florentine banker and patron of Renaissance art and letters, passed away on April 8, 1492. Which reminds me that literary patronage seems to be on the decline, or maybe I meet the wrong people. I once asked the only millionaire I ever met if he wouldn't like to support some struggling author who had lots of talent but couldn't seem to get along, somehow. I didn't succeed in getting his views, because he pulled out his watch and said he just remembered a very important engagement. Nothing much came of *that* conversation.

May 23

General Ambrose Everett Burnside, who fought on the Union side in the Civil War, was born in Liberty, Indiana, on May 23, 1824. He has been blamed for losing a couple of battles and for wearing an odd kind of whiskers called burnsides or sideburns, a hirsute drapery covering both cheeks and the upper lip and leaving the chin and laryngeal region bare naked—some people say you can have sideburns without a mustache, but that is merely a quibble.

There were whiskers like that before, but somehow they became associated with General Burnside and he never heard the last of them. Practically all the generals in the Civil War had beards or facial foliage of some kind, and most of them just let nature take its course, like Grant and Lee. General Burnside was about the only one who went in for formal landscape gardening. And that reminds me that in his twenties he was getting married to a girl from Kentucky, and when the clergyman asked her if she would have Ambrose for her wedded husband she said no, she wouldn't. I often wonder whether he had the sideburns at the time.

P.S.—The girl finally married another fellow, who told her he'd shoot her if she pulled that on *him*. Young Ambrose got a wife, too, so everything ended happily.

June 20

"Dear Sir: Please tell me some of Queen Victoria's witty sayings, as I am writing a paper for my club.

Bookish"

Why don't you try to think up something a little zippier, *Bookish?* The subject you suggest has been regarded as pretty well closed since about 1887, the Diamond Jubilee year. I wouldn't bother to answer you except that today is the anniversary of Queen Victoria's accession to the throne of Great Britain and Ireland—yes, June 20, 1837. Now, let's see! When she learned of her future greatness, at the age of eleven, she said: "I will be good." That isn't what is technically called wit, but it is a fine saying and will do your club no harm.

I don't know what you'd better do about "We are not amused," for that isn't so awfully witty, either. Queen Victoria first used the expression after she had forced a perspiring young man named Eric to repeat the imitation of herself with which he had been convulsing the court. My own feeling is that her implied criticism of Eric's art was probably just, to put it mildly—and, naturally, Eric was at his worst. Of course, there's also that thing that Mr. Gladstone said, or rather that she said Mr. Gladstone said—or perhaps you could get up a nice paper on current events.

P.S.—Why not leave town?

July 13

It's amazing how many superstitions one encounters among otherwise intelligent people. I know a lady who practically has a fit if a black cat crosses her path. Yet nothing very terrible ever happened to me after a black cat crossed my path. I wish I could say the same for tortoise-shell cats.

Superstition is plain, downright ignorance. Such beliefs merely shackle the mind and hold you back. Of course, if you break a leg on account of a tortoise-shell cat, that would shackle you even worse, so I keep my eye on them just in case.

One of my friends carries a rabbit's left hind foot in his pocket the year round. He gets along very well and he lays it all to this charm. He doesn't seem to know that in order to be any good the rabbit must be killed in a churchyard at midnight in the dark of the moon. He's simply a victim of ignorance.

Any child should know that breaking a mirror couldn't possibly cause seven years of bad luck, though I'd as soon not break one myself. I went into that scientifically once by breaking a mirror and keeping track of my luck for the next seven years. The experiment didn't prove much, really. I hadn't been so awfully lucky before that, either.

August 21

"Dear Sir: How can I get my husband to stop reading the paper at breakfast? I simply hate it.

Housewife"

As your husband doubtless reads the paper at breakfast in order to find out what is going on in the world and thus fit himself for his daily grind at the office, you might ask him to give up his business or profession. Tell him you married him for himself alone and that you don't care a bit whether he makes any money or not. If you feel strongly enough on the subject, you might let him know in a tactful way that you will go out and earn the living if he will only give up this annoying habit. Maybe you can work it so there won't *be* any breakfast. That might solve your problem.

332

September 23

What with the influence of elementary education upon the growing mind, it is not too much to say that McGuffey's Eclectic Readers explain why millions of American citizens are the way they are. This is a good day to say it because William Holmes McGuffey, author and compiler, was born in Washington County, Pennsylvania, on September 23, 1800.

As some one has put it, Mr. McGuffey taught the moral and intellectual virtues of integrity, honesty, industry, temperance, true patriotism, courage, politeness, and then some. He not only taught them, he rubbed them in.

Perhaps I was considered too backward for the First Reader, for I had a Primer, in which there was a cat and a rat. Ann was there, too, and the rat ran at Ann and the cat ran at the rat. Then Nat arrived, and the rat ran at Nat. Nat had a fat dog named Rab, who saw a frog on a log. So Rab ran at the frog for a change.

A very strange thing happened to Ann and Nat in Lesson VIII, where they suddenly grew up, as you could see by the picture. It seems that Ann had a mat and Nat had a lamp. They had pooled their resources for the evening, because the lamp is on the mat, all lighted up, right between Ann and Nat. Nat must have brought the lamp with him when he came to call.

Next day, though, Ann and Nat were themselves again. Nat was on Tom's nag and Ann was on the log, where the frog had been. The rat was still at large.

October 16

This is Noah Webster's birthday. No, not Daniel—*Noah*. Noah Webster was born October 16, 1758, at West Hartford, Connecticut, and was not, as I had always believed until a few minutes ago, a brother of Daniel's. Daniel was a much more emotional type, rather given to flowery quotations, such as "Sink or swim, live or die, survive or perish, I give my hand and my heart to this vote." Noah would mull over his learned books for hours in absolute silence and then startle everybody by remarking: "The Zarp is a species of Zimp indigenous to Madagascar and Eastern Abyssinia."

333

His dictionary was published in 1828 and is still going strong in a bigger and better edition. Of Noah's great work, some of us can say, with an elderly friend of a friend of mine: "I've hefted it and I respect it, but I ain't read it."

November 16

"Dear Sir: Is it *ee-ther* or *eye-ther?* I never know which to say and I feel that the time has come to face it.

Louise"

I hesitate to speak freely on this matter, as I might say something I'd regret. Moreover, it is a problem that each of us must solve for himself. It must come from inside, if you follow me. But I can give you a hint, *Louise.* Look about you, listen to people talking, watch them at work and at play, and if you want to be like the ones who say *eye-ther* I wouldn't lay a straw in your way. Much the same line of reasoning applies to *to-may-to* and *to-mah-to.* Unless you come honestly by it, have nothing to do with *to-mah-to.* I tried it once, and I felt something awful for weeks afterwards. It simply isn't in me.

December 9

Socrates was considered to be one of the greatest thinkers of his time. He said that Happiness is Virtue and Virtue is Happiness, and therefore no man will do wrong if he can help it, for if he does wrong he will not be virtuous and therefore he will not be happy, since Happiness is Virtue and Virtue is Happiness.

The Socratic Method consisted mostly of asking questions. Socrates would listen to people talking and then he would ask them exactly what they meant by what they said and whether they knew what they were talking about. This was embarrassing for the people, because they had not meant much of anything. They were just talking. If they had known what they were talking about, they would not have been talking. Then Socrates would prove to them that they had no sense whatever. He seems to have thought this would please them. As you probably know, he was forced to drink hemlock, in 399 B.C. At his trial he denied that he was a wise man, but nobody would believe him.

334